# Applied Linear Programming

NORMAN J. DRIEBEEK
*Arthur D. Little, Inc., Cambridge, Massachusetts*

**ADDISON-WESLEY PUBLISHING COMPANY**

Reading, Massachusetts · Menlo Park, California · London · Don Mills, Ontario

# Preface

This manuscript describes how mathematical programming techniques and especially linear programming can be applied to operational problems. Since the original development of linear programming in the late 1940's and early 1950's, the practical uses of this technique have grown at an unprecedented rate. Among current applications are optimization of product blending, product manufacture, transport system analysis, manpower utilization, production allocation, and advertising media selection. Until recently, the widest use of linear programming had been by the processing industries, especially the petroleum industry, and by animal feed manufacturers. Today, linear programming has penetrated many other sectors of industrial life, especially in medium range operations planning.

While linear programming applications have been varied and diverse, common denominators have been the development of mathematical models of operations and the use of standard general purpose solution routines. This book is aimed at students and at the industrial engineer, the planning manager, and the plant coordinator who can be expected to apply linear programming. The emphasis is on the development of linear programming models, and on the application of these models to industrial problems. Algorithm development and mathematical proofs are de-emphasized in favor of detailed descriptions of operational procedures which have been found useful in solving a large number of industrial problems that can be formulated in linear programming formats.

iii

A major part of this book was initially developed as a series of lecture notes for a second-year graduate course at Harvard Business School. I have assembled, detailed, and extended these lecture notes on the urging of my colleagues at Harvard and at Arthur D. Little, Inc., who felt that a work of this nature would find a ready audience.

A rigorous mathematical treatment of linear programming and its many extensions is beyond the scope of this work. The bibliography contains a detailed list of some excellent reference works in this area. Rather than a discussion of theory, the primary emphasis is on assisting those that may be called upon to develop applications of linear programming to existing problems.

Linear programming and its many extensions are powerful tools in the development of optimum allocation strategies. Many managerial decisions concern themselves with allocation of resources, whether it be production capacity, labor, inventory, or funds for investment. Detailed descriptions of several mathematical models used in a wide variety of industries are contained in the following chapters. It is my sincere wish that those who read this book will find it easier to develop linear programming applications to their allocation problems, or that they will gain a greater understanding of the results obtainable from the use of linear programming as an operations planning tool, and for evaluation of alternatives in long range corporate plans.

The overall organization of the book is as follows:

| | |
|---|---|
| Chapters 1 & 2 | Introduction to linear programming and the supporting mathematics |
| Chapters 3, 4, 5, & 6 | A description of linear programming model components, specific model structures, and comments on the objective function |
| Chapter 7 | How to solve linear programming problems |
| Chapters 8 & 9 | How to get additional information out of computer solved linear programming models |
| Chapters 10, 11, & 12 | Extensions of linear programming models and specialized solution procedures |
| Chapter 13 | A discussion on computers in general, and how computers can help in linear programming solutions |
| Chapters 14, 15, 16, & 17 | Case study examples in which linear programming was used to solve specific problems. |

Chapter 16 was authored by J. W. Traenkle, and Chapter 17 was authored by H. L. Dick, J. L. Russel, and J. L. Lewis, former students who carried out the research described in this chapter as partial fulfillment of the requirements for the MBA degree from the Harvard Business School. These papers are included in this book with permission of the authors. The various case studies are included because they give an indication into the diverse problems that lend themselves to treatment by linear programming methods.

*Cambridge, Mass.*                                                                             N.J.D.
*May 1969*

# Contents

# Introduction to Linear Programming

Historically, scientists and economists have been interested in optimization problems, problems which seek to maximize or minimize a numerical function of a number of variables. Optimization problems occurred primarily in the physical sciences and geometry, and the classical optimization techniques, such as differential calculus of variations, were developed to deal with them. A new class of optimization problems has since become of considerable interest, consisting of problems dealing with the optimum allocation of limited resources. These are *programming problems*, and their solution involves a *program* of action, or a strategy. One seeks the optimum program or best strategy available within the imposed limitations. Such a program may involve men, machines, material, land, or financial assets, all of which contribute to the production of one or more items.

Almost all industrial operations are faced with programming problems. Some of these problems are small, and others are easily solved, but there remain many situations in which the application of mathematical programming techniques can be very fruitful. For example, a distribution manager in a nationwide company must decide how much of a variety of products to ship from his several warehouses. This is a programming problem, because the manager must develop a schedule of deliveries. He will want to minimize his total delivery cost, but he is faced with warehouse capacity constraints. He therefore "allocates" his warehouse capacity to the many potential delivery activities.

A processed foods manufacturer has a requirement for a blend of instant coffee with several quality specifications. He selects coffee supplies from among his many bins so that the final blend meets the buyers' specifications. This is a programming problem because it involves the development of a strategy in component selection to minimize cost.

A planning manager in an industry with seasonable variations in demand must plan to inventory selected items before the peak selling season. He must decide which products to store when and where. This can be viewed as a programming problem because the manager must develop a plan of allocating machines to production and warehouse space to finished goods.

Linear programming techniques have successfully been applied to these problems, and many other similar problems in industry and government.

Linear programming is the best known and most widely used of the various mathematical programming techniques. It deals only with those problems for which all the relationships between the variables are linear (i.e., the variables are equated in the first power only). The price paid for gasoline at a filling station exhibits a linear relationship in that the seventeenth gallon costs just as much as the first gallon. The price paid for orange juice in a supermarket, on the other hand, often represents a nonlinear relationship since it can be 20¢ for one can but six cans for $1.

Linear programming is the most advanced of all mathematical programming techniques. It has wide application in many industries, and, even though it is realized that many activities are not related to one another in strictly a linear sense, linear programming has been able to cope with such problems by using linear approximations of nonlinear relationships.

Linear programming will find without fail the very best of all possible solutions in a stated problem, it will indicate when alternative equally good solutions exist, and it will produce an indication on how profit will change if one elected not to use the suggested best or optimum solution. Linear programming is a quite powerful technique, and despite its recent inception in the late 1940's by Professor G. Dantzig, it has become a fully integrated procedure in many industrial corporations. The most prolific users of linear programming are the major petroleum companies who started applying the technique to their gasoline and heating oil blending problems in the late 1950's. One of the first things learned was that the quality of input data (accuracy and consistency) was oftentimes lacking. Programs were initiated to improve the data gathering procedures, and after that, the linear programming calculated blends invariably represented a lower cost operation.

The next step in the application of linear programming to the petroleum industry was the development of entire refinery scheduling models. These served to indicate the preferred crude oils to be run in the refineries, and the preferred mix of products to be manufactured under a given set of product prices. Oil companies soon developed models for pipeline optimization and tanker scheduling. Next came models for optimizing crude oil development and marketing strategies. Today most of the large oil companies are using (or developing) total corporate models which take in all the portions of the total operations covered by all the models just mentioned.

Cost reductions or profit improvements attributable to linear programming solutions have generally been in the 1 to 3% range. This may not sound big, but it can make quite a difference on total corporate operating costs.

While the petroleum companies have been the pioneers in linear programming applications, other industries have not been idle. Steel, textile, electronic equipment, wholesale, and many other industries use linear programming models regularly in their operations. Many of the examples shown throughout this book are representative of such actual industrial linear programming applications.

## USES OF LINEAR PROGRAMMING IN OPERATIONS PLANNING

Industrial operations are always confronted with operations planning problems. These problems vary from one industry to another, and they tend to deal with different aspects of the operations. Also, the specific planning steps and timing requirements differ. Nevertheless, operations planning can be divided into three broad categories as diagrammed in Fig. 1-1.

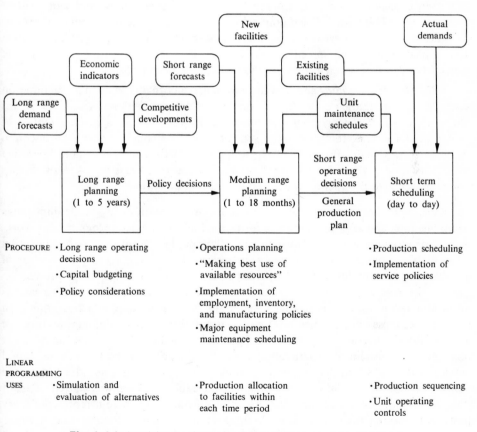

Fig. 1-1 Industrial operations planning and linear programming uses.

• *Long range planning* includes capital budgeting, corporate policy, corporate image, and long range marketing strategy development. Long range planning usually has a time horizon of 1 to 5 years. New facilities and/or modifications of facilities are planned to meet long term business forecasts, and appropriate plans will recognize that these forecasts are apt to be in error. Long range planning often concerns itself primarily with future facilities planning, and the time horizon is often related to the lead time for new major facilities. Power utilities thus have longer planning horizons than most manufacturing companies.

• *Medium range planning* generally deals with the development of operating plans or programs using existing equipment and resources to meet business requirements. The time horizon often extends from 1 month to 1 year or more, with the shorter time span being representative of manufacturing cycle time, and the longer time period being representative of the lead time for new major facilities. In nonseasonal businesses, a short time span is usually covered by such medium range planning. But where the business has definite seasonal variations, such planning generally covers at least a full year of operations. The operating plans must take into account manufacturing capacities, business requirements, seasonal inventories, and employment fluctuations. This type of planning allocates production requirements to various facilities in each time period and, as such, it establishes the operating rules for short term scheduling. Medium range planning deals with averages, e.g., equipment downtimes can be averaged out over the total planning periods.

• *Short term scheduling* specifies the actual product that is to be manufactured on each facility during the next shift, day, or week. Such production scheduling involves the assignment of specific men and machines to manufacture a given quantity of material. Of course, the production schedule must be consistent with the medium range operating plan. Production scheduling deals with specific units and operating rates; the time horizon is often so short that cognizance must be taken of startup times, anticipated production rates, and actual unit downtimes.

Linear programming has found its initial implementations in the medium range planning area, and such planning still forms the bulk of all linear programming work. Linear programming is well suited to such planning because it covers the allocation of available resources—men, machines, materials—to the manufacture of an array of products, and it can develop such operating plans on the basis of average production rates. The amount of uncertainty in the form of product forecast errors, variations in production rates, etc., is relatively small and as such a single best operating plan that ignores these uncertainties is extremely useful. Linear programming can produce such a plan or program of operations. We should note here though that the planning managers who use linear programming procedures generally consider them as "good advice"; they will take the linear programming prepared plan and adjust it on the basis of insight or new information obtained since the operation was started. Part of this occurs because a mathematical model of an operation seldom represents every last detail of the operation. The planning manager may recognize that a linear programming produced operating plan is unworkable because of some small detail not incorporated in the model. He then adjusts accordingly. Another aspect is that planning managers tend to initially distrust linear programming solutions. The feeling is that mathematical models can hardly be expected to be able to cope with all the operational details that the manager has learned in his many years of experience. If, however, the planning manager can overcome his initial anxieties and become familiar with the linear programming produced operating plans, he will invariably embrace them wholeheartedly and use them because they will provide better operating plans and eliminate considerable manual scheduling tedium.

Linear programming is finding more and more applications in the long range planning area. When a firm has a mathematical model of its medium term scheduling operations, it is relatively easy to incorporate into such a model a variety of new and still nonexistent facilities, and then to use the model to simulate future operations. In this mode, alternative capital investments are evaluated in conjunction with existing facilities, taking into account all system interactions. Of course such long range planning involves many uncertainties, but extensions of linear programming as described in Chapters 9 and 10 can be used in such cases. There have been applications of linear programming to long range planning that have preceded the development of medium range planning models, but such applications have been rare. It is preferable to develop a linear programming model of an operation with fewer uncertainties first, and then extend it when confidence and competence in linear programming become established.

Linear programming has made fewer inroads into short term scheduling, partially due to the fact that linear programming technology cannot yet deal too well with models containing many discrete operating units that must be scheduled for discrete time periods. Also, delegating direct on-line control of production scheduling to a mathematical model and a computer is not readily accepted. As mathematical competence grows, and a few successful operations become publicized, we will undoubtedly see more linear programming applications in short term production scheduling.

While the bulk of linear programming applications deals with operations planning and the development of operating strategies, many other useful applications exist. These include the use of linear programming in price determination, final product prices as well as appropriate transfer prices, some uses in curve fitting, and even some uses to simulate competitive operations. The cases and examples discussed in the later chapters of this book describe some of these applications.

## SAMPLE LINEAR PROGRAMMING MODEL

As an introduction, it may be helpful to illustrate a small linear programming problem to indicate some of the major concepts of linear programming and to detail the methods used for finding the optimum soluion to a linear programming problem.

A plant manager can use a machine M to manufacture two types of insulating material B and R. Because of the difference in the densities of these products, he can make 16.67 carloads of B in a day but only 8.33 carloads of R, or any combination

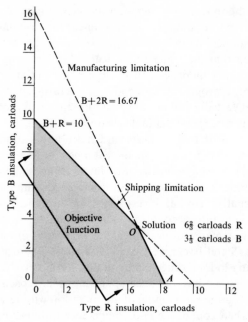

**Fig. 1-2** Graphic representation of a two-variable linear programming model.

of these two activities, as long as the total does not exceed 16.67 carloads of B equivalent, where the manufacture of 1 carload of R equals 2 carloads of B. The plant makes a profit of $3 per carload on R and only $2 per carload on B. The plant can be run many ways on a given day since any combination of these products, given these same manufacturing rates, can be produced. However, the manufacturing operation is constrained by the capacity of machine M and by the availability of transportation— only 10 boxcars are available for shipping the final product to the customers. What is the optimum strategy of the plant manager whose objective is to maximize profits?

Figure 1-2 shows a graphical representation of this manufacturing problem. As can be seen, the total of B and R must be less than 10 carloads.

Thus $R = 0$ and $B = 10$ is an admissible solution. So are $R = 5$ and $B = 5$ or even $R = 1$ and $B = 3$. However, $R = -2$ or $B = -6$ is not allowed, since obviously we cannot use machine M to produce negative quantities of material. We thus see that any point in the triangle $R = 10$, $B = 10$; $R = 0$, $B = 0$; and $R = 0$, $B = 10$ satisfies the limitations that only 10 boxcars are available and only positive quantities may be produced.

Simultaneously, the manufacturing limit implies that the total of B and R produced must lie on or to the left of the manufacturing constraint line in Fig. 1-2. Thus any solution that falls in the shaded area is a *feasible solution* which satisfies the two linear constraints on the problem. For example, $R = 4$ and $B = 4$ is a feasible solution; it is possible to manufacture these volumes within the operating constraints.

**Optimum Solution**

Maximizing a profit in the situation shown in Fig. 1-2 is equivalent to pushing through the solution space a line that represents the plant manager's objective. This is known as the objective function. The slope of this line shown in Fig. 1-2 indicates equal profit potential for 6 × B as for 4 × R. The optimum solution to this problem is, of course, the point marked O, which is at one of the vertices of the solution space. When the objective is a straight line and the solution space is bounded by straight lines, an optimum solution will always lie at one of the vertices of the solution space. If the slope of the line which represents the objective function is parallel to one of the constraint lines, both vertices on this line and any point in between them may represent an optimum solution. In our example, the optimum solution falls where both constraints in the problem are simultaneously binding, i.e., the point at which we should make $6\frac{2}{3}$ carloads of R and $3\frac{1}{3}$ carloads of B.

Such an optimal solution can be determined by linear programming methods. Since we have intuitively seen that the optimum solution must be at a vertex of the feasible solution space, it is quite safe to start at any one vertex and walk around the perimeter of the solution space until we have found an optimum solution. An easy assumption is to start at the point R = 0, B = 0, which is the intersection of the X- and Y-axes. It is a perfectly valid and feasible solution to the problem for us to make neither R nor B; at this point, of course, our profit is zero. By walking around the solution space, starting from R = 0, B = 0, we can either make $8\frac{1}{4}$ carloads of R and none of B, or 10 carloads of B and none of R. For each carload of B, we make a profit of $2 and for each carload of R, we make a profit of $3, so it appears more attractive to go the R route. This then moves us to point A $(8\frac{1}{4}, 0)$, where the profit is $25. From point A, we can return to the point R = 0, B = 0, or we can move up along the constraint line which is implied by the manufacturing limitation. If we move upward, we start making B in exchange for R in a two for one ratio, so we gain 2 × $2 and lose 1 × $3, for a net gain of $1 per carload. This alternative is attractive, so we continue on this line to the point where we make $6\frac{2}{3}$ carloads of R and $3\frac{1}{3}$ carloads of B. At this point, total profit for the operation is $(6\frac{2}{3} \times \$3) + (3\frac{1}{3} + \$2)$ or $26.67. The binding constraints are both the number of boxcars available and the manufacturing limitation.

If we proceed farther along this line from point O, our exchange (linear relationship) is one boxcar more of B for every boxcar less of R, which decreases the profit by $2 per carload − $3 per carload = −$1 per carload. This is unattractive. Since going back from point O to the horizontal axis would also result in a loss of $1 per carload, we must conclude that we have found the optimum solution to the problem.

The above is a very simple example of a linear programming problem that can be solved graphically. Since there are only two variables, it is a two-dimensional problem, and at each point or vertex our decision involves only two choices. When we reached the point at which neither choice was attractive, we had found the optimum solution to the problem.

### Cost Sensitivity Analysis

In addition to indicating the optimum solution to the problem, linear programming also gives the range of coefficients in the objective function within which the solution remains optimal. For example, we can determine that the point $R = 6\frac{2}{3}$, $B = 3\frac{1}{3}$ remains optimal when the value or profit margin of B varies from \$1.5 per carload all the way up to \$3 per carload. In manufacturing operations the exact costs are often not known and product prices can vary considerably. This immediate by-product indicates that our solution is not very sensitive to the profit margin of B, and, therefore, it would be little worth while to do additional studies aimed at developing a better profit margin analysis for B.

Varying the profit margins for B and R is equivalent to changing the slope of the objective function line. If the profit margin on B is lowered, we must sell more B to make the same profit, and the slope of the objective function becomes steeper. As long as the objective function line passes through $O$, we retain the strategy of $B = 3\frac{1}{3}$, $R = 6\frac{2}{3}$; but when the objective slope becomes as steep as or steeper than the manufacturing constraint (B at \$1.5 per carload), the projected strategy, or optimum solution, changes to $R = 8\frac{1}{3}$, $B = 0$. Conversely, not until the profit on B becomes \$3 per carload or more does the strategy become $B = 10$, $R = 0$. Thus the strategy $B = 3\frac{1}{3}$, $R = 6\frac{2}{3}$ remains optimal for the range of profit margins for B between \$1.5 and \$3 per carload. For further details of cost sensitivity analysis, see Chapter 8.

### Fractional Answers

Another observation which we should make is that in linear programming, all the variables are considered to be continuous between their lower and upper bounds; i.e., they can assume values in fractions as well as whole numbers. If we round off our answer to $R = 7$ and $B = 3$, it becomes infeasible, because it exceeds the manufacturing capacity (i.e., 8.5 instead of 8.33). Rounding down to $R = 6$ and $B = 3$ gives a feasible answer, but a little inspection shows that $R = 6$ and $B = 4$ is a better answer. Our example thus illustrates one of the limitations of linear programming—the answers cannot always be rounded to whole numbers when ordinary linear programming algorithms are used. Some algorithms will solve problems and give whole number answers. A brief discussion of these algorithms, which are called integer programming algorithms, is contained in Chapter 10.

### Starting Solution

It is very easy to develop a starting solution for this problem. The solution $R = 0$, $B = 0$, although not optimal, is feasible. However, if there were an additional constraint, such as "insulation must be produced at a rate equal to 5 carloads per day of R or 10 carloads of B or machine M will not work satisfactorily," a different problem would exist, and the solution $R = 0$, $B = 0$ would not be feasible. Figure 1-3 shows the now feasible solution space to this problem. Since we know that the optimal solution to our problem must be at a vertex of the feasible solution space, we can still start at $R = 0$, $B = 0$. But, our first objective will be to find the feasible solution space. Once this has been determined, we can follow the normal optimization policy.

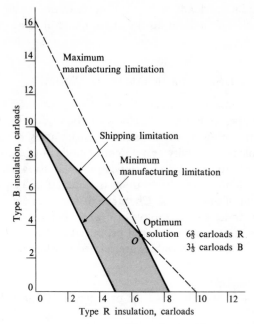

**Fig. 1-3** Graphic representation of a revised two-variable linear programming model.

The mathematical procedure is no different than the method used by an operations planning manager. Both begin by finding a possible or feasible solution; once this is found, an attempt is made to improve the solution. One of the differences between manual and computer based methods is that the computer can start from an absolute null position (make no products, use no resources) and perform all the necessary calculations to find an optimum solution. The operations planning manager will generally begin with an estimate of a good solution and improve on it subsequently. Due to the necessary computational effort, the manual process is often terminated before an optimum solution is found.

The modern high-speed computer programs available for the solution of linear programming problems adequately cope with the infeasibility problem, and the demands on the originator of the problem are minimal. At the beginning of a problem, the computer program effectively amends a hypothetical objective function which measures the amount by which the starting solution is not feasible. When using this hypothetical objective function, the programs move around the perimeter of total solution space (feasible, as well as infeasible) until a feasible solution is reached. At the conclusion of this first operation, the computer programs switch to the true objective function of the problem and perform the optimization calculation.

In formulating problems, particularly new problems, the originator sometimes specifies the problem in such a way that no feasible solution exists. For example, if we stated that machine *M* must produce at least 10 carloads of R or 20 of B, no single solution would be feasible because manufacturing cannot produce more than 8.33

carloads of R and 16.67 carloads of B. This specification is obviously inconsistent, yet such inconsistencies often occur during initial linear programming model development.

## COMPONENTS OF A LINEAR PROGRAMMING MODEL

A linear programming model is a description of an operation in mathematical terms. The behavior of the operation which it depicts can be studied by adjusting the model. Such a linear programming model consists of two classes of items: *variables* and *constraints*. A variable is an activity or a potential mode of operation. Using machine M to produce B is an activity and so is the possibility of using machine M to produce R. A constraint is a limiting condition upon the operation, i.e., only 10 boxcars are available for shipment of final goods. Chapter 3 discusses in detail the components of linear programming models. The example of Fig. 1-2 contains two variables B and R, where B is the amount of type *B* material produced and R is the amount of type *R* material produced. These two variables are related to each other by the constraints:

*Shipping limitation:*

$$B + R \text{ must be less than or equal to 10 carloads,}$$

or

$$B + R \leq 10. \tag{1-1}$$

*Manufacturing limitation:*

$$B + 2R \text{ must be less than or equal to 16.67 carloads,}$$

or

$$B + 2R \leq 16.67. \tag{1-2}$$

The variables are also related to each other by the profit maximization objective. If we let this relationship be $Z = 2B + 3R$, the objective is to maximize

$$Z = 2B + 3R. \tag{1-3}$$

The two relationships, (1-1) and (1-2), along with the tacit understanding that B and R must not be negative, form the total mathematical model of the sample problem. In these expressions, all that is known about the operation is described; all that remains is to solve the linear programming problem according to the specified objective (1-3). Chapter 2 describes how this is accomplished.

A set of mathematical equations is most easily expressed in matrix format. It is conventional to speak of a $2 \times 4$ matrix; a matrix with two rows and four columns, or in other words, with two constraints and four variables.

Within this volume, we will describe the development, solution, and analysis of problems with hundreds of equations and thousands of variables. Such large problems are being solved routinely. Reliable general purpose computer programs to carry out these solutions (see Chapter 7) exist and they are readily available. A word of caution, however, is in order. The development of large models is relatively straightforward, but the data collection aspects can become staggering. Consider, for example, a model with 1000 constraints and 2000 variables. Even if this matrix contains only 1% nonzero elements (the other 99% are zero), it is still necessary to develop $1000 \times 2000 \times 0.01 = 20,000$ data points. Actual experience in the development of a great many linear programming models has indicated that the collection of reliable input data is by far the most difficult and time consuming part of a mathematical programming project. Even after all the data has been collected, and the problem is solved, one invariably finds that further refinement of selected input data is still necessary. Chapter 8 describes in detail how such data refinement can be carried out in an interactive mode, with a linear programming model indicating the sensitive coefficients and the problem originator sharpening up on these coefficients, with this cycle repeating.

# The
# Simplex
# Method

2

Linear programming is a mathematical prodecure. A problem formulated as a linear program can be solved graphically, as was done in the example in Chapter 1, only if the problem is very small and almost trivial. Larger problems cannot be solved by graphical means, and one has to resort to mathematical manipulation and execution. As soon as these actions become routine and repetitive, they are, of course, best delegated to electronic computing equipment. For most of the common electronic computers there exist good and reliable general purpose linear programming procedures. Chapter 7 describes in detail how these procedures or programs can best be used for solving linear programming problems. Also, Chapter 13 contains a description of the historical development of electronic computers and how the computer and linear programming technologies have matured simultaneously. Large scale linear programming problems can never be solved without electronic computers, and oftentimes only the largest machines suffice. Conversely, linear programming technology has to some extent influenced computer technology, especially in the earlier stages. Linear programming and computers are inseparable, and meaningful linear programming problems can be solved only with the help of an electronic computer. Despite this, the problem originator will understand the overall solution process only if he understands the underlying mathematical manipulation that forms the basis for linear programming solutions. Because of this, we present here a simple example of the *simplex method* of linear programming. This procedure was originated by Professor

George B. Dantzig of the University of California in 1949. Since then, there have been many extensions and improvements to the original procedure, and all modern computer programs employ these modifications, especially the product form of the inverse technique (see references 40, 51, 52). For our purposes, however, we will restrict ourselves to a basic description of the simplex algorithm as applied to the sample problem of Chapter 1.

This problem was: maximize $Z$, where

$$Z = 2B + 3R, \tag{1-3}$$

subject to the limitation or constraints

$$B + R \leq 10, \tag{1-1}$$

$$B + 2R \leq 16.67. \tag{1-2}$$

Also understood but not specified was that B and R could only be positive or zero; a negative value for B or R would be meaningless, because one cannot be expected to manufacture negative quantities of a product. Thus,

$$B \text{ and } R \geq 0. \tag{2-1}$$

The inequalities (1-1) and (1-2) are difficult to deal with mathematically. They imply, in an operational sense, that the limitations imposed by shipping and manufacturing capabilities impose an upper bound, i.e., they state the maximum shipping and manufacturing capacities. The inequalities can be changed to exact equalities through the introduction of new variables or unknowns whose value represents the difference between the exact equality and the sum of the other components.

Consider, for example, the equation

$$B + R \leq 10. \tag{1-1}$$

If we could introduce a new variable $S_s$ that represents the amount of shipping capacity *not used*, then we can easily state

$$B + R + S_s = 10, \tag{2-2}$$

or in words B type insulation + R type insulation + shipping capacity not used will equal 10 carloads.

Similarly we can state

$$B + 2R + S_m = 16.67, \tag{2-3}$$

where $S_m$ represents the spare or *slack* manufacturing capacity that exists.

Chapter 3 describes in more detail the use of such slack variables. Let us accept at the present that new variables like $S_s$ and $S_m$ can be introduced so that inequalities can be changed to equalities. This then leaves us the problem: Max $Z$, where

$$Z = 2B + 3R, \tag{1-3}$$

or

$$Z - 2B - 3R = 0 \tag{2-4}$$

subject to

$$B + R + S_s = 10.00, \tag{2-2}$$

$$B + 2R + S_m = 16.67. \tag{2-3}$$

We can write this set of equations in matrix or tabular format as in Tableau 2-1.

Obviously, we now have three equations with five unknowns, i.e., $Z$, $B$, $R$, $S_s$, and $S_m$, and we are to find a best or optimum solution for this set.

An initial solution is quite easy. If we let $S_s = 10$, $S_m = 16.67$, and $Z = 0$, we have in effect stated that by leaving all the shipping and all the manufacturing capacity *slack*, we have a feasible solution with a value of 0, or in other words, we are still at the origin of the graph shown in Fig. 1-2. This is an acceptable solution to the problem, but not necessarily the best solution.

Tableau 2-1

|  | Z | B | R | $S_s$ | $S_m$ | = b |
|---|---|---|---|---|---|---|
| Max | 1 | −2 | −3 | | | = 0 |
| | | 1 | 1 | 1 | | = 10.00 = $S_s$ |
| | | 1 | 2 | | 1 | = 16.67 = $S_m$ |

The overall solution is

$$S_s = 10.00, \qquad S_m = 16.67, \qquad Z = 0,$$

and as a necessary consequence,

$$B = 0 \quad \text{and} \quad R = 0.$$

From Tableau 2-1 we can, however, see that a better solution may exist, because, as shown in the top line, the overall profit can be improved by $2.00 per unit of B produced, and by $3.00 for each unit of R. This occurs because our objective is to maximize $Z$, and

$$Z = 2B + 3R. \tag{1-3}$$

Since B and R are 0, $Z = 0$, but by letting B or R increase, $Z$ will increase by $2.00 or $3.00 per unit, respectively.

Of the two alternatives, to start producing B or R, R is, of course, more attractive. Now, when manufacturing R improves the overall profit, then we should produce as much R as possible. From Tableau 2-1 we learn that if we selected to produce R up to the shipping limitations (and thus setting $S_s$ equal to 0), we would start making $10.0/1.0 = 10.0$ units of R. Note here that the coefficient 1.0 indicates the relationship between R and $S_s$. In a similar manner, we may consider to produce R up to the manufacturing limitation (and thus setting $S_m$ equal to 0). This we can do up to a level of $16.67/2.0 = 8.33$ units of R.

From these choices, we must conclude that R can be produced only up to the manufacturing limitation of 8.33 units. By increasing R up to 10.0 units, the manufacturing capacity would be exceeded. In the graphical presentation of Fig. 1-2, we can see that producing R is equivalent to moving along the horizontal axis, with the point $A$ becoming first limiting.

For our overall new solution, we therefore decide to introduce the manufacture of R and to eliminate the slack manufacturing capacity. We learned this from examining Tableau 2-1, where we found that (1) introducing R is more attractive than introducing B ($3.00 versus $2.00) and (2) we should introduce R up to the limit imposed by the manufacturing capacity, because it has the smallest positive ratio $16.67/2.00 = 8.33$ (versus $10.0/1.0 = 10.0$) between the right-hand side vector $b$ and the new vector R to be introduced. We will thus shift (iterate) to a new solution in which $S_m$ and B will be 0 and we are to solve for Z, R, and $S_s$.

We have

$$Z - 3R \qquad = 0, \tag{2-5}$$

$$1R + S_s = 10, \tag{2-6}$$

$$2R \qquad = 16.67. \tag{2-7}$$

This represents three equations and three unknowns, which solve to

$$R = 8.33,$$

$$S_s = 10.0 - 8.33 = 1.67,$$

$$Z = 3R = 25.00.$$

In the graphical solution, this is the point $A$!

The actual mathematical rules described here are:

*Rule 1.* Select as a promising new activity the one with the greatest profit potential, i.e., the one with the largest negative number in the objective function row.*

*Rule 2.* Introduce this variable to its maximum as limited by the smallest positive ratio between the right-hand side coefficients and the corresponding coefficients in the selected column. As will be seen later, negative ratios do not represent limiting conditions, and as such are of little interest in this step.

After these two rules have been followed, a new solution can be calculated. This can be done by normal algebraic methods for solving simultaneous equations. The remaining problem then is to express the entire *new* solution in a format similar to that of Tableau 2-1 and to examine it to determine if further improvements can be achieved. A specific method for constructing the new tableau observes the following additional rules:

*Rule 3.* In the key row that represents the intersection between the incoming variable R and the outgoing variable $S_m$, divide each element by the pivotal coefficient, the

---

* This criterion applies when maximizing profit or reducing costs is the objective; in a minimization situation one should select the variable with the largest positive coefficient.

coefficient that occurs in the incoming or key column and the key or outgoing row. In our example this coefficient is 2.0.

This rule thus converts

| | Z | B | R | $S_s$ | $S_m = b$ |
|---|---|---|---|---|---|
| | 0.0 | 1.0 | 2.0 | 0.0 | 1.0 = 16.67 |

into

| | 0.0 | 0.5 | 1.0 | 0.0 | 0.5 = 8.33. |
|---|---|---|---|---|---|

In mathematical terms this is $arj' = arj/ark$, where the prime indicates new, $a$ is any coefficient, $r$ is a selected row, $j$ is a running index within the row, and $k$ is the index for the incoming column. Readers familiar with FORTRAN can quickly see the computer equivalent of this rule. It should be clear that when $j = k$, the new coefficient $arj' = arj/ark = 1.0$. In our example this is $arj' = 2.0/2.0 = 1.0$. By this rule, the replacement of the pivot element becomes 1.0.

*Rule 4.* Convert *all* other tableau entries (all that are not in the key row) by subtracting from them the product of the new coefficient at the intersection of the current column and the modified key row with the coefficient in the current row and the key column.

In Tableau 2-1 we can thus execute

$$a'_{1Z} = a_{1Z} - a_{3Z} \times a_{1R},$$

or

$$a'_{1Z} = 1.0 - 0.0 \times -3.0 = 1.0.$$

Also

$$a'_{2Z} = a_{2Z} - a_{3Z} \times a_{2R},$$

or

$$a'_{2Z} = 0.0 - 0.0 \times 1.0 = 0.0.$$

The coefficient $a'_{3Z}$ is already converted by Rule 3, so it falls outside of the current computation.

In column B we see

$$a'_{1B} = a_{1B} - a_{3B} \times a_{1R},$$

or

$$a'_{1B} = -2.0 - 0.5 \times -3.0 = -0.5,$$

and

$$a'_{2B} = a_{2B} - a_{3B} \times a_{2R},$$

or

$$a'_{2B} = 1.0 - 0.5 \times 1.0 = 0.5.$$

The coefficient $a'_{3B}$ has already been converted by Rule 3 since it is part of the key row.

In column R we see

$$a'_{1R} = -3.0 - 1.0 \times -3 = 0.0,$$

$$a'_{2R} = 1.0 - 1.0 \times 1.0 = 0.0.$$

In column $S_s$ we see

$$a'_{1S_s} = 0.0 - 0.0 \times -3.0 = 0.0,$$

$$a'_{2S_s} = 1.0 - 0.0 \times -3.0 = 1.0.$$

In column $S_m$ we see

$$a'_{1S_m} = 0.0 - 0.5 \times -3.0 = 1.5,$$

$$a'_{2S_m} = 0.0 - 0.5 \times 1.0 = -0.5.$$

In column $b$ we see

$$a'_{1b} = 0.0 - 8.33 \times -3.0 = 25.00,$$

$$a'_{2b} = 10.0 - 8.33 \times 1.0 = 1.67.$$

The new tableau therefore looks like Tableau 2-2. This tableau represents the new solution that corresponds to the point $A$ in the graph. The production of R is 8.33 units, there is a slack shipping capacity of 1.67 units, and the overall profit is $25.00.

**Tableau 2-2**

| $Z$ | B | R | $S_s$ | $S_m = b$ |
|-----|------|-----|-----|-----------|
| 1.0 | −0.5 | 0.0 | 0.0 | $1.5 = 25.0 = Z$ |
| 0.0 | 0.5 | 0.0 | 1.0 | $-0.5 = 1.67 = S_s$ |
| 0.0 | 0.5 | 1.0 | 0.0 | $0.5 = 8.33 = R$ |

By this process we have found a new and better solution. The remaining question is whether we can further improve on our current situation. Applying Rule 1 quickly indicates that there is only one candidate for introduction, i.e., B. All other variables or potential activities either would have no effect on the profit potential (coefficient 0.0) or they would decrease the profit (coefficient positive).

By now applying the four rules we can proceed to Tableau 2-3. In the graphical solution, this is equivalent to the point $O$, where 6.67 carloads of R and 3.33 carloads of B are produced for a total profit of $26.67.

**Tableau 2-3**

| $Z$ | B | R | $S_s$ | $S_m = b$ |
|-----|-----|-----|------|-----------|
| 1.0 | 0.0 | 0.0 | 1.0 | $1.0 = 26.67 = Z$ |
| 0.0 | 1.0 | 0.0 | 2.0 | $-1.0 = 3.33 = B$ |
| 0.0 | 0.0 | 1.0 | −1.0 | $1.0 = 6.67 = R$ |

Following the procedure of Rules 1 through 4 again indicates that no further improvement is possible because there are no new potential activities that can improve the solution, i.e., there are no more negative coefficients in the objective row. We thus see that the optimum solution has been obtained. But that is not the only thing learned. We can also see directly the potential effects of deviating from the optimum solution, because if we were to introduce some slack shipping capacity $S_s$, we would lose $1.00 per unit introduced. The same holds true for the manufacturing capacity. These are interesting things to know because they can also be expressed as: "We could increase our profit by $1.00 for each unit of additional shipping capacity." The same applies to manufacturing capacity—each additional unit will increase profits by $1.00.

This is an important aspect of linear programming work; the proposed solution not only provides a suggested strategy, it gives as an immediate by-product an indication on the marginal costs of the limiting constraints. It shows how profits are affected by changes in the various constraints. Thus a linear programming solution not only provides a best strategy, it also indicates the cost deviations that occur if one were to deviate from the suggested strategy.

There are still further insights on a problem that can be gained from analyzing a linear programming solution. These deal with the ranges of costs or requirements and availabilities within which the proposed solution will remain valid. These procedures are described in more detail in Chapters 7 and 8.

# Components
# of a Linear
# Programming
# Model                                                             3

From the introductory remarks of the foregoing chapters, it should be clear that a linear programming model is a description in mathematical terms of an operation. It is a model because it depicts or describes an operation, and we can study the behavior of the operation by adjusting the model. Linear programming models consist of *variables* or activities and *constraints* or *equations* that describe the interrelationships between the variables.

## VARIABLES

A variable is a potential activity or operation. It is a possible action, and we are interested in the optimum amount of this action. Examples of variables in a linear programming model are:

- Using machine A to produce product P.
- Shipping product P from origin A to destination B.
- Putting product P in inventory at site S.
- Using component C in a mixture that will become end product E.

These are just a few of the possible activities that can or have been incorporated into linear programming models. Each activity is a unique event or at least a potential unique event.  Each activity can assume different values.  For example, machine A can be used for 10 hours to make product P, or it may be used only 6 hours.  Similarly, the amount of produce shipped from origin A to destination B can be 10 tons, 73 tons, or 0.  A variable or an activity merely indicates a feasible operating procedure, i.e., it is possible to use machine M to make product P.  The function of the linear programming procedure is to select an optimum set of variables or activities and then to solve for this selected set.  One of the resulting answers will then be the amount of P to produce on machine M, which may be zero or a positive quantity.

In the example of Chapter 1, the capability to manufacture *B* is a variable, and so is the capability to produce *R*.

## CONSTRAINTS

The many variables in a linear programming model cannot assume any value at will; rather there are many constraints on an operation, and these constraints will limit the values that the variables can assume.  In the example of Chapter 1, there existed a manufacturing constraint as well as a shipping constraint.  In developing linear programming models of operations, the following types of constraints may occur:

• *Equipment capacity limitations.*  Machine M can produce 100 tons per hour maximum or warehouse W can hold no more than 500 carloads of material.

• *Material balances.*  Production plus opening inventory must equal shipments plus closing inventory.

• *Product specifications.*  The octane rating of a given gasoline blend must at least be 97, or the protein content of an animal feed mixture must at least be 30%.

• *Quantity requirements.*  At least 50 tons of P are required at site S or, 1000 barrels of premium gasoline must be made.

• *Technical limitations.*  The pressure on vessel V must not exceed 500 pounds per square inch.

• *Regulatory limitations.*  The amount of sulfur dioxide emitted to the air by a large boiler shall not exceed 0.2 part per million.

• *Policy considerations.*  A plant shall be so operated as to provide work for at least 50 men.

Many other examples of limiting conditions or constraints can and do exist. When describing an operation in mathematical terms (as a mathematical model) such constraints will occur in the form of equations or inequalities.  Note, for example, that of the seven examples above, six contain a statement of "at least" or "at most," implying that any answer up to or beyond a stated figure is acceptable.  In mathematical terms, such a statement is described by an inequality.  A minimum constraint, such as a minimum quantity requirement, may be exceeded; it is allowable to ship more or a surplus beyond the specified amount.  This constraint is therefore binding only on the low side.

A maximum constraint, such as the maximum amount of warehouse space available to store inventory, need not be met exactly either. It is entirely acceptable to store fewer goods in the warehouse than the maximum capacity allows, in effect, keeping some of the warehouse unoccupied. The amount by which the warehouse is not filled up is known as *slack capacity*.

No matter how these equations are formulated, there is always the allowable procedure to exceed the minimum or to stay below the maximum, and only exact equalities such as the material balance equations need be met exactly.

## SLACK AND SURPLUS VARIABLES

From the above discussion it should be clear that linear programming constraints are often in the form of inequalities. When a constraint consists of a minimum quantity specification, it is entirely admissible to exceed such a specification. At the same time, a maximum constraint such as the inventory space available in a warehouse need not be met. In the development of linear programming problems, new variables or activities are quickly introduced to handle the amounts by which minima are exceeded, or maxima not met. Such variables are known as *surplus variables*, indicating the surplus quantity available, or *slack variables*, indicating the amount of slack capacity that exists. Using the prior examples, this is what happens. If we let $P$ be the amount of product shipped, we can state

$$P \geq 50. \tag{3-1}$$

We can introduce a new variable $S_P$ that represents the surplus shipped so that

$$P = 50 + S_P \tag{3-2}$$

or

$$P - S_P = 50 \tag{3-2a}$$

by the addition of a new variable that makes up for the difference between the requirement and the actual amount shipped.

A similar example for the maximum consideration is: Let $I_A$ be the inventory of product A, and $I_B$ be the inventory of product B, with the constraint

$$I_A + I_B \leq 300 \text{ ft}^3. \tag{3-3}$$

This equation can be changed into an equality by stating

$$I_A + I_B + I_S = 300 \text{ ft}^3, \tag{3-4}$$

where $I_S$ is the slack inventory space, or the inventory space not used in the solution of the problem.

Another important consideration in linear programming problems is that all of the variables are normally limited to positive values. It is, of course, not possible to add a negative amount of component $Q_A$ into a gasoline blend. Neither is it possible to store a negative amount of item $I_A$ in a warehouse. The amount to be stored in the warehouse, or the amount of the product component to be blended must either be zero or positive; a negative value of such a variable is meaningless. The electronic computer routines or programs for the solution of linear programs generally create appropriate slack and surplus variables as part of the normal solution procedure.

## EXACT EQUALITIES

In the development of linear programming problems, it is also frequently possible that exact equalities must be met. For example, in a manufacturing operation, the amount of the opening inventory plus the amount produced in a given time period must equal the amount delivered to customers plus the amount of closing inventory. In this case, neither slack nor surplus variables may be introduced into the problem, since only an exact equality will satisfy the "balance" constraint. If we let $I_o$ be the opening inventory, $I_c$ be the closing inventory, $D$ be the customer demand, and $P$ be the production, then

$$I_o + P - D - I_c = 0 \tag{3-5}$$

is the equation that describes the above material balance.

## ARTIFICIAL VARIABLES

Of course, with an exact equality, there is no need to create a slack or surplus variable. However, in order to start the computer solution procedure, it is convenient to introduce a so-called *artificial variable*, a variable that represents the apparent difference in the equality. Through this expedient, it becomes possible to state an initial, albeit infeasible, solution that can be used as the starting point of the complete solution procedure. For example, we can begin by letting $P$, $D$, and $I_c$ be zero. However, $I_o$ is not zero when there is material on hand at the start of the problem. When we introduce an artificial variable $A_b$ so that

$$I_o + P + D - I_c + A_b = 0 \tag{3-6}$$

and we let $A_b = -I_o$, $P = 0$, $D = 0$, and $I_c = 0$, we satisfy Eq. (3-6) mathematically. As long as $A_b$ is not zero, Eq. (3-5) is not satisfied, so we see that the artificial variable $A_b$ represents an infeasibility. Just as with slack and surplus variables, the commercially available computer procedures will automatically create such artificial variables when necessary.

## TYPES OF CONSTRAINTS

The constraints in linear programming models can be considered in a different manner. When there is maximum availability of a resource or maximum requirement for a commodity, we can think of an upper limit or *upper bound*. Consider, for example the warehouse limitation from the inventory example above:

$$I_A + I_B \le 300. \tag{3-3}$$

This is an upper bound condition. In a similar manner, there can exist lower limits or *lower bounds*, e.g.,

$$P \geq 50. \tag{3-2}$$

At times, only a single variable has an upper and/or lower bound. In this case we can speak of a *bounded variable*, as in this example, where $P$ is limited to a minimum of 50 tons. In this sense, $P$ is a bounded variable. Bounded variables are important because many of the more sophisticated computer programs are capable of dealing with bounded variables directly, without requiring the insertion of special "upper or lower bound" constraints. Exact equalities can also be thought of as balance equations; the inputs must be equal to the outputs, or there must be a balance between inputs and outputs. Equation (3-5) is of this type, $I_o + P$ must be equal to $D + I_c$. In this instance, the equation represents a material balance.

All the equations in a linear programming problem are of three types:

- Upper bounds,
- Lower bounds,
- Balance equations.

In order to arrive at an initial starting solution, upper bound equations are augmented with a slack variable, one for each upper bound equation; lower bound equations are augmented with a surplus variable, one for each lower bound equation; and balance equations are augmented with an artificial variable, one for each balance equation. We see thus that the total number of variables in a linear programming problem is equal to the number of variables introduced by the problem originator (structural variables) plus a number of variables equal to the number of constraints in the model.

## DIMENSIONS

We have observed that there are many varieties of problem constraints. Each constraint specifies in a single mathematical equation a certain operating condition, i.e., an octane rating must be met or exceeded, total inventory must be less than the total space available, or a balance between input and output must be met. Each of these equations can have a different dimension. In the product quality specifications, the dimension for the equation consisted of octane quality times the number of gallons. In the inventory equation, the variables are expressed as the number of units stored. Each unit occupies some number of cubic feet and the dimensions for the constraint can be cubic feet or some other volumetric unit such as carloads. In the product balance equation, the dimension for the equation consisted of merely units produced, units stored, and units purchased. Hence, the dimension for this equation is merely units. The various equations that together form a linear programming model need not all have the same dimensions; in fact, they seldom do. For simplicity's sake, it is advisable to keep the number of different dimensions small. Since each equation is an entity, it is possible, but undesirable, for each equation to have its own special dimension.

We should note here also that constraints on a linear programming problem can be physical constraints, such as hours of equipment availability, or they can be policy constraints, i.e., we will not operate the plant with less than 15 men. The motivation for including the constraint into the model is as unimportant as the dimension used for the constraint. It is necessary only that *all* true operational constraints, be they physical or based on policy considerations, are included in the model.

## FEASIBLE SOLUTIONS

In the development of linear programming problems, one is not sure that the problem, as specified, is feasible. For example, we could have an equation that specified that a minimum of man-days of work must be incurred at a given plant. Such a specification may be the result of a labor contract, or it may be just a desirable operating policy imposed by management of the corporation. The possibility of shutting this plant down entirely or using it below the level as defined in the constraint is unadmissible. If a linear programming model contains such equations, then producing zero at that plant can only be accomplished by having the surplus manpower variable assume a negative value. This is known as an infeasibility. If we let $M_A$ be the manpower of type $A$, $M_B$ be the manpower of type $B$, and $M_S$ be the surplus manpower, and if we have an equation

$$M_A + M_B - M_S = 50, \tag{3-7}$$

we cannot tolerate $M_A = 0$ *and* $M_B = 0$ because this would yield $M_S = -50$, or the surplus manpower is 50 men short. It is not feasible to satisfy the operating constraint when not producing anything at the plant.

An infeasibility can also exist due to an equality constraint. For example, if there is an opening inventory of a product, but no demand, no production, and no closing inventory, then this represents an infeasible condition.

Let $I_o$ be the amount of opening inventory, $I_c$ be the amount of closing inventory, $D$ be the product demand, and $P$ be the production volume. Then, if $I_o = 10$, $D = 0$, $P = 0$, and $I_c = 0$, the equation

$$I_o + P - D - I_c = 0 \tag{3-5}$$

is not satisfied. It can be satisfied by the introduction of an artificial variable.

Linear programming methods are intended to find an optimum operating strategy using the variables provided in the problem, while satisfying the constraints imposed. However, prior to being able to search for an optimum solution, all linear programming solution procedures must first establish that a feasible solution exists. This has given rise to the so-called *two-phase approach*. Once a problem is presented to the computer, the first step is to develop a feasible solution and the subsequent step is to develop an optimum solution while maintaining feasibility. A problem is feasible when all artificial variables are zero and all other variables including the slack and surplus variables are nonnegative (zero or positive).

The various computer codes available for the multitude of electronic computers treat this procedure in varying manners. Some will entirely ignore optimization until feasibility is established, while others will attempt to simultaneously attain feasibility and optimality. The exact mode of operation is unimportant so long as it is recognized that feasibility and optimality are both required.

## OPTIMAL SOLUTIONS

What is an optimal solution? Many of the operations modeled contain operating cost, or alternatively, a special variable can represent the potential profit. In industrial terms, the objective of solving a linear program is generally to minimize operating costs or to maximize the profits. When the problem is formulated so as to produce a maximum profit, generally final product prices are included as parts of the model, and the model is requested to provide the optimum operating strategy given these prices. In other cases, the requirement is not so much to maximize the profit in the face of given product prices, because product prices will frequently vary with the quantity sold. In these cases, it is usually specified first that the product demands be exactly met (feasibility), and subsequently the objective becomes to minimize the operating cost to manufacture the exact quantities of the product. All good linear program solution codes are capable of either minimizing the costs or maximizing the profits.

In normal manufacturing operations, the objectives are frequently quite clear, yet when manpower considerations or military strategy are involved, the true objective of the operation at times may be more difficult to ascertain. We should note here that a linear program can only find an optimal solution to a given single objective. One must instruct the computer routine with distinctive guidelines and only a single objective at a time can be optimized. This does not mean that the linear program solution code cannot be asked to solve a problem with different objectives. We merely indicate that only a single objective at a time can be optimized. In actual operations the same is true. We can instruct a plant manager to minimize his operating costs, and he will look for a minimum cost operating plan, given certain raw material, labor, and utilities costs. If however, raw material costs fluctuate, his strategy may vary; for each set of raw material costs he can develop a "best" strategy, but differing strategies are frequently inevitable as costs change. In linear programming terminology, a full set of costs is a single objective function for which a best strategy can be found. A different set of costs will form a different objective function for which a different "best" solution can be found.

## ALTERNATIVE SOLUTIONS

A linear program routine will find a feasible and an optimal solution to a problem if such a solution exists. Relatively frequently there are several solutions that all satisfy the optimality criteria, just as there can be equally good operating strategies in industrial situations. Alternative optimum solutions can be observed from the printouts available from all linear program computer solution programs. They are manifested by having variables with zero marginal cost not in the optimum solution. When the marginal cost is zero, the total objective is not altered by introducing the variable into the solution and hence a different solution, containing a different activity, exists at the same minimum cost. This thus represents an alternative optimum solution. For a detailed discussion of these concepts see Chapter 8.

## DISCUSSION TOPICS AND PROBLEMS

1. In developing a model of a part of your operation, what operational constraints can apply? (Manufacturing capacities, raw material supplies, finished goods outlets, policy considerations, etc.)
2. What kind of possible activities or variables exist for your operations? (Manufacturing, mining, transportation, conversion, product upgrading, etc.)
3. In developing a mathematical model of an operation should you include only those activities that have been employed in the past, or should you also include other possibilities, even though they have not been considered before?

# Models of
# Production
# Operations                                                            4

The producing industries provide by far the largest number of linear programming applications. Linear programming models are used to schedule or plan such operations. Each industry, of course, has its own type of model and its own special considerations. However, a number of similar types of operations do exist in a variety of industries, and these have given rise to some common problem formulations. For example, final product blending operations exist in petroleum refining, primary steel manufacture, feed manufacture, textile operations, etc. Each of these industries has, of course, different component availabilities, finished goods requirements, and product specifications. The mathematical model that describes a blending operation is, however, the same for all of these processing industries.

In a similar manner, there are other operational systems that can be described by common mathematical programming models. These include simultaneous multiproduct manufacturing operations, batchwise multiproduct manufacturing, and transportation models.

In many instances, an industrial linear programming application will entail one or more of these various types of operation. In these cases, the various models are combined into an overall model that represents such a company's operating process.

## A PRODUCT MIXING MODEL

Probably the most common linear programming model is one that describes a product mixing operation. The common aspects of such an operation are that a number of

**Table 4-1**

**Blending Components**

| Component | Availability, thousands of barrels | Research octane number | Vapor pressure | Volatility index | Code name | Cost, cents per gallon |
|---|---|---|---|---|---|---|
| Butane | 1.7 | 120.0 | 60.0 | 105 | BU | 5.2 |
| Light naphtha | 1.0 | 84.5 | 18.0 | 30 | LN | 6.4 |
| Heavy naphtha | 2.3 | 73.0 | 4.0 | 12 | HN | 8.3 |
| Catalytic naphtha | 6.2 | 96.0 | 6.4 | 15 | CN | 10.2 |
| Catalytic reformate | 4.0 | 99.0 | 2.5 | 3 | CR | 11.0 |

raw or intermediate materials are blended together to form a finished product with strictly defined qualities.

Table 4-1 describes a number of components in a petroleum refinery that can be used to blend a regular gasoline as described in Table 4-2. In this problem, the variables or activities are the amounts of each of the components used in making up the regular gasoline blend. These variables are butane (BU), light naphtha (LN), heavy naphtha (HN), catalytic naphtha (CN), and catalytic reformate (CR). The first constraint is a volume requirement:

$$BU + LN + HN + CN + CR = 10 \text{ thousand barrels.} \qquad (4\text{-}1)$$

This states that the sum of the volumes of the components must equal 10 thousand barrels. Note that none of the variables has been assigned a value as yet; the actual amounts are undetermined except that negative quantities are not tolerated.

The next set of constraints relates to the availability of the components:

$$BU \leq 1.7, \qquad (4\text{-}2)$$

$$LN \leq 1.0, \qquad (4\text{-}3)$$

$$HN \leq 2.3, \qquad (4\text{-}4)$$

$$CN \leq 6.2, \qquad (4\text{-}5)$$

$$CR \leq 4.0, \qquad (4\text{-}6)$$

The final set of constraints is concerned with the product qualities:

Octane $\quad 120BU + 84.5LN + 73HN + 96CN + 99CR \geq 95GAS.$ $\qquad (4\text{-}7)$

This specifies that the octane of the final product, expressed in thousands of octane barrels, must at least be 95 or more for each barrel of gas manufactured; and since

**Table 4-2**

**Regular Gasoline Requirement**

| Needed volume, thousands of barrels | Minimum research octane number | Maximum vapor pressure | Minimum volatility index | Code name |
|---|---|---|---|---|
| 10.0 | 95.0 | 11.0 | 18 | GAS |

Eq. (4-1) specifies that 10 thousand barrels must be made, there is a requirement for $95 \times 10 = 950$ thousand octane barrels.

Vapor pressure    $60BU + 18LN + 4HN + 6.4CN + 2.5CR \leq 11.0GAS.$    (4-8)

This specifies that the vapor pressure of the final blend must be less than or equal to 11.0.

Volatility    $105BU + 30LN + 12HN + 15CN + 3CR \geq 18.0GAS.$    (4-9)

The above nine equations describe the entire blending operation and as such they are the "model" of the operation.

The objective of course is to produce the final product at minimum cost. Thus

$$\text{Min } [5.2BU + 6.4LN + 8.3HN + 10.2CN + 11.0CR]    (4-10)$$

states the objective.

The model with the objective function but without the slack and surplus variables can also be shown in matrix format:

| | BU | LN | HN | CN | CR | Requirements |
|---|---|---|---|---|---|---|
| Objective | 5.2 | 6.4 | 8.3 | 10.2 | 11.0 | in thousands |
| Total volume | 1 | 1 | 1 | 1 | 1 | = 10.0 |
| BU volume | 1 | | | | | ≤ 1.7 |
| LN volume | | 1 | | | | ≤ 1.0 |
| HN volume | | | 1 | | | ≤ 2.3 |
| CN volume | | | | 1 | | ≤ 6.2 |
| CR volume | | | | | 1 | ≤ 4.0 |
| Octane specification | 120 | 84.5 | 73 | 96 | 99 | ≥ 950.0 |
| Vapor pressure | 60 | 18 | 4 | 6.4 | 2.5 | ≤ 110.0 |
| Volatility | 105 | 30 | 12 | 15 | 3.0 | ≥ 180.0 |

Note here that the amount of GAS requirement is 10.0 thousand barrels, and hence that in the product quality constraints, the requirements are for $95.0 \times 10.0 = 950.0$

thousand octane barrels, $11.0 \times 10.0 = 110.0$ thousand vapor pressure barrels, and $18.0 \times 10.0 = 180.0$ thousand volatility unit barrels. All single product blending models, irrespective of the industry that they pertain to, exhibit this same matrix pattern where the heavy black lines represent a series of 1.0's:

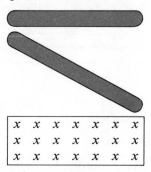

Similarly, a two-product blending model with common components to be used in both products looks in matrix format like:

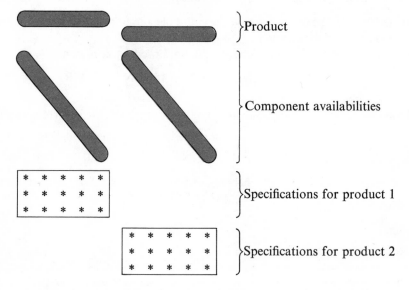

## SIMULTANEOUS MULTIPRODUCT MANUFACTURING MODELS

Many industries, while geared to manufacture one main product, will also automatically produce several coproducts or by-products. In oil refining, the distillation of a barrel of crude oil yields some gases, some propane, some gasoline, some jet fuel, some diesel fuel, and some fuel oil. All of these are coproducts; they are manufactured simultaneously by a single process. In the meat packing industry, the slaughter of a single hog produces some pork, some ham, some bacon, a hide, and other commodities. A rock crushing operation produces some fine dust, some small rocks, some medium size rocks, and maybe even a few large rocks. There are, of course, many other examples of simultaneous coproduct manufacturing operations, but the above examples should be adequate to demonstrate the common aspect of these operations.

The mathematical model describing these various operations is quite straightforward and similar for all the operations mentioned. Let us work out the example of the rock crushing operation. When the crusher runs, it produces:

| | |
|---|---|
| Dust | 10% |
| Fine gravel | 40% |
| Medium rocks | 30% |
| Large rocks | 20% |

Of course, during operation, 100% of raw material is consumed.

If we now have demands for 2 tons dust, 40 tons fine gravel, 25 tons medium rock, and 20 tons large rocks, and a maximum availability of 100 tons of raw materials, and if we let our crusher operation be known as O, we can state:

Dust requirement

$$0.10O \geq 2, \tag{4-11}$$

Fine gravel requirement

$$0.40O \geq 40, \tag{4-12}$$

Medium rock requirement

$$0.30O \geq 25, \tag{4-13}$$

Large rock requirement

$$0.20O \geq 20, \tag{4-14}$$

Raw material supply

$$1.00O \leq 100. \tag{4-15}$$

If we let the surplus and slack variable be named SD for dust, SFG for fine gravel, SMR for medium rock, SLR for large rock, and SRAW for raw material, we have

$$0.10O - SD = 2, \tag{4-16}$$

$$0.40O - SFG = 40, \tag{4-17}$$

$$0.30O - SMR = 25, \tag{4-18}$$

$$0.20O - SLR = 20, \tag{4-19}$$

$$1.00O + SRAW = 100. \tag{4-20}$$

This last equation can also be converted to:

$$-1.00\,O - SRAW = -100 \tag{4-20a}$$

This converts into matrix form:

| O | SD | SFG | SMR | SLR | SRAW | Requirement |
|---|----|-----|-----|-----|------|-------------|
| 0.10 | −1 | | | | | = 2 |
| 0.40 | | −1 | | | | = 40 |
| 0.30 | | | −1 | | | = 25 |
| 0.20 | | | | −1 | | = 20 |
| −1.00 | | | | | −1 | = −100 |

This is a typical pattern for a simultaneous multiproduct manufacturing model, with the column of numbers under O generally known as the *activity vector* or the *manufacturing variable*. In a simultaneous multiproduct manufacturing model there are always at least as many nonzero coefficients in the vector as there are product interactions, with finished products as well as with the raw material. In this model of five equations, the supply is debited for rocks consumed, and the other four are credited with the amount of material produced. In this example, all material balances are on a weight basis, and hence, the sum of the quantities produced equals the quantity consumed.

Many manufacturing operations also have some manufacturing losses, and hence a ton of rock may not yield a full ton of crushed material. This is so because some of the dust is so fine that it just blows away. Under such circumstances, it is generally best to incorporate into the model the exact volume flows resulting from the activity. For example, in the rock crushing example,

| | |
|---|---|
| Rock supply balance | −1.0 |
| Dust | 0.085 |
| Fine gravel | 0.395 |
| Medium rocks | 0.30 |
| Large rocks | 0.20 |

may represent the actual material flows on a weight basis, taking into consderation the loss of the fine dust and the fine gravel.

The above described primarily the material balance aspects of a simultaneous product manufacturing model. Other constraints that frequently occur in production models are manpower balances and utility balances. For example, if the rock crusher required a crew of 3 men, and 1000 tons of rocks can be crushed in a single shift, then there should also be an entry of (−0.003) in the manpower per ton balance equation. Similarly, if the crusher consumed 2000 kilowatt-hours (kWh) of power on a single shift, then if there is an electric power balance equation, it should be debited by −2000/1000 or −2 kWh for every ton of rock crushed. Note here that the crushing activity is expressed in tons of rock crushed, while the manpower and electric power balance equations are expressed in men per ton rock and kWh per ton rock, respectively. Other utility services that can be variable with the amount of the activity are heat, fuel, air-conditioning, cooling water, and steam.

**Table 4-3.**

| Activity | Fine operation | Medium operation | Constraint |
|---|---|---|---|
| Rock supply balance | −1.0 | −1.0 | ≥ −100 |
| Dust | 0.085 | 0.05 | ≥ 2 |
| Fine gravel | 0.39 | 0.265 | ≥ 40 |
| Medium | 0.30 | 0.42 | ≥ 25 |
| Large rocks | 0.20 | 0.25 | ≥ 20 |
| Manpower | −0.003 | −0.003 | ≥ −3 |
| Electric power | −2.0 | −1.7 | ≥ −1000 |
| Crusher capacity | −1.00 | −0.80 | ≥ −150 |

A further important element in an activity vector is the capacity constraint element. This is especially important if the process can be operated at various severities and if the linear programming model would be requested to in effect suggest the severity of the operation. If, for example, our rock crusher could be operated for maximum fine gravel, or for maximum medium rocks, our model without the slack and surplus vectors could look like Table 4-3. This model now represents the two possible modes of operation of the crusher. The second mode of operation is less severe; it consumes less power and less crusher capacity (it can run faster) while still requiring the same amount of manpower.

If there are two separate variables or activity vectors that describe different operating modes for a single unit, it frequently happens that the optimum solution to the problem suggests to use both modes, but each a fraction of the total available capacity. This is quite straightforward. The solution may for example say: Use mode 1 38% of the time and use mode 2 62% of the time.

If more than two modes of operation are described in the model, it may occur that the solution suggests to use modes 1 and 3 each 50% of the time, but not to use

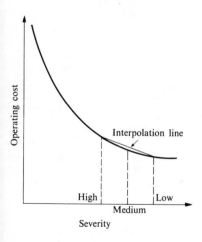

Fig. 4-1 Typical cost of operation vs. severity of operation.

mode 2. This may be proper, but it is quite unlikely to happen in a normal industrial environment.

For example, if the rock crusher can be operated at three severities, with low, medium, and high yields of fine materials, then it is most likely that the medium operation by itself is less expensive than operating the crusher 50% of the time at high and 50% of the time at low severity. There are of course exceptions to such a rule of thumb, but in most cases it is wise to verify the input data into the model if the solution suggests to use the high and low severity operations simultaneously, instead of medium severity with possibly one of the other two operating modes. This is a problem in convexity as shown in Fig. 4-1. It can easily be seen that the medium severity mode of operation is less costly than a mixture of high and low severity operations. For a more detailed discussion of such nonlinear relationships, see Chapter 11.

### BATCHWISE MULTIPRODUCT MANUFACTURING MODEL

In many industrial operations, a single machine or unit can be used to manufacture various end products, but only one product at a time. Especially if there are a large number of manufacturing units each with different costs and different production rates, scheduling the entire operation becomes a tremendous task, and linear programming can possibly help. Consider, for example, a steel company that has three open hearth furnaces (OH1, OH2, OH3), a basic oxygen furnace (BO), and an electrical furnace (ELEC). This firm normally manufactures carbon (C), armor (A), alloy (L), and stainless (S) steels. The open hearth furnaces are usually reserved for the manufacture of carbon and armor steel, alloy is usually produced on the basic oxygen furnace, and stainless on the electric furnace. Other manufacturing activities are possible, but they have not been used. Table 4-4 describes a possible set of operating conditions and product requirements for the steel-making operation.

**Table 4-4**
**Steel Production (Tons Per Day) with Five Furnaces**

| Steel Type | OH1 | OH2 | OH3 | BO | ELEC | Requirement, tons |
|---|---|---|---|---|---|---|
| Carbon | 120 | 140 | 87 | 103 | 45 | 8100 |
| Armor | 104 | 130 | 80 | 94 | 42 | 1938 |
| Alloy | — | — | — | 97 | 35 | 2128 |
| Stainless | 62 | 70 | 55 | 88 | 37 | 1020 |
| Days available | 30 | 29 | 27 | 30 | 28 | |

Standard production rates: tons per day
Availability: stream days per month
Requirement: total tonnage forecast

**Table 4-5**

**Multiproduct Manufacturing Model**

| O | O | O | O | O | O | O | O | O | B | B | B | B | E | E | E | E | | D* / C† |
|---|---|---|---|---|---|---|---|---|---|---|---|---|---|---|---|---|---|---|
| H | H | H | H | H | H | H | H | H | O | O | O | O | L | L | L | L | | E & A |
| 1 | 1 | 1 | 2 | 2 | 2 | 3 | 3 | 3 | | | | | E | E | E | E | | M      P |
| | | | | | | | | | | | | | C | C | C | C | | |
| C | A | S | C | A | S | C | A | S | C | A | L | S | C | A | L | S | | |
| 1 | 1 | 1 | | | | | | | | | | | | | | | ≤ | 30 |
| | | | 1 | 1 | 1 | | | | | | | | | | | | ≤ | 29 |
| | | | | | | 1 | 1 | 1 | | | | | | | | | ≤ | 27 |
| | | | | | | | | | 1 | 1 | 1 | 1 | | | | | ≤ | 30 |
| | | | | | | | | | | | | | 1 | 1 | 1 | 1 | ≤ | 28 |
| 120 | | | 140 | | | 87 | | | 103 | | | | 45 | | | | = | 8100 |
| | 104 | | | 130 | | | 80 | | | 94 | | | | 42 | | | = | 1938 |
| | | 62 | | | 70 | | | 55 | | | 88 | | | | 37 | | = | 1020 |
| | | | | | | | | | | | | 97 | | | | 35 | = | 2128 |

\* DEM = demand.

† CAP = capacity.

The actual mathematical model of this operation has three possible modes of operation for the open hearth furnaces, and four modes of operations for the basic oxygen and electric furnaces. In total, there are 17 potential operating modes, or 17 possible activities, resulting in 17 column vectors in the linear planning matrix.

In addition to the objective function, there are five capacity constraint rows for the five furnaces, and there are four demand equation rows for the four types of steel to be manufactured, giving a total of nine constraint rows. The entire model of the operation, but without the objective function, is shown in Table 4-5.

The observant reader will note that the structure of this model is similar to the structure of the blending model, i.e., machine capacities are distributed over the various final product requirements. Additional constraints, not shown in Table 4-5, that frequently apply are manpower usage and utility usage, much as they occur in simultaneous multiproduct manufacturing models. As noted before, the matrix shown in Table 4-5 is a model of the operation, and this model will be used to develop an operating program for the plant that it represents.

## TRANSPORTATION MODELS

When goods are distributed from plants to warehouses, or even from warehouses to delivery points, it is often attractive to model this distribution operation along with the model of manufacturing operations. Delivery costs of finished goods frequently exceed 10% of the variable manufacturing costs, and the development of an appropriate distribution schedule along with a manufacturing schedule can be highly attractive. Furthermore, some companies are in the distribution business only, and for these firms an analysis by linear programming methods can be highly beneficial.

**Table 4-6**

**Transportation Model with Three Sources and Five Sinks**

| W | W | W | W | W | W | W | W | W | W | W | W | W | W | W | D | C |
|---|---|---|---|---|---|---|---|---|---|---|---|---|---|---|---|---|
| 1 | 1 | 1 | 1 | 1 | 2 | 2 | 2 | 2 | 2 | 3 | 3 | 3 | 3 | 3 | E & | A |
| D | D | D | D | D | D | D | D | D | D | D | D | D | D | D | M | P |
| 1 | 2 | 3 | 4 | 5 | 1 | 2 | 3 | 4 | 5 | 1 | 2 | 3 | 4 | 5 | | |
| 1 | 1 | 1 | 1 | 1 | | | | | | | | | | | ≤ 100 | W1 |
| | | | | | 1 | 1 | 1 | 1 | 1 | | | | | | ≤ 70 | W2 |
| | | | | | | | | | | 1 | 1 | 1 | 1 | 1 | ≤ 60 | W3 |
| 1 | | | | | 1 | | | | | 1 | | | | | = 50 | D1 |
| | 1 | | | | | 1 | | | | | 1 | | | | = 40 | D2 |
| | | 1 | | | | | 1 | | | | | 1 | | | = 20 | D3 |
| | | | 1 | | | | | 1 | | | | | 1 | | = 40 | D4 |
| | | | | 1 | | | | | 1 | | | | | 1 | = 30 | D5 |

The basic distribution or transportation model is very straightforward. The main body of the matrix will consist of only 0's and 1's. These models, when expressed in general linear programming formats, look just like blending models without quality constraints. Table 4-6 is an example of a transportation model with three warehouses (W) and five destinations (D) for a single commodity. Not shown in Table 4–6 are the transportation costs from each warehouse to each destination. Each column vector in such a model represents the activity of shipping a unit of goods from a warehouse to a destination. When there is more than a single commodity to be shipped, an activity will consist of shipping a specific commodity from one warehouse or source to a given destination or sink. Therefore, if the model is to encompass 40 commodities from 5 sources to 120 sinks, the model would consist of $40 \times 5 \times 120 = 24{,}000$ variables, and there would be $40 \times 5 = 200$ supply constraints and $40 \times 120 = 4800$ demand constraints. By any standard, that is a large linear programming model. However, due to the special nature and structure of the pure transportation problem, it has been possible to devise special algorithms so that problems of this size are actually quite easily solved. Difficulties arise when such a transportation model forms part of a much larger problem so that the special transportation formulation cannot be used. Chapters 7 and 12 contains some suggestions that may be helpful in such cases.

The efficient formulation of a pure transportation model is a matrix that contains the transportation costs only, with the rest of the model structure implied. Table 4-7 gives such an efficient formulation for the same operation as depicted in Table 4-6. Table 4-7 also includes the transportation costs.

Two additional observations apply to the pure transportation linear programming model:

1. Inhibited routes, impossible delivery routes, or even highly unlikely delivery activities can be effectively blocked by inserting an artificially high transportation

**Table 4-7**

**Efficient Formulation of a Pure Transportation Model**

| Sources | | W1 | W2 | W3 | |
|---|---|---|---|---|---|
| Source capacity | | 100 | 70 | 60 | Sink demands |
| Sinks | D1 | $11.20 | $16.20 | $4.30 | 50 |
| | D2 | $12.30 | $8.40 | $6.50 | 40 |
| | D3 | $8.90 | $3.70 | $7.30 | 20 |
| | D4 | $7.60 | $9.20 | $5.20 | 40 |
| | D5 | $9.25 | $8.65 | $999.00 | 30 |

cost in the cell for that route. In Table 4-7, for example, the route from warehouse 3 to destination 5 is effectively blocked. Such a blocking procedure is necessary because the structure of the total model is implied. If $0 had been inserted in the route W3–D5, the algorithm would surely suggest to ship all it could via the "cheap" route from W3 to D5.

2. If supply capacities and demands are expressed in integers or whole numbers, then the solution to the transportation problem will also be in integers. This is not a normal circumstance in linear programs (see the example in Chapter 1), rather it is a special effect in pure transportation problems, and it results from the structure of the model itself.

## TRANSPORTATION MODEL SOLUTION

As we have seen, a pure transportation model can be presented in a compact format. The solution to a pure transportation problem is also much simpler than the simplex procedure described in Chapter 2. Consider for example, the three sources and five sinks problem shown in Table 4-7. Our objective is to find the quantities or flows to be shipped from each source to each sink, while minimizing the total transportation cost. We can show both the transportation costs *and* the flows in a combined table as in Table 4-8.

Once this tabulation form is established, one should proceed to:

1. Find a feasible solution.
2. Find better solutions until the optimum solution has been found.

As such, one can clearly see that this approach matches the simplex algorithm. Let us see how we can proceed, beginning by finding a feasible solution first. If we establish a flow of 50 units from W1 to D1, we satisfy all the D1 requirements, and still have a capacity of 50 units left at W1. Let us therefore assign a flow of 40 units from W1 to D2. This fulfills the demand for D2, leaving still a capacity of 10 units

Table 4-8

**Combined Cost and Flow Table for a Transportation Problem**

| Sources | | W1 | W2 | W3 | Sink Demands |
|---|---|---|---|---|---|
| Source capacity | | 100 | 70 | 60 | |
| Sinks | D1 | $11.20 | $16.20 | $4.30 | 50 |
| | D2 | $12.30 | $8.40 | $6.50 | 40 |
| | D3 | $8.90 | $3.70 | $7.30 | 20 |
| | D4 | $7.60 | $9.20 | $5.20 | 40 |
| | D5 | $9.25 | $8.65 | $999.00 | 30 |
| Unused capacity | | 100 | 70 | 60 | |

Table 4-9

| Sources | | W1 | W2 | W3 | Sink demands |
|---|---|---|---|---|---|
| Source capacity | | 100 | 70 | 60 | |
| Sinks | | $11.20 | $16.20 | $4.30 | |
| | D1 | 50 | | | 50 |
| | | $12.30 | $8.40 | $6.50 | |
| | D2 | 40 | | | 40 |
| | | $8.90 | $3.70 | $7.30 | |
| | D3 | 10 | 10 | | 20 |
| | | $7.60 | $9.20 | $5.20 | |
| | D4 | | 40 | | 40 |
| | | $9.25 | $8.65 | $999.00 | |
| | D5 | | 20 | 10 | 30 |
| Unused capacity | | 0 | 0 | 50 | |

at W1.  Next, we will establish a flow of 10 units from W1 to D3.  This exhausts the capacity of W1, but it does not yet fill the complete requirements for D3.  So now we must establish an additional flow of 10 units from W2 to D3.  This process can go on, resulting in the flows shown in Table 4-9.  This now represents a feasible solution, even though most likely a nonoptimal solution since 10 units are shipped at the exhorbitant rate of $999.00 per unit.  The process by which the feasible solution was found is generally known as the "northwest corner rule"; by starting to fill demands in the northwest corner and gradually moving toward the southeast a feasible solution is found.  There are a great many varieties of methods to find a feasible solution, and much has been written about the relative merits of the various procedures.  For our purposes we will only indicate one easy to understand procedure, leaving it to the user to employ other procedures if he so desires.

Now that there exists a feasible solution, we should determine if a better solution can be found.  In our following discussion we will denote each cell by its source-sink combination so that (1-3) denotes the source 1 sink 3 cell.  Examining Table 4-9 we see that cell (3-5) represents a high cost flow.  We examine therefore if this cost can be reduced.  If we ship 1 unit in (3-4), 39 in (2-4), and 21 in (2-5), we see that the solution stays feasible but that a cost saving of $999.00 − $5.20 + $9.20 − $8.65 = $994.35 can be achieved.  Obviously, this is attractive and it should be attractive for as many units as can be shifted in this manner.  The limit here is the 10 units in cell (3-5).  This thus results in a new flow plan as depicted in Table 4-10.

**Table 4-10**

| Sources | | W1 | W2 | W3 | |
|---|---|---|---|---|---|
| Source capacity | | 100 | 70 | 60 | Sink demands |
| Sinks | | $11.20 | $16.20 | $4.30 | |
| | D1 | 50 | | | 50 |
| | | $12.30 | $8.40 | $6.50 | |
| | D2 | 40 | | | 40 |
| | | $8.90 | $3.70 | $7.30 | |
| | D3 | 10 | 10 | | 20 |
| | | $7.60 | $9.20 | $5.20 | |
| | D4 | | 30 | 10 | 40 |
| | | $9.25 | $8.65 | $999.00 | |
| | D5 | | 30 | 0 | 30 |
| Unused capacity | | 0 | 0 | 50 | |

**Table 4-11**

| Sources | | W1 | W2 | W3 | |
|---|---|---|---|---|---|
| Source capacity | | 100 | 70 | 60 | Sink demands |
| Sinks | D1 | $11.20<br>50 | $16.20 | $4.30 | 50 |
| | D2 | $12.30 | $8.40 | $6.50<br>40 | 40 |
| | D3 | $8.90<br>10 | $3.70<br>10 | $7.30 | 20 |
| | D4 | $7.60 | $9.20<br>30 | $5.20<br>10 | 40 |
| | D5 | $9.25 | $8.65<br>30 | $999.00 | 30 |
| Unused capacity | | 40 | 0 | 10 | |

**Table 4-12**

| Sources | | W1 | W2 | W3 | |
|---|---|---|---|---|---|
| Source capacity | | 100 | 70 | 60 | Sink demands |
| Sinks | D1 | $11.20 | $16.20 | $4.30<br>50 | 50 |
| | D2 | $12.30 | $8.40<br>30 | $6.50<br>10 | 40 |
| | D3 | $8.90 | $3.70<br>20 | $7.30 | 20 |
| | D4 | $7.60<br>40 | $9.20 | $5.20 | 40 |
| | D5 | $9.25<br>10 | $8.65<br>20 | $999.00 | 30 |
| Unused capacity | | 50 | 0 | 0 | |

This now represents one full iteration toward the optimum solution. Let us examine a second step. The highest cost cell with a flow is now (1-2) at $12.30 per unit. Let us see if this "highest" cost can be reduced. If we let the unused capacity be equal to demand 6, then we can see that shifting via (1-2) to (3-2) to (3-6) to (1-6) causes a cost reduction of $12.30 − 6.50 + 0.0 − 0.0 = $5.80 per unit. This solution remains feasible and 40 units can be so shifted. So the next solution is depicted in Table 4-11.

We can continue this process:

1. Examine the highest cost flow.

2. See if there is a potential substitution. If none, the problem is finished.

3. Evaluate the substitution: Return to step 1.

The observant reader should note that this overall procedure is essentially identical to the simplex method shown in Chapter 2. The only difference is that the actual evaluation procedure is much simpler than the full simplex procedure in recognition of the simpler problem posed by the transportation problem. The final solution is shown in Table 4-12.

As noted earlier, only one procedure for finding the optimum solution to a transportation problem is shown here. Actually, there are many very good solution procedures and the interested reader is referred to the references in this regard.

## DISCUSSION TOPICS AND PROBLEMS

1. What distinguishes a simultaneous multiproduct manufacturing model from a batchwise multiproduct model?

2. How can a blending model be added to a simultaneous multiproduct manufacturing model? For example, the rock crusher discussed in Table 4-3 can be operated in two modes, fine and medium. The demand for products is as follows:

| Grade | A | B | C |
|---|---|---|---|
| Max fine | 35% | 75% | 45% |
| Min fine | 30% | 60% | 40% |
| Max medium | 35% | 25% | 30% |
| Max large | 35% | 10% | 30% |
| Volume, tons | 100 | 60 | 40 |

Construct the combined model for crushing and blending.

3. Why can transportation models be treated in a more compact manner? What precautions should be taken when using the more compact form.

# Multiplant
# and Multitime
# Period Models                                                    5

The previous chapter contained a detailed description of linear programming models that represent various typical industrial operations. However, the models described in Chapter 4 were concerned only with a single plant, a single operation, or a plant operation in a single time period. Many industrial situations concern themselves with production or planning problems covering several plants in a single time period, or alternatively, the development of a single plant operation schedule extending over many time periods. In addition, there often are problems concerning the development of multiplant and multitime period operation schedules. The development of appropriate mathematical programming models of such multiplant and multitime period models is discussed here. It is this aspect of mathematical programming application that is growing most rapidly, because mathematical programming models can be used to suggest total corporate operating strategies.

## MULTIPLANT MODELS

Multiplant models apply to those corporations that manufacture similar goods at a number of different plants, located remote from one another. When such operating conditions exist, there exists the possibility to transship intermediate and finished goods between the various plants or to allocate demands to the individual plants to reduce costs. In this way, capacity shortages at one plant site can be alleviated at the expense of a transportation charge. When the various plants produce several intermediate and final products, there is undoubtedly a large number of possible operating strategies, representing the possibilities to transship one or more commodities between the various plants. In these cases, mathematical programming is useful in determining the best operating strategy available for all plants.

Multiplant models contain sections that describe the individual plant operations. In addition, they contain a section that describes the interplant transportation operations. The tie-ins between the individual plant model sections and the transportation section all occur in the product balancing equations, because transshipments in or out affect the quantity that is available at each plant site. Care must be taken that different variables are constructed for shipment from plant A to plant B and from plant B to plant A, even for a single unique product. This is so because linear programming algorithms will consider only positive values for any variable in the problem. If both the *to* and *from* transshipments were described by a single variable, then this variable would have to be allowed to take on negative values. A second consideration is that there is a charge for transporting goods from A to B, and there is a charge to transport goods from B to A. Even if a variable were allowed to go negative, a positive transportation charge would still have to be incurred; hence the necessity for two variables to describe the two possible directions of flow of the goods.

Figure 5-1 shows in matrix form the typical tie-ins occurring in a two-plant, two-product model for a single time period. In this model, the plants are numbered 1 and 2, the products are P and Q, machines K and L are located at plant 1, and machines M, N, and O are located at plant 2. The demand for product P at plant 1 is encoded as P1. The other demand combinations are coded as Q1, P2, and Q2. The machine upper bounds, i.e., the total time that the machines are available, are expressed in stream days (i.e., days that they can be on stream). The time schedule for the example is 1 month of operation. The sectionalized structure for the individual plants and for the transportation subsection can clearly be seen from Fig. 5-1.

When the actual operation employs many different products, the transportation section of the total model can become quite large, because each individual product-route combination represents a different activity, and hence an individual column vector in the model. For example, if there are five plants and ten products, then each plant will be able to ship its goods to the other four plants. So there will be $4 \times 10 = 40$ outbound transshipment variables for each plant, and a total of $5 \times 4 \times 10 = 200$ transshipment variables in the model. In general, the number of constraint rows in a multiplant model will be equal to the sum of the number of constraint rows in the individual plant models, since the transportation section generally does not carry with it additional constraints. From this it should be clear that multiplant models tend to have a proportionally greater number of columns versus rows than an individual plant model. Multiplant models with 500 constraint rows and 5000 column variables are not unusual. The large number of columns in these models actually represents the many potential strategies that are available to the operation, and even though many of these activities will be zero, or in other words, no transshipment will take place, the possibility of using an activity should be incorporated in the model,

| | K\|P | K\|Q | L\|P | L\|Q | $T^{P}_{12}$ | $T^{P}_{21}$ | $T^{Q}_{12}$ | $T^{Q}_{21}$ | M\|P | M\|Q | N\|P | N\|Q | O\|P | O\|Q | |
|---|---|---|---|---|---|---|---|---|---|---|---|---|---|---|---|
| Operating cost | 100 | 102 | 105 | 108 | 10 | 10 | 12 | 12 | 92 | 94 | 104 | 107 | 110 | 113 | |
| P1 balance | 40 | | 50 | | −1 | +1 | | | | | | | | | = 1400 units |
| Q1 balance | | 35 | | 42 | | | −1 | +1 | | | | | | | = 1020 units |
| K upper bound | 1 | 1 | | | | | | | | | | | | | ≤ 30 days |
| L upper bound | | | 1 | 1 | | | | | | | | | | | ≤ 24 days |
| P2 balance | | | | | +1 | −1 | | | 35 | | 50 | | 60 | | = 1350 units |
| Q2 balance | | | | | | | +1 | −1 | | 32 | | 45 | | 58 | = 1820 units |
| M upper bound | | | | | | | | | 1 | 1 | | | | | ≤ 30 days |
| N upper bound | | | | | | | | | | | 1 | 1 | | | ≤ 28 days |
| O upper bound | | | | | | | | | | | | | 1 | 1 | ≤ 30 days |

Plant 1 model                Transportation model                Plant 2 model

**Fig. 5-1** A two-plant, two-product model for a single time period.

because under unusual circumstances, some of these "far out" possibilities do become attractive.

Multiplant models are also known as production allocation models, because they suggest a possible strategy for allocating production to the various plants, taking into consideration the demand at the individual plant locations as well as the machine and manufacturing capabilities that exist at each plant site.

## MULTITIME PERIOD MODELS

In addition to production allocation problems, many industrial firms are faced with the development of operating strategies in the face of seasonally varying demand or supply. If there exists a seasonality in demand, or, in other words, if sales are higher at certain times of the year than at others, and if there exists inadequate production capacity to manufacture the peak demand in the time period that it occurs, then operating management must use a strategy for premanufacturing and storing seasonal inventories. Early manufacture of finished goods has several disadvantages: it uses up warehouse space, the finished goods may deteriorate, the finished goods may become obsolete if the actual demand does not meet the forecasted quantity, and most of all, early manufacture of finished goods ties up working capital of the firm. The development of a good strategy for seasonal production is therefore quite important in many industries. Seasonality in demand exists in such diverse industries as steel making, automobile manufacture, appliance manufacture, petroleum refining, home building, and brewing.

Besides seasonality in demand, some firms are faced with seasonality in supply. Examples are the steel industry and the glass industry. Both of these industries use large furnaces that have a very distinct life cycle, often 2 to 4 years. When such a furnace reaches the end of its useful life, the furnace must be essentially rebuilt, and this may involve 60 to 90 days. This, coupled with seasonality in demand, gives rise to development of operating plans to best match equipment downtimes with product demands. Multitime period models are built up from single time period models with inventory variables. In a similar manner as the multiplant models, the inventory section of multitime period models affects primarily the product balance equations.

In commercial operations, there exist several different categories of warehouse space. Most industrial firms operate some wholly owned warehouse space that can be used for seasonal stocking of goods. Other possibilities are to lease warehouse space on a contractual arrangement. Such leases can run from 6 months to 3 years or more and lease payments are due whether the space is used or not. Finally, there is a possibility of storing seasonal inventory in commercial warehouses. Under such conditions, the cost for warehousing is generally related only to the handling cost plus a time rental charge. We see here that different costs apply to the different modes for storage for seasonal inventories. For wholly owned warehouse space, the variable operating cost generally consists only of handling and deterioration charge plus, of course, an appropriate charge for capital tied up by the seasonal inventory. In leased warehouse space, the variable operating cost is similar, but since the leased

| | $1KP$ | $1KQ$ | $1LP$ | $1LQ$ | $WP_{12}$ | $WP_{13}$ | $WQ_{12}$ | $WQ_{13}$ | $WLP_{12}$ | $WLP_{13}$ | $WLQ_{12}$ | $WLQ_{13}$ | $2KP$ | $2KQ$ | $2LP$ | $2LQ$ | $WP_{23}$ | $WQ_{23}$ | $WLP_{23}$ | $WLQ_{23}$ | $3KP$ | $3KQ$ | $3LP$ | $3LQ$ | RHS |
|---|---|---|---|---|---|---|---|---|---|---|---|---|---|---|---|---|---|---|---|---|---|---|---|---|---|
| Cost | 100 | 102 | 105 | 108 | 8 | 8 | 9 | 9 | 12 | 14 | 13 | 15 | 90 | 92 | 95 | 98 | 7 | 8 | 11 | 12 | 80 | 82 | 85 | 88 | |
| Balance 1P | 40 | | 50 | | −1 | −1 | | | −1 | −1 | | | | | | | | | | | | | | | = 1200 |
| Balance 1Q | | 35 | | 42 | | | −1 | −1 | | | −1 | −1 | | | | | | | | | | | | | = 800 |
| Capacity 1K | 1 | 1 | | | | | | | | | | | | | | | | | | | | | | | ≤ 26 |
| Capacity 1L | | | 1 | 1 | | | | | | | | | | | | | | | | | | | | | ≤ 28 |
| Balance 2P | | | | | +1 | | | | +1 | | | | 40 | | 50 | | −1 | | −1 | | | | | | = 1400 |
| Balance 2Q | | | | | | | +1 | | | | +1 | | | 35 | | 42 | | −1 | | −1 | | | | | = 900 |
| Capacity 2K | | | | | | | | | | | | | 1 | 1 | | | | | | | | | | | ≤ 26 |
| Capacity 2L | | | | | | | | | | | | | | | 1 | 1 | | | | | | | | | ≤ 27 |
| Balance 3P | | | | | | +1 | | | | +1 | | | | | | | +1 | | +1 | | 40 | | 50 | | = 1550 |
| Balance 3Q | | | | | | | | +1 | | | | +1 | | | | | | +1 | | +1 | | 35 | | 42 | = 1150 |
| Capacity 3K | | | | | | | | | | | | | | | | | | | | | 1 | 1 | | | ≤ 29 |
| Capacity 3L | | | | | | | | | | | | | | | | | | | | | | | 1 | 1 | ≤ 30 |

Fig. 5-2 A single plant, multitime period model.

warehouse space is generally not adjacent to the plant, the actual handling and deterioration costs are frequently higher than they are for a wholly owned warehouse. Finally, for commercial warehouse space, there exists a handling charge, deterioration cost, and a monthly storage fee.

In all of these cases, the handling charges are a one-time cost, while the capital charges and space rental charges are time dependent. Total warehouse cost, therefore, is not linear with respect to the time that the goods are stored. Because of this, it is not feasible to construct a single variable activity that describes the storage of goods that can be withdrawn over a multiple number of time periods; rather, it is necessary to construct an independent variable for each possible combination of storage time, withdrawal time, type of warehouse space used, and material stored. For example, if a firm produced only two items or types of products, and could use self-owned warehouse space or commercial warehouse space, and it is planned to model 3 months of operations, then there will be independent inventory variables for each type of product for manufacture in the first month and withdrawal in the second, for manufacture in the first month and withdrawal in the third, and for all other combinations. We see, thus, that for two products, two types of warehouse space, and three possible manufacture-withdrawal combinations, there will be 12 inventory variables.

Figure 5-2 depicts an example of a time-phased model. The nomenclature employed in this model is similar to that of Fig. 5-1. The products are P and Q, and the manufacturing units in the plant are machines K and L. The time periods are indicated by a prefix 1, 2, or 3 representing month 1, 2, and 3. From Fig. 5-2, it can again be seen that models describing multiple time periods of operations tend to increase the number of possible activities or potential modes of operation quicker than they extend the number of constraint equations.

Multitime period models should concern themselves with the time value of money. This is especially important where goods are stored in inventory and actually do tie up cash within the firm. An appropriate way in which to handle the time value of money is to express future cost and revenues on a present value basis using an appropriate discount rate. For example, if a unit has an operating cost of $110, and if the appropriate discount rate is $10\%$, then the present value of operating that machine next year is $1/1.10 \times 110$ or $100. In other words, the present value of an operation at a future time period is lower than it is today. When such a cost structure is used within a multitime period linear programming model, the optimum solution will be to delay all manufacturing to as late as possible. In the normal planning condition, this is what is generally desirable anyway, because any materials that are produced too early are carried in stock for a longer period and hence tie up capital for a longer period. When the present value approach is used, the costs associated with inventory variables consist only of handling, spoilage, and space rental costs, because the time value of money is now incorporated into the manufacturing cost at later time periods rather than directly incorporated into inventory costs themselves. The cost factors in Fig. 5-2 are an approximation of this present volume approach. Additional constraints may exist in multitime period models, because the available warehousing space that is self-owned is most likely limiting. Similarly, upper bound constraints may exist for leased warehouse space. Multitime period models of current operations must take into account the current volumes of seasonal inventories. Materials that are stored for other than seasonal buildups (i.e., safety stocks, cycle stocks, etc.) need not be considered, but goods that are stored for drawdown during a peak selling season should be credited to the product balance equation for that time period. This can be accomplished by stating the production requirements for that period as the forecasted demand minus the already manufactured volume. For instance, if the peak season demand is 120 tons, and current seasonal inventory is 28 tons, then a production requirement of only 92 tons remains.

Another method for dealing with such "opening inventories" is to credit the volume of the inventory to the product balance equation of the first time period and in effect let the model develop the operating strategy for the remaining time periods after the opening inventory is "worked off" in the initial time period. A difficulty may arise if the demand for the inventoried product is less than the stored volume because the only feasible solution then is to reinventory the difference between the opening inventory and the demand. For example, if the opening inventory is 200 units and the demand in the first period is 128 units, then it will be necessary to reinventory 72 units. In this case, the model will assume another handling charge to reinventory the goods, while in actual practice, the seasonal inventory most likely will stay in storage without additional handling.

The time horizon, or in other words, the total time period covered by the model, should always extend beyond the next peak demand or beyond the next valley in supply. Time-phased models are primarily intended to develop seasonal inventory strategy, and as such the horizon of the model must of course extend beyond the next "season." The actual duration of each time period represented by the model need not be equal. Frequently, operating plans are drawn up for the next 3 months and the subsequent 3 quarters, thus spanning an entire year, but with more detailed emphasis on the near term operations. Actually, a time scale consisting of three individual months followed by five or six full quarters of operations may be preferable because in this manner one is assured that the next peak season is always included in the model. Other variations in time span are of course entirely feasible and production schedules for individual shifts, days, weeks, months, quarters, half years, and full years have all been used with good results.

While time-phased models must explicitly deal with opening inventories, there do not exist good procedures to deal with closing inventories. This happens because it is difficult if not impossible to specify an objective for storing goods beyond the period under consideration. Different approaches have been tried, but so far none have appeared to give reasonably satisfactory answers on a continuing basis. Some of these approaches have tried to specify that the model's closing inventory should be at least as large as the similar inventory one year prior to the end of the last time period. On the face of it, this sounds reasonable. However, this procedure fails when a full year's operation contains a large one-time demand, or a large equipment shutdown. In both of these cases, one would want to build up a sizeable inventory before the beginning of the period, but this would then force a similar inventory to exist at the end of the year. This may not be possible. In fact, a rule such as: "closing inventories must be equal to or exceed opening inventories," will in fact require that the total demand in the full time period not exceed the manufacturing capacity in that time period. In spot situations, this rule can be overly restrictive.

## TWO-STAGE MANUFACTURING OPERATION

The models described heretofore have all been concerned with a single-stage manufacturing operation. A set of raw materials was converted in a single step from raw materials into one or more finished products. The following example portrays a two-stage manufacturing operation.

An aluminum company has bauxite (raw material) deposits in Guinea (Africa), Surinam (north coast of South America), and in Arkansas. There exist ore plants where bauxite is converted into alumina (an intermediate product) in Surinam, Baltimore, Arkansas, and Kitimat, British Columbia. Also, there are aluminum smelting facilities in Baltimore and Kitimat.

The initial conversion to alumina is a relatively inexpensive process. Smelting, however, is expensive, since electric furnaces (pot lines) are used. A ton of alumina yields 0.4 ton finished aluminum ingots.

The following data are available:*

| Bauxite mining | $/ton | Annual bauxite capacity, tons | Alumina yield |
|---|---|---|---|
| Guinea | $4.20 | 36,000 | 6% |
| Surinam | $3.60 | 52,000 | 8% |
| Arkansas | $5.40 | 28,000 | 6.2% |

*Bauxite to alumina conversion*

| | $/ton alumina | Annual bauxite capacity, tons |
|---|---|---|
| Surinam | 3.30 | 40,000 |
| Baltimore | 3.80 | 30,000 |
| Arkansas | 3.20 | 20,000 |
| Kitimat | 2.40 | 80,000 |

*Smelting*

| | $/ton alumina | Annual alumina capacity, tons |
|---|---|---|
| Baltimore | 85.0 | 4000 |
| Kitimat | 52.0 | 7000 |

* These data are not representative of actual mining, transportation, bauxite conversion, or smelting operations. They are merely presented to depict typical mathematical model building aspects.

*Finished product demands*

|  | Annual sales of aluminum ingots, tons |
|---|---|
| Baltimore | 1000 |
| Kitimat | 1200 |

*Bauxite transportation costs, $/ton*

| From ↓ To→ | Surinam | Baltimore | Arkansas | Kitimat |
|---|---|---|---|---|
| Guinea | 4.00 | 5.10 | 20.10 | 19.20 |
| Surinam | 0.10 | 2.20 | 16.30 | 15.10 |
| Arkansas | 16.30 | 6.20 | 0.10 | 9.40 |

*Alumina transportation costs, $/ton*

| From ↓ To→ | Baltimore | Kitimat |
|---|---|---|
| Surinam | 2.20 | 15.10 |
| Baltimore | 0.00 | 16.15 |
| Arkansas | 6.20 | 9.40 |
| Kitimat | 14.65 | 0.00 |

Finished ingots are not transported between Baltimore and Kitimat or vice versa.

## Constraints

An examination of this "system" reveals that a model of the overall operation must contain several capacity constraints. For example, the amount of bauxite mined in Guinea must be equal to or less than 36,000 tons per year. But since there does not exist a bauxite to alumina conversion facility in Guinea, all the material mined must be shipped to such a plant.

We can thus state that the sum of the materials mined in Guinea *and* shipped in bauxite form to Surinam, Baltimore, Arkansas, and Kitimat must be equal to or less than 36,000 tons per year. Similarly, there are capacity constraints on the mining operations at the other locations. There will also be capacity constraints on the conversion capacities at Surinam, Baltimore, Arkansas, and Kitimat, and on the smelting capacities at Kitimat and Baltimore. Finally there must be two constraints defining the finished product requirements at Baltimore and Kitimat. This now represents a total of three mining, four conversion, two smelting, and two demand equations or a total of 11 equations. This is an absolute minimum; in actually developing the model it often is advisable to also include some product balance equations.

### Variables

The variables or activities are of different forms. They should include mining, transportation, reduction, transportation, and smelting operations. Each one of these variables can be expressed separately, or a set of combination variables can be defined. For example, one variable can be constructed for each of the mining *and* initial transportation variables. Let (G − S) be the amout mined in Guinea *and* shipped to Surinam. Similarly, (G − B), (G − A), and (G − K) are the variables for mining in Guinea and shipment to, respectively, Baltimore, Arkansas, and Kitimat. These variables are then related to one another through the constraint

$$(G - S) + (G - B) + (G - A) + (G - K) \leq 36{,}000,$$

which is the mining constraint for Guinea.

The next set of variables, after those describing mining and transportation, will be the conversion variables. If we name these R.S., R.B., R.A., and R.K. for ore conversion in Surinam, Baltimore, Arkansas, and Kitimat, we can construct the constraint

$$(G - S) + (S - S) + (A - S) = R.S.$$

which states that the volumes mined in Guinea, Surinam, and Arkansas, and shipped to Surinam must equal the volume converted in Surinam. This now is a new balance equation; it equates a volume of inputs with a volume of outputs. Care must be taken with the dimension of this equation, since the alumina content of the three source materials differs. Expressing it in tons of bauxite is erroneous; instead it is best to express the volumes in tons of alumina. So we will have

$$0.06 \times (G - S) + 0.08 \times (S - S) + 0.062 \times (A - S) = R.S.$$

Now the variable R.S. is expressed in tons of alumina represented by the various raw materials. By a similar process, involving conversion, transportation, and smelting, the entire model of the operation can be completed. This total model, from mining to final products, is shown in matrix form in Fig. 5-3. This is a model with 11 capacity and demand constraints, 10 product balance equations, and a total of 26 variables; 12 for mining and transport, 4 for conversion, 8 for shipping alumina, and 2 for smelting operations. The actual cost function, which is to minimize, is also shown in Fig. 5-3.

### *Compact formulation*

The entire operation could have been modeled in a different manner as well. For example, we could have expressed the total process from mining all the way to the final product by individual variables which represent combined activities. With three mines, four conversion facilities, and two smelters we can express in a single variable, for example, mine in Guinea, convert in Surinam, and smelt in Kitimat. By using this approach we would have $3 \times 4 \times 2 = 24$ variables and only 11 equations; a much more compact model. When using this approach, care must be taken to express all of these variables in a common dimension, e.g., tons of alumina. By doing so,

| | $\frac{G}{S}$ | $\frac{G}{B}$ | $\frac{G}{A}$ | $\frac{G}{K}$ | $\frac{S}{S}$ | $\frac{S}{B}$ | $\frac{S}{A}$ | $\frac{S}{K}$ | $\frac{A}{S}$ | $\frac{A}{B}$ | $\frac{A}{A}$ |
|---|---|---|---|---|---|---|---|---|---|---|---|
| Mining constraint | 1 | 1 | 1 | 1 | | | | | | | |
| | | | | | 1 | 1 | 1 | 1 | | | |
| | | | | | | | | | 1 | 1 | 1 |
| Bauxite balance equations in tons alumina | 0.06 | | | | 0.08 | | | | 0.062 | | |
| | | 0.06 | | | | 0.08 | | | | 0.062 | |
| | | | 0.06 | | | | 0.08 | | | | 0.062 |
| | | | | 0.06 | | | | 0.08 | | | |
| Conversion capacity constraints in tons bauxite | 1 | | | | 1 | | | | 1 | | |
| | | 1 | | | | 1 | | | | 1 | |
| | | | 1 | | | | 1 | | | | 1 |
| | | | | 1 | | | | 1 | | | |
| Alumina balance equations in tons alumina | | | | | | | | | | | |
| Smelter input balances | | | | | | | | | | | |
| Smelter capacity | | | | | | | | | | | |
| Final product | | | | | | | | | | | |
| Cost | 8.20 | 9.30 | 24.30 | 23.40 | 3.70 | 5.80 | 19.90 | 18.70 | 21.70 | 11.60 | 5.50 |

**Fig. 5-3** Model of two-stage production process.

| | G S B | G S K | G A B | G A K | G B B | G B K | G K B | G K K | S S B | S S K | S A B | S A K | S B B |
|---|---|---|---|---|---|---|---|---|---|---|---|---|---|
| MINE G | 1 | 1 | 1 | 1 | 1 | 1 | 1 | 1 | | | | | |
| MINE S | | | | | | | | | 1 | 1 | 1 | 1 | 1 |
| MINE A | | | | | | | | | | | | | |
| CONV S | 1/0.06 | 1/0.06 | | | | | | | 1/0.08 | 1/0.08 | | | |
| CONV A | | | 1/0.06 | 1/0.06 | | | | | | | 1/0.08 | 1/0.08 | |
| CONV B | | | | | 1/0.06 | 1/0.06 | | | | | | | 1/0. |
| CONV K | | | | | | | 1/0.06 | 1/0.06 | | | | | |
| SMLT B | 1 | | 1 | | 1 | | 1 | | 1 | | 1 | | 1 |
| SMLT K | | 1 | | 1 | | 1 | | 1 | | 1 | | 1 | |
| DEM B | 0.4 | | 0.4 | | 0.4 | | 0.4 | | 0.4 | | 0.4 | | 0. |
| DEM K | | 0.4 | | 0.4 | | 0.4 | | 0.4 | | 0.4 | | 0.4 | |

**Fig. 5-4** Compact configuration of two-stage production process.

| R.S | R.B | R.A | R.K | S*B | S*K | B*B | B*K | A*B | A*K | K*B | K*K | SMB | SMK | | |
|---|---|---|---|---|---|---|---|---|---|---|---|---|---|---|---|
| | | | | | | | | | | | | | | ≤ | 36,000 |
| | | | | | | | | | | | | | | ≤ | 52,000 |
| | | | | | | | | | | | | | | ≤ | 28,000 |
| −1 | | | | | | | | | | | | | | = | 0 |
| | −1 | | | | | | | | | | | | | = | 0 |
| | | −1 | | | | | | | | | | | | = | 0 |
| | | | −1 | | | | | | | | | | | = | 0 |
| | | | | | | | | | | | | | | ≤ | 40,000 |
| | | | | | | | | | | | | | | ≤ | 30,000 |
| | | | | | | | | | | | | | | ≤ | 20,000 |
| | | | | | | | | | | | | | | ≤ | 80,000 |
| 1 | | | | −1 | −1 | | | | | | | | | = | 0 |
| | 1 | | | | | −1 | −1 | | | | | | | = | 0 |
| | | 1 | | | | | | −1 | −1 | | | | | = | 0 |
| | | | 1 | | | | | | | −1 | −1 | | | = | 0 |
| | | | | 1 | | 1 | | 1 | | 1 | | −1 | | = | 0 |
| | | | | | 1 | | 1 | | 1 | | 1 | | −1 | = | 0 |
| | | | | | | | | | | | | 1 | | ≤ | 4000 |
| | | | | | | | | | | | | | 1 | ≤ | 7000 |
| | | | | | | | | | | | | 0.4 | | = | 1000 |
| | | | | | | | | | | | | | 0.4 | = | 1200 |
| 3.30 | 3.80 | 3.20 | 2.40 | 2.20 | 15.10 | 0.0 | 16.15 | 6.20 | 9.40 | 14.65 | 0.0 | 85.0 | 52.0 | | |

(marginal, cut off at left edge: "52" beside the R.A −1 row; leading "0" before 3.30 in the cost row)

| SKB | SKK | ASB | ASK | AAB | AAK | ABB | ABK | AKB | AKK | | |
|---|---|---|---|---|---|---|---|---|---|---|---|
| 1 | 1 | | | | | | | | | ≤ | 36,000 × 0.06 |
| | | | | | | | | | | ≤ | 52,000 × 0.08 |
| | | 1 | 1 | 1 | 1 | 1 | 1 | 1 | 1 | ≤ | 28,000 × 0.062 |
| | | 1/0.062 | 1/0.062 | | | | | | | ≤ | 40,000 |
| | | | | 1/0.062 | 1/0.062 | | | | | ≤ | 20,000 |
| | | | | | | 1/0.062 | 1/0.062 | | | ≤ | 30,000 |
| 1/0.08 | 1/0.08 | | | | | | | 1/0.062 | 1/0.062 | ≤ | 80,000 |
| 1 | | 1 | | 1 | | 1 | | 1 | | ≤ | 4000 |
| | 1 | | 1 | | 1 | | 1 | | 1 | ≤ | 7000 |
| 0.4 | | 0.4 | | 0.4 | | 0.4 | | 0.4 | | = | 1000 |
| | 0.4 | | 0.4 | | 0.4 | | 0.4 | | 0.4 | = | 1200 |

appropriate conversion factors must be used in the various constraint equations. Figure 5-4 shows the matrix for this more compact formluation.

The cost associated with each activity now is

Mining

Transport

Conversion

Transport

Smelting

With the activity expressed in tons alumina rather than in tons bauxite or finished product, a sample cost calculation for the variable $(G - S - K)$ is

| | | |
|---|---|---|
| Mining, \$4.20/0.06 | = | \$ 70.00 |
| Transport $(G - S)$, \$4.00/0.06 | = | \$ 66.67 |
| Bauxite conversion, \$3.30 | = | 3.30 |
| Transport, $(S - K)$ | = | 15.10 |
| Smelting | = | 52.00 |
| | | \$207.07 |

All other cost factors for this compact model are developed in a similar manner.

Actual model construction times for the two different approaches are quite similar, but computer solution time can be somewhat less for the more compact model. Of course, the results obtained from solving the two models are identical. One advantage of the more elaborate model is that it is easier to modify or extend. For example, the introduction of a new smelter in the operation in the more elaborate model necessitates the development of four new alumina transportation variables and two new smelting *and* transporting to final market variables, plus one new balance equation and one new capacity constraint. In the compact model, 12 new variables describing mining, conversion, and smelting would be required, plus a new capacity constraint. Also, the compact model is somewhat more difficult to use in sensitivity analyses (see Chapter 9), and the compact model fails to establish appropriate transfer prices (see Chapter 8). As noted, neither method is very superior to the other; for flexibility it may be better to be expansive, but for computer time economies, it may be better to use the compact model approach.

Essentially all multistage manufacturing models can similarly be expressed in an expansive or in a compact form and frequently a combination approach is used. It is here that the versatility of the model builder is tested! One final note is that in a multistage manufacturing model that includes transportation of materials, it is generally infeasible to describe the transportation operation in its compact form as described earlier, especially when the transportation links the various manufacturing phases.

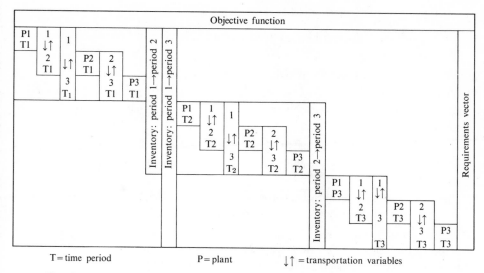

T = time period          P = plant          ↓↑ = transportation variables

**Fig. 5-5** Sample multiplant, multitime period linear programming model structure.

## TOTAL CORPORATE MODELS

The development of operating strategies for an entire company can involve several plants *and* several time periods. A model describing such total corporate operations can be built up by combining the various models described in the earlier portions of this chapter, and if necessary extended with appropriate models from Chapter 4. Total corporate models extending over several time periods tend to be very large. The problem originator faced with an assignment for a total corporate model is well advised to begin with developing a model that covers only a subset of the operation in order to gain insight into model building, solution methods, and solution analysis procedures. Such a subset can cover only a few of all the products, or only a few of the several plants, or even only two or three distinct time periods. Another possible simplification is to group products or to group plants and to develop an optimum operating strategy for these groupings. Further sub-division can then take place once good solutions to the simplified model are obtained.

Multiplant and multitime period models when laid out in matrix form can take on a "staircase" configuration. This is pictorially shown in Fig. 5-5. With this staircase-type structure, it can easily be seen that as the matrices themselves become larger, they also become sparcer, because the spaces underneath and well above the staircase are entirely zero. All efficient computer codes for linear programs do take into account the sparcity of the matrices, and this is part of the reason that even large problems, exceeding 1000 constraint equations and 8000 to 10,000 variables can be solved by electronic computing equipment. Chapter 14 describes a case study of a total corporate model development.

## DISCUSSION TOPICS AND PROBLEMS

1. What is necessary to describe a multiplant operation when not every plant produces all products?

2. When are multitime period models important?

3. What distinguishes multistage manufacturing models from single-stage models? Does this difference apply only when the various stages are remote from one another?

4. What would be the effect of strategies suggested by a multitime period model when the objective function does or does not take into account the time value of money?

5. Can you suggest alternative approaches to closing inventory strategies? What would be the consequences of each suggested approach?

6. In the two-stage manufacturing model described, what changes would have to be made to the objective function if the bauxite to alumina conversion cost is based on tons bauxite processed rather than on tons alumina produced?

# The Objective Function

6

The purpose of a linear programming problem is to maximize a profit, minimize an operating cost, or some combinatorial effect. A linear programming model is a description of an operation. The main use of such a model is to study the actual operation as represented by the model. A linear programming solution is a recommended schedule of operation, based on some desired objective. Whether the objective is to maximize profits or to minimize operating costs is immaterial at this time. The objective in effect becomes the driving force or motivation for the problem at hand. Hence, within a given problem, only a single objective can be pursued at any one time. Linear programming problems can be equipped with several objective functions, but optimization can take place only with one objective or one goal at a time.

Linear programming models generally represent operations in which limited resources are to be allocated in an optimum manner. Resources or variables may be available machine hours, available blending components, available man-hours of various grades of operating personnel, or available space in warehouses. All of these "available" commodities are resources that should be best allocated among a set of requirements. Most frequently, linear programming models describe current or near term future operations, and the objective is to develop a best operating strategy within the expected available resources.

57

**Table 6-1**

**Standard Costs (in Cents Per Pound) for Machine M**

| Costs / Product | A | B | C |
|---|---|---|---|
| Fixed cost | 1.22 | 1.124 | 1.31 |
| Depreciation and maintenance | 2.30 | 2.14 | 1.44 |
| Direct labor | 0.51 | 0.38 | 0.758 |
| Raw materials | 1.17 | 1.23 | 1.06 |
| Special supplies | 0.23 | 0.48 | 0.26 |
| Packaging | 0.15 | 0.32 | 0.05 |
| Warehouse | 0.03 | 0.05 | 0.02 |
| Total standard cost | 5.61 | 5.724 | 4.898 |

## USE OF VARIABLE OPERATING COSTS

When an optimum strategy is to be calculated for existing equipment only variable (also known as direct or controllable) operating costs are meaningful. Fixed costs for equipment and overhead charges are not affected whether the linear programming problem suggests one strategy or another. For example, we can make product P on machine A or machine B. Also we have specified that we will make all of product P. In this case the fixed costs associated with machine A and machine B are immaterial. The only important thing is whether the true variable or out-of-pocket costs for making product P are less on machine A than they are on machine B. In a similar vein, the overhead expenses in the form of factory management and sales department expense are not affected whether we make product P on machine A or machine B, and, hence, our optimization strategy need not concern itself with these and *similar other fixed* expenses.

The suggested procedure for using only variable or direct cost for allocation planning is frequently contrary to company policy and/or practices. In many instances operating decisions are made on the basis of standard costs, *prorata* costs, or other cost factors that include all or a portion of the fixed expenses associated with a given operation. This is faulty. True fixed expenses cannot be reduced except by a total elimination of the operation. This, of course, is a relatively discrete event and it can be handled in a mathematical programming environment using discrete or integer programming methods. In general linear programming problems, however, such discrete events cannot be incorporated into the model, and hence fixed expenses associated with an operation are meaningless. Table 6-1 gives a typical standard cost breakdown table.

Some of the costs in Table 6-1 are truly fixed, others are truly variable, and still others are questionable. Depreciation is a fixed cost, but maintenance may vary by the type of product manufactured on machine M. Direct labor, raw materials, special

**Table 6-2**

**Cost Breakdown (in Cents Per Pound) for Linear Programming Model for Machine M**

| Costs            Product | A | B | C |
|---|---|---|---|
| Fixed cost | 1.22 | 1.124 | 1.31 |
| Depreciation and maintenance | 2.30 | 2.14 | 1.44 |
| Warehouse | 0.03 | 0.05 | 0.12 |
| Total fixed cost | 3.55 | 3.214 | 2.77 |
| Direct labor | 0.51 | 0.38 | 0.758 |
| Raw materials | 1.17 | 1.23 | 1.06 |
| Special supplies | 0.23 | 0.48 | 0.26 |
| Packaging | 0.15 | 0.32 | 0.05 |
| Total variable cost | 2.06 | 2.41 | 2.128 |

supplies, and packaging vary of course with the quantity of material produced, and as such they represent variable costs.

Warehousing costs are questionable; they may include fixed warehouse costs such as depreciation, and they may include materials handling costs. Some review with the cost accountants is inevitable, and at times it may even become quite time consuming. However, it is a necessary step in the development of linear programming models.

Given the costs shown in Table 6-1, we would suggest using direct labor, raw materials, special supplies, and packaging as the variable costs, leaving fixed cost, depreciation and maintenance, and warehousing as the fixed cost components. This is shown in Table 6-2.

It should be clear that different operating strategies can result from using only variable costs rather than total standard costs. For example, product C has the lowest total standard cost, yet its variable cost places it between products A and B.

## FUTURE OPERATING COSTS

Most linear programming applications concern themselves with future operations. Linear programming is a tool for finding optimum operating strategy for future operations. Simulation of historical operating conditions is generally done only for checking purposes. We see, thus, that linear programming models are used as planning tools or as procedures to suggest future operating plans. Because of this, the variable operating costs to be incorporated in a linear programming model should by all rights be the expected *future variable* operating costs. Using historical variable operating costs is often an excellent first approach to the problem; however, if future modifications on machine B are contemplated, then a mathematical programming model

**Table 6-3**

**Future Variable Operating Costs (in Cents Per Pound) for Machine M**

| Costs        Product | A | B | C |
|---|---|---|---|
| Direct labor | 0.510 | 0.380 | 0.758 |
| Labor increase | 0.031 | 0.023 | 0.046 |
| Raw materials | 1.170 | 1.230 | 1.060 |
| Increase in materials cost | 0.117 | 0.123 | 0.106 |
| Special supplies | 0.230 | 0.480 | 0.260 |
| Packaging | 0.150 | 0.320 | 0.050 |
| Total future variable cost | 2.208 | 2.556 | 2.280 |

describing this future operation should have incorporated into it the best estimate of future operating costs of machine B. If only historical operating costs are used, the linear programming model will describe and calculate a best future operating strategy for the case that the old manufacturing facilities would have persisted. However, if we know that changes and improvements will be incorporated in the manufacturing facilities, then we should also include this knowledge in the linear programming model that describes such future operations. For example, if we expect raw materials costs to increase 10% in the next year, and if we expect union negotiations to result in a 6% increase in labor costs, then our future variable operating costs, those that we should use for our future operations plan, should be constructed as shown in Table 6-3.

## COSTS MUST BE LINEAR

The costs associated with an activity must be linear, or in other words, they must be a constant multiplier with the amount of activity consumed. Frequently, variable operating costs are not linear over the total range of operations but rather, as the volume of operations increases, the unit cost decreases. This phenomenon cannot be incorporated into a linear programming model *per se*. The best initial approach is to

**Table 6-4**

**Variable Operating Cost (in Cents Per Pound) Versus Quantity**

| Volume, units       Product | A | B |
|---|---|---|
| 0 to 99 | 3.468 | 4.680 |
| 100 to 199 | 3.242 | 4.482 |
| 200 to 300 | 3.162 | 4.350 |

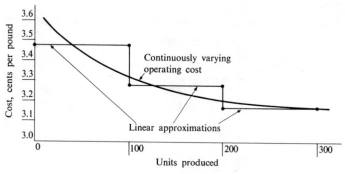

Figure 6-1

estimate the approximate answer for the variable, and to use as the initial attempt for the operating cost the unit cost at the prevailing operating rate.  Table 6-4 gives an example of a nonlinear operating cost.

When such a cost structure exists, the best and most practical approach is to "guess" at the quantity that will be produced and to use the operating cost for the range in which the "guessed" amount lies.  Actually, it is doubtful that costs so described are truly accurate; most likely, the actual costs, if they are known with enough precision, may well vary continuously with the quantity produced, as shown in Fig. 6-1.  The costs shown in Table 6-4 are then a linear approximation of such continuously varying operating costs.  One might ask whether it is not possible to construct separate variables, one for each separate level of production.  The difficulty here is that the linear programming solution will always try to use the lowest cost variable first, and so if the demand is say 60 units, the linear programming will select to make 200 to 260 units, ignoring all units between 0 and 200.  This, of course, is not permissible.  More elaborate procedures for handling nonlinear costs are described in Chapter 11.

## THE COST FACTOR DEVELOPMENT

The actual development of meaningful costs to be incorporated into a linear programming model is frequently the most time-consuming task in total model development and evaluation.  Meaningful variable costs are hard to come by and although no hard and fast rules can be given here, there is a suggested procedure of development.  In modeling a new operation, one can begin by requesting that the accounting department or the standard cost department develop the appropriate variable operating costs.  In the case of manufacturing facilities, these will include raw materials cost, direct labor charges, utilities, and product losses or scrapped materials.  In case of a product transportation activity, the variable costs will include loading costs, out-of-pocket transportation costs, unloading costs, and a small factor for potential spoilage or wastage enroute.  Table 6-5 gives an example of transportation cost factors.

**Table 6-5**

**Transportation Cost (in Dollars Per Carload) for Product B**

| Costs / Route | Chicago–New York | Chicago–Memphis |
|---|---|---|
| Loading | 23.50 | 23.50 |
| Transport | 811.00 | 267.00 |
| Unloading | 31.00 | 18.50 |
| Spoilage | 4.00 | 2.50 |
| Total | 909.50 | 311.50 |

**Table 6-6**

**Warehousing Costs (in Dollars Per Carload)**

| Costs / Product | P | R |
|---|---|---|
| Materials handling (in and out) | 2.44 | 0.39 |
| Spoilage | 0.20 | 0.15 |
| 1 month capital value at 20% | 9.63 | 12.15 |
| Subtotal | 12.27 | 12.69 |
| Commercial warehouse cost per month | 28.50 | 32.00 |
| Total | 40.77 | 44.69 |

For storing materials in inventory, the costs will include the handling costs into storage, the handling costs out of storage, possible storage costs, and an actual cost for warehouse space used when such warehouse space is leased. In self-owned warehouses, the variable costs for the space used is generally zero (unless space can be leased to third parties). In addition, there should be a charge equivalent to the interest component of the monetary value of the goods stored, because if the goods were *not* stored, the firm would have a larger cash position, and would most likely be able to reduce its bank loans. The actual "capital charge" often is a major portion of the total variable inventory cost. Some industrial firms, primarily those in a stable industrial sector, consider their *cost of capital* to be equal to the current prevailing bank rate. This, in effect, implies that these firms can borrow additional funds from banks at that rate if they so desire. Other companies, especially those in the faster growing sectors of the economy, frequently cannot borrow additional funds from the banks, and hence the *cost of capital* is somewhat irrelevant. In such instances, the company may select to use the *value of capital* or in other words an arbitrary measure describing the potential rate of return available to that company if additional cash exists within that firm. While the *cost* of capital is generally considered to be between 5 and 7%, the *value* of capital is frequently between 15 and 30%. Table 6-6 gives an example of warehousing costs.

Table 6-7

Labor Costs (in Dollars Per Hour)

| Costs | Class of labor | A | B | C |
|---|---|---|---|---|
| Direct labor | | 3.75 | 3.42 | 3.20 |
| Direct fringe benefits | | 1.30 | 1.20 | 1.10 |
| Total | | 5.05 | 4.62 | 4.30 |

Commercial warehouse cost applies only if the material is actually stored in nonowned warehouse space. If there exists the possibility to store the materials in owned or leased warehouses, it is generally best to make up separate inventory variables, one for owned and the other for the leased warehouse space.

In a blending variable, or in other words a variable that is introduced into a pool that will ultimately become a final product, the associated cost is usually only the variable operating cost of the blending operation for the quantity of material blended. Actual blending losses are generally better introduced into the equations themselves rather than as an adjustment in the blending operating cost. For example, if there is generally a 5% blending loss, then one gallon of this product blended into the pool can be described as adding only 0.95 gallon to the pool volume. This is the preferable manner in which to describe blending losses. Chapter 4 contains a detailed example of a blending model.

Manpower variables should normally carry the direct labor cost, including the direct fringe benefits, but excluding overhead expenses, and indirect labor expenses. Table 6-7 gives an example. All indirect expenses such as hiring, firing, and pension plans are not considered here.

## ARBITRARY COSTS

In many instances, and especially in profit maximization problems, an estimate of product selling price should be used in the models. This is especially so if a product price is fairly stable and there are large markets for the various products. At times, however, companies find themselves in the fortunate position that they can sell all of their output, or in other words, that they are in a seller's market. Under such conditions, when primarily the availability of raw materials or manufacturing capability is limiting, it is entirely appropriate to use artificial selling costs (i.e., artificial costs that well exceed the normal selling price of the various products manufactured). For example, if a petroleum refiner can sell all the output from its refinery and, in effect, is capacity limited, it is entirely feasible and proper to assign an arbitrary value of $5 per gallon for each gallon sold. This, of course, is a shortcut, but it is a frequently used procedure in the development of linear programming models. In a similar vein, one may at times find some variables or activities that essentially carry zero cost. A true zero variable cost for an activity is essentially unthinkable. At times, therefore, the expedient of using an arbitrarily small cost for such activity will attempt to keep the activity to its lowest desired levels and not let it range up toward its upper bounds. Extreme care should be used when employing such artificial costs; in using an arbitrary large product value, one must make sure that this product value well exceeds the actual product value and, in effect, produces enough "driving force" to ascertain that the product will really be made, despite normal raw material and operating costs. Similarly, the small arbitrary costs assigned to the low cost activities must truly be so small they that do not materially affect the strategy proposed by the linear programming solution.

Arbitrary costs or even rough cost estimates are frequently used during early model development stages. A model containing estimated costs can be constructed and checked out simultaneously with accurate cost factor development by others than the model builders. In many instances, initial or trial models contain a large percentage of estimated costs. By cost sensitivity analyses as explained in Chapter 8, the trial model is then actually used to find those costs to which the operation is sensitive; these costs may need refinement and all others can stay as they are.

## NEW INVESTMENTS

When linear programming models are used to develop longer range operating strategies that include considerations for new investments, it becomes necessary to tread with caution. At such times, it may occur that the consideration is whether or not to invest in one, two, or three new manufacturing units. This requires discrete investment decisions as described in Chapter 10. In other instances, it is possible to increase manufacturing capacity in a more or less continuous manner. For example, a trucking firm with 100 or more trucks can, for all practical purposes, extend its fleet in a more or less continuous manner. When this happens, new investments are made, and the company will undoubtedly want a return on these investments. In linear programming models this is frequently handled by applying an appropriate capital charge to the variable that describes the volume of new capacity. In the trucking example we might see

$$\text{Total usage} \leq 100 \text{ trucks} + \text{new trucks.}$$

By now applying an appropriate capital charge to the new trucks only and regular operating costs to all trucks, the model will use only the new trucks if they, in effect, will also produce a return on investment. The electronic power generation industry has often used an annual capital charge equal to 14% of investment. Other industries, such as primary metals, oil refining, etc., may use annual capital charges or desired return on investment of 17 to 23%. A breakdown of such charges can be as shown in Table 6-8.

It should be realized that such a treatment of new investment funds is only a first approximation, and although it is frequently adequate for averaging or long range planning purposes, a more rigorous treatment is generally desired when evaluating individual new capital investments.

**Table 6-8**

**Cash Flow**

| Charges | Cash flow before taxes | Cash flow after taxes |
|---|---|---|
| Interest | $-6.5\%$ | — |
| Depreciation (15 years straight line) | $-6.7\%$ | 6.7 |
| Insurance and local taxes | $-2.0\%$ | — |
| Desired return on investment | $20.0\%$ | 2.4 |
| Tax payment | $-2.4$ | — |
| Total net cash flow | $2.4\%$ | $9.1\%$ |

## DISCUSSION TOPICS AND PROBLEMS

1. What is the purpose of an objective function in a linear program?

2. What is the composition of appropriate cost figures to be used in a linear program model of (a) an existing operation, (b) a newly to be expanded operation?

3. What is the effect of using average costs (including depreciation, etc.) on the strategy suggested by a linear programming model?

4. Would it be possible to construct a model of your operations using primarily artificial costs?

# Practical
# Solution
# Methods
7

From the description of the development of linear programming models in the previous chapters, it should be clear that only truly small problems can routinely be solved by manual means. Any linear programming problem with more than 10 constraints will take an inordinate amount of time to solve by hand, even if a desk calculator is available.

There are many linear programming solution procedures or "computer codes" available for the various makes and models of computers. The majority of these programs have been well tested and as such they are readily available for use. A major drawback has existed in the past in that the control language or the control commands to properly execute linear program solutions are difficult to learn and difficult to use properly. This chapter provides some hints that may make the use of available linear programming computer programs somewhat easier.

## SOLUTION PROCEDURES

Essentially all the available computer programs use one version or another of the simplex method. This method was originally developed by Dr. George B. Dantzig in the late 1940's. The actual procedures used on modern high speed computers vary to some extent from the original algorithm, but these variations concern themselves only with the mode of carrying out the solution, and not with the concepts embodied in the solution procedure as described in Chapter 2. A nonmathematically oriented narrative description of the procedure follows.

The basic premise of the simplex method of linear programming is to start with a plausible solution to the problem and to improve on this solution by a detailed procedure. The "improvement" process is stepwise; at each step a new, more promising activity is introduced into the solution and a less promising activity is deleted. Activities are selected for introduction into the solution only if they will improve the solution or at worst keep the solution at the same level. By continuously introducing promising activities, and deleting unpromising activities, the entire procedure is ultimately bound to reach a best or optimum solution available to the problem.

In the example in Chapters 1 and 2, there are four potential activities, i.e., manufacture type B insulation, manufacture type R insulation, don't use all the ship-ping capacity, and don't use all the manufacturing capacity. It may seem odd to call "not using a resource" a possible activity, but in a mathematical sense this is quite acceptable. In addition, by incorporating the "don't use activities" in the problem formulation there exists a very straightforward starting point for the simplex method, since "not using" any of the manufacturing or shipping capacity is a plausible solution to the problem, even though it is a highly undesirable one. However, since it is a possible mode of operation, it is entirely acceptable as a starting point from which to investigate possible improvements in strategy or operating schedule. Figures 7-1, 7-2, and 7-3 show the card deck computer input as well as the full computer solution to this problem.

As we saw in Chapters 1 and 2 (and as shown in Fig. 7-3), starting from the initial point, where all manufacturing and shipping capacity is left idle (SOLUTION FEASIBLE), the procedure investigates the possible profit improvement by manufacturing either type R insulation or type B insulation. Type R insulation appears to be the most promising of the two alternatives available, and hence the activity to produce R is introduced into the solution (CHOSEN VECTOR = R), and the activity to leave manufac-turing capacity idle is removed from the solution (VECTOR REMOVD = +MANUF). At

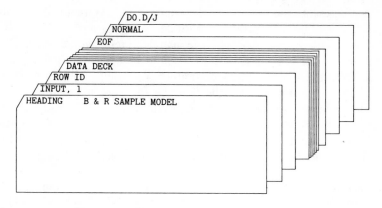

**Fig. 7-1** Sample card deck input to a computer.

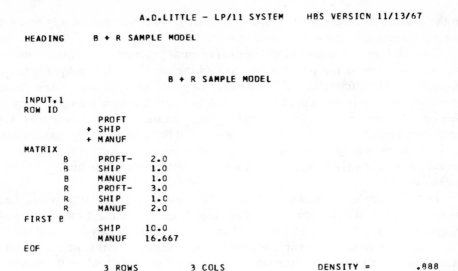

B + R SAMPLE MODEL

NORMAL

Fig. 7-2 Sample computer log of a small linear programming model.

this point, a profit of $25 per day is obtained (SUM OF INFEAS. = 25)* and the suggested operating schedule is to manufacture 8⅓ carloads of R, none of B, to use all manufacturing capacity, and to leave 1⅔ carloads of shipping capacity idle. (These items are not shown by the computer.)   At this point, the simplex method again examines the operation to see if a further improvement in profit is possible.   Of the total of four activities available, two are at zero, and the question is, if, after introducing one of these two activities into the solution, profit will improve.   As we noted, manufacturing type B insulation appears attractive, even though it implies a tradeoff with the manufacture of some type R insulation.   So the manufacture of type B insulation activity is introduced into the solution (CHOSEN VECTOR = B), and the idle shipping capacity is removed from the solution (VECTOR REMOVD = +SHIP).   By this manner, a new solution is obtained: B = 3⅓ carloads, R = 6⅔ carloads, idle shipping capacity is zero, idle manufacturing capacity is zero; profit is now $26.67 (SUM OF INFEAS. = 26.67).   Again, at this second solution, an examination is made of the activities that are zero to determine if by introducing them into the solution, profit will improve. It is found that no further improvements are possible, and hence the optimum

* The computer solution procedure used here should state "Value of the Objective" instead of "Sum of Infeasibilities" after a feasible solution has been reached.  This is an unfortunate shortcoming of the specific code used here.

B + R SAMPLE MODEL

| TOTAL ITERS | ROW IDENT. | SUM OF INFEAS. | CHOSEN VECTOR | VECTOR REMOVD | NEG D/J |
|---|---|---|---|---|---|

SOLUTION FEASIBLE

B + R SAMPLE MODEL

| TOTAL ITERS | ROW IDENT. | SUM OF INFEAS. | CHOSEN VECTOR | VECTOR REMOVD | NEG D/J |
|---|---|---|---|---|---|
| 1 | PROFT | 25.000 | R | + MANUF | 2 |
| 2 | PROFT | 26.667 | B | + SHIP | 1 |

PRIMAL SOLUTION

B + R SAMPLE MODEL

SOLUTION PRINT — FUNCTION ROW   PROFT      26.667   RHS        1

| VARIABLE | LEVEL | | C/J |
|---|---|---|---|
| B | 3.333 | − | 2.000 |
| R | 6.667 | − | 3.000 |

A PROFT        26.667

DO.D/J                        B + R SAMPLE MODEL

| VARIABLE | | D/J |
|---|---|---|
| + SHIP | | 1.000 |
| + MANUF | | 1.000 |
| R | 1 | 26.667 |

Fig. 7-3 Sample output of a linear programming solution.

solution or the best schedule of operation has been found, (PRIMAL SOLUTION) and is printed.

All of the available linear programming computer programs proceed in an entirely similar manner.  Starting from a possible solution, the profit potential of all activities not in the solution or schedule of operations is examined and the activity with the greatest profit margin potential is introduced into the schedule.  An appropriate other activity is deleted from the schedule of operations.  In computer printouts these incoming and outgoing activities are generally known as the incoming and outgoing variables.

Finding an initial feasible schedule of operations is frequently not easy.  Oftentimes there are exact equalities that must be met.  Also, there can be minimum constraints, in which it is specified that the sum of a total of some other activities

MULTIPRODUCT MANUFACT. MODEL

| TOTAL ITERS | ROW IDENT.[1] | SUM OF INFEAS.[2] | CHOSEN VECTOR | VECTOR REMOVD | NEG D/J [4] |
|---|---|---|---|---|---|
| 1 | FUNCT | − 9126.000 | OH2−C | + OH2 | 17 |
| 2 | FUNCT | − 5526.000 | OH1−C | + OH1 | 14 |
| 3 | FUNCT | − 5086.000 | BO −C | A CARB | 11 |
| 4 | FUNCT | − 4066.000 | BO −S | A STNLS | 12 |
| 5 | FUNCT | − 2636.007 | BO −A | + BO | 7 |
| 6 | FUNCT | − 2128.000 | OH3−A | A ARMOR | 8 |
| 7 | FUNCT | − 789.283 | BO −L | BO −A | 2 |
| 8 | FUNCT | − 583.017 | OH3−C | + OH3 | 5 |
| 9 | FUNCT | 0.0 | ELECL | A ALLOY | 5 |

SOLUTION FEASIBLE

MULTIPRODUCT MANUFACT. MODEL

| TOTAL ITERS | ROW IDENT. | SUM OF INFEAS.[3] | CHOSEN VECTOR | VECTOR REMOVD | NEG D/J |
|---|---|---|---|---|---|
| 10 | FUNCT | −53302.354 | ELECC | BO −C | 3 |

PRIMAL SOLUTION

**Fig. 7-4** Sample log of operations. (1) This identifies the name of the objective function. (2) The sum of infeasibilities is the number of units of infeasibility. (3) This should properly be named "value of the objective" since feasibility has been obtained. (4) This indicates the number of variables that are potential candidates for entrance into the solution on each iteration. Zero candidates implies that first a feasible, then an optimum solution has been found.

must exceed a given minimum amount. In these cases, and in fact in the majority of normal industrial linear programming problems, an initial feasible solution or schedule of operations is not obvious. However, all of the available computer programs have the capability of finding a feasible schedule of operations, even when starting from an otherwise infeasible schedule. The procedure used to arrive at such a feasible solution is similar to that of finding an optimum solution. The only difference is that the driving mechanism is not an economic consideration such as maximizing profit; instead it is the physical consideration of finding a feasible schedule of operation.

When a linear programming problem is submitted to a computer, the computer program generally assumes that the initial or starting point is infeasible, and hence the code will proceed to calculate a feasible schedule of operations. This is also known as phase 1 of the solution. The stepwise replacement (iteration) procedure will continue until a feasible solution has been obtained. At that time, the log of operations will generally state "solution feasible" and the code will automatically proceed with the optimization cycle, or phase 2. Figure 7-4 contains a sample computer printout for the multiproduct manufacturing model originally described in Chapter 4 and shown again here in Table 7-1. It can easily be seen that in this model with nine constraints and 17 potential activities or variables, the computer program required nine *iterations* to reach a feasible solution, and then one more iteration to arrive at an optimum solution to the problem.

**Table 7-1**

**Multiproduct Manufacturing Data**

| Steel type | Production, tons per day | | | | | Requirement, tons |
|---|---|---|---|---|---|---|
| | OH1 | OH2 | OH3 | BO | ELEC | |
| Carbon | 120 | 140 | 87 | 103 | 45 | 8100 |
| Armour | 104 | 130 | 80 | 94 | 42 | 1938 |
| Alloy | — | — | — | 97 | 35 | 2128 |
| Stainless | 62 | 70 | 55 | 88 | 37 | 1020 |
| Days available | 30 | 29 | 27 | 30 | 28 | |

Standard production rates: tons per day
Availability: stream days per month
Requirement: total tonnage forecast

In the past, there have been many estimates made of the number of iterations required to reach an optimum solution to a linear programming problem. These estimates have ranged from $1.0m$ to $3.0m$, where $m$ is the number of constraint rows in the problem. Practical experience, especially with large linear programming problems, has indicated that the actual number of iterations depends greatly on the structure of the model and also on its size. Especially important appears to be the ratio between the number of variables and the number of constraints, i.e., if there are 10 times more variables than there are constraints, the number of iterations needed to reach an optimum solution will tend to be on the high side of the norms.

## OPERATING COMMANDS

In order to solve a linear programming problem with existing computer codes, a number of commands must be issued to the code to instruct it what to do. The minimum number of commands are:

• READ INPUT DATA

• SOLVE AND PRINT SOLUTION

Many variations of these commands, however, can exist, and specific details are necessary. READ INPUT DATA alone is inadequate if the code is capable of reading input data in different formats and from different storage media. For example, some input data may be in the form of punched cards; other input data may be stored on magnetic tapes or on disk storage units. Yet other data may be developed as a result of special purpose matrix generator programs, and this data may be in a different format and/or storage medium. Hence, the command to a linear programming code to read input data must specify both the format and the medium of the input data, unless these are tacitly understood to be in a single standard form and medium.

MULTIPRODUCT MANUFACT. MODEL

```
INPUT,1
ROW ID
              FUNCT
         +  OH1
         +  OH2
         +  OH3
         +  BO
         +  ELEC
            CARB
            ARMOR
            ALLOY
            STNLS
MATRIX
         OH1-C  OH1      1.0
         OH1-C  CARB   120.0
         OH1-C  FUNCT  400.0
         OH1-A  FUNCT  440.0
         OH1-A  OH1      1.0
         OH1-A  ARMOR  104.0
         OH1-S  FUNCT  480.0
         OH1-S  OH1      1.0
         OH1-S  STNLS   62.0
         OH2-C  FUNCT  440.0
         OH2-C  CARB   140.0
         OH2-C  OH2      1.0
         OH2-A  FUNCT  484.0
         OH2-A  ARMOR  130.0
         OH2-A  OH2      1.0
         OH2-S  FUNCT  528.0
         OH2-S  STNLS   70.0
         OH2-S  OH2      1.0
         OH3-C  FUNCT  360.0
         OH3-C  OH3      1.0
         OH3-C  CARB    87.0
         OH3-A  FUNCT  380.0
         OH3-A  ARMOR   80.0
         OH3-A  OH3      1.0
         OH3-S  FUNCT  410.0
         OH3-S  STNLS   55.0
         OH3-S  OH3      1.0
         BO -C  FUNCT  380.0
         BO -C  CARB   103.0
         BO -C  BO       1.0
         BO -A  FUNCT  406.0
         BO -A  ARMOR   94.0
         BO -A  BO       1.0
         BO -L  FUNCT  416.0
         BO -L  ALLOY   88.0
         BO -L  BO       1.0
         BO -S  FUNCT  426.0
         BO -S  STNLS   97.0
         BO -S  BO       1.0
         ELECC  FUNCT  300.0
         ELECC  CARB    45.0
         ELECC  ELEC     1.0
         ELECA  FUNCT  350.0
         ELECA  ARMOR   42.0
         ELECA  ELEC     1.0
```

```
         ELECL  FUNCT  375.0
         ELECL  ALLOY   35.0
         ELECL  ELEC     1.0
         ELECS  FUNCT  400.0
         ELECS  STNLS   37.0
         ELECS  ELEC     1.0
FIRST B
                OH1       30.0
                OH2       29.0
                OH3       27.0
                BO        30.0
                ELEC      28.
                CARB    8100.0
                ARMOR   1938.0
                ALLOY   2128.0
                STNLS   1020.0
EOF
```

```
10 ROWS         18 COLS.          DENSITY =         .333
```

Fig. 7-5 Computer input of a multiproduct manufacturing model.

Another item of necessary information pertains to the number of objective functions that are carried with the linear programming matrix. Traditionally, the objective function(s) has been the top row(s) in the matrix, and it is necessary to specify how many objectives functions are contained within the matrix. This is especially important when sensitivity analyses on cost elements are contemplated. These actions are described in detail in Chapter 8. At other times, the first constraint row name is specified and all rows preceding this constraint row are considered as objective rows.

The READ DATA or INPUT control cards frequently also contain the possibility to specify that certain statistics regarding the entire matrix be printed out. Such statistics are the number of rows in the matrix, the number of columns in the matrix, the density of the matrix, the value of the largest element in the matrix, the value of the smallest element in the matrix, the number of right-hand side vectors contained with the matrix, the number of function rows in the matrix, the largest and smallest sizes of the elements in the right-hand side and function row, vectors, etc. All of these statistics are interesting, especially when new models are presented for their initial runs, because these statistics may point out some errors in model formulations. Figure 7-5 shows the input data of the multiproduct manufacturing model in a format that has been in wide use for a number of years, along with some matrix statistics.

The command to SOLVE or OPTIMIZE may take on different forms. Specificially, the computer code should be instructed whether the problem is to be maximized or minimized. In addition, if several cost rows and several right-hand side vectors are presented with the problem, it must be specified which of the various cost rows and/or various right-hand side vectors to use in the optimization process. This command is also known as: NORMAL, MAXIMIZE, MINIMIZE, PRIMAL, or GOGOGO, depending on the

### MULTIPRODUCT MANUFACT. MODEL

SOLUTION PRINT - FUNCTION ROW   FUNCT  -53302.354   RHS        1

| VARIABLE | LEVEL | C/J |
|----------|-------|-----|
| OH1-C | 30.000 | 400.000 |
| OH2-C | 29.000 | 440.000 |
| OH3-C | 2.775 | 360.000 |
| OH3-A | 24.225 | 380.000 |
| BO -L | 19.484 | 416.000 |
| BO -S | 10.515 | 426.000 |
| ELECC | 4.412 | 300.000 |
| ELECL | 11.810 | 375.000 |

A FUNCT   -53302.354

+ ELEC       11.776

**Fig. 7-6** Sample computer output—LP/11 code.

specific code used. *Solution printouts* are frequently obtainable only if called for with a special control command. This happens because different media such as tape or printer can often be used for solution printouts. Also, different sets of output may be desirable. Common forms of output are: OUTPUT, SOLUTION, etc. Generally, the solution printout contains the name of the variable and the level at which it is in the solution. In addition, the original cost of the variable, known as $C_j$, is frequently shown on the printout sheet. All the good computer programs will present the variables on the output form in the same sequence as used in input. This eases somewhat the reading of the normal output sheets. Figure 7-6 contains a sample output sheet from a small-scale computer system. We should note here that the product of the cost × level of the variable represents the cost contribution of that variable, and that the sum of these cost contributions plus the objective value will be zero. Figure 7-7 shows the same results as Fig. 7-6, but now prepared by a larger scale computer system that actually calculates this total cost contribution, along with the reduced costs, shadow prices, and ranges as discussed below. Figure 7-8 shows the same problem output, but prepared by still another computer program. Most users will generally have access to only one, or at most two different linear programming codes. Familiarity with the output formats can then be established with a minimum of confusion. The standard linear programming output is generally unsuitable for management reporting, due to its highly cryptic nature, and special report writers should often be employed as discussed later in this chapter.

MULTIPRODUCT MANUFACTURING MODEL          11/21/68 AT 22 13 PAGE 3 VARIABLE SUMMARY   PAGE-1
                                          1* FUNCT                        1*RHS001

| F | VARBLE | VALUE | CJ | EXT COST | DJ | RANGE LOWER | VEAL | RANGE UPPER | VEAU |
|---|--------|-------|-----|----------|-----|-------------|------|-------------|------|
| * | OH1 | | .000000 | | 400.000000 | -400.000000 | OH1 | UNBNDED | |
| * | OH2 | | .000000 | | 493.333333 | -493.333333 | OH2 | UNBNDED | |
| * | OH3 | | .000000 | | 220.000000 | -220.000000 | OH3 | UNBNDED | |
| * | BO | | .000000 | | 526.857143 | -526.857143 | BO | UNBNDED | |
| * | ELEC | 11.776913 | .000000 | .000000 | .000000 | -76.363637 | OH2-A | 113.793104 | OH3 |
| | OH1-C | 30.000000 | 400.000000 | .1200000+05 | .000000 | UNBNDED | | 460.000000 | OH1-A |
| | OH1-A | | 440.000000 | | 60.000000 | 380.000000 | OH1-A | UNBNDED | |
| | OH1-S | | 480.000000 | | 270.957290 | 209.042710 | OH1-S | UNBNDED | |
| | OH2-C | 29.000000 | 440.000000 | .1276000+05 | .000000 | UNBNDED | | 442.333333 | OH2-A |
| | OH2-A | | 484.000000 | | 2.333333 | 481.666667 | OH2-A | UNBNDED | |
| | OH2-S | | 528.000000 | | 333.704467 | 194.295533 | OH2-S | UNBNDED | |
| | OH3-C | 2.775000 | 360.000000 | 999.000000 | .000000 | 358.564103 | OH2-A | 449.720177 | OH3-S |
| | OH3-A | 24.225000 | 380.000000 | 9205.500000 | .000000 | UNBNDED | | 381.435898 | OH2-A |
| | OH3-S | | 410.000000 | | 89.720177 | 320.279823 | OH3-S | UNBNDED | |
| | BO -C | | 380.000000 | | 220.190476 | 159.809524 | BO -C | UNBNDED | |
| | BO -A | | 406.000000 | | 227.857143 | 178.142857 | BO -A | UNBNDED | |
| | BO -L | 19.484536 | 416.000000 | 8105.567010 | .000000 | 320.208494 | ELECS | 636.190476 | BO -C |
| | BO -S | 10.515464 | 426.000000 | 4479.587629 | .000000 | UNBNDED | | 521.791506 | ELECS |
| | ELECC | 4.412778 | 300.000000 | 1323.833334 | .000000 | 253.593012 | OH3-S | 334.482759 | ELECA |
| | ELECA | | 350.000000 | | 35.000000 | 315.000000 | ELECA | UNBNDED | |
| | ELECL | 11.810309 | 375.000000 | 4428.865980 | .000000 | 287.424243 | BO -C | 413.098894 | ELECS |
| | ELECS | | 400.000000 | | 36.539028 | 363.460972 | ELECS | UNBNDED | |

MULTIPRODUCT MANUFACTURING MODEL          11/21/68 AT 22 13 PAGE 4 CONSTRAINT SUMMARY  PAGE-1
                                          1* FUNCT                        1*RHS001

| VARBLE | VALUE | CJ | EXT COST | ROW NM | DUAL | RHS VALUE | RANGE LOWER | VLAL | RANGE UPPER | VLAU |
|--------|-------|-----|----------|--------|------|-----------|-------------|------|-------------|------|
| FUNCT | -.5330235+05 | .000000 | .000000 | FUNCT | 1.000000 | .000000 | | | | |
| OH1-C | 30.000000 | 400.000000 | .1200000+05 | OH1 | 400.000000 | 30.000000 | 25.583658 | ELEC | 31.654792 | ELECC |
| OH2-C | 29.000000 | 440.000000 | .1276000+05 | OH2 | 493.333333 | 29.000000 | 25.214564 | ELEC | 30.418393 | ELECC |
| ELEC | 11.776913 | .000000 | .000000 | OH3 | 220.000000 | 27.000000 | 24.225000 | OH3-C | 29.282471 | ELECC |
| BO -L | 19.484536 | 416.000000 | 8105.567010 | BO | 526.857143 | 30.000000 | 25.316001 | ELEC | 34.697282 | ELECL |
| ELECC | 4.412778 | 300.000000 | 1323.833334 | ELEC | .000000 | 28.000000 | 16.223087 | ELEC | UNBNDED | |
| BO -S | 10.515464 | 426.000000 | 4479.587629 | CARB | -6.666667 | 8100.000000 | 7901.425000 | ELECC | 8629.961082 | ELEC |
| ELECL | 11.810309 | 375.000000 | 4428.865980 | ARMOR | -7.500000 | 1938.000000 | 1755.402299 | ELECC | 2160.000000 | OH3-C |
| OH3-A | 24.225000 | 380.000000 | 9205.500000 | ALLOY | -10.714286 | 2128.000000 | 1714.639175 | ELECL | 2540.191953 | ELEC |
| OH3-C | 2.775000 | 360.000000 | 999.000000 | STNLS | -9.823270 | 1020.000000 | 564.363636 | ELECL | 1474.347948 | ELEC |

**Fig. 7-7** Sample computer output—Allegro code, CDC-3600 computer.

In addition to the key commands INPUT and SOLVE, there are generally a great variety of other commands that can be useful for special problem solution procedures, sensitivity analysis, etc. The commands INPUT and SOLVE specify to calculate a given solution. If, however, a good schedule of operations is known, it is highly advisable to instruct the computer of this schedule of operations before commencing the optimization cycle. This is equivalent to informing the computer of an advanced starting point. This process is also known as matrix inversion or reinversion to a specified solution.

As we have seen earlier, the simplex procedure determines at each iteration the profit potential represented by the activities that are zero and not part of the current schedule of operations to select a new promising activity; this is also known as "pricing." Once the most promising activity has been selected, the determination must be made of an activity to leave the schedule. Finally, the new solution as the result of the iteration must be calculated. Of these three major functions, pricing generally takes 75 to 80% of the time consumed by the entire iteration. Because of this, prespecifying a good solution or basis and using the INVERT mode of operation can save a tremendous amount of computer time, because a lot of "pricing" activities can be bypassed. All good linear programming solution codes do have the possibility to invert directly to a prespecified solution. In addition, all good solution codes also have the capability to punch out such a BASIS or otherwise save the appropriate information required for a later reinversion to such a given solution. The actual

SECTION 1 - ROWS

| NUMBER | ...ROW.. | AT | ...ACTIVITY... | SLACK ACTIVITY | ..LOWER LIMIT. | ..UPPER LIMIT. | .DUAL ACTIVITY |
|---|---|---|---|---|---|---|---|
| 1 | FUNCT | BS | 53302.35395 | 53302.35395- | NONE | NONE | 1.00000 |
| 2 | DCOST | BS | . | . | NONE | NONE | . |
| 3 | OH1 | UL | 30.00000 | . | NONE | 30.00000 | 400.00000 |
| 4 | OH2 | UL | 29.00000 | . | NONE | 29.00000 | 493.33333 |
| 5 | OH3 | UL | 27.00000 | . | NONE | 27.00000 | 220.00000 |
| 6 | BO | UL | 30.00000 | . | NONE | 30.00000 | 526.85714 |
| 7 | ELEC | BS | 16.22309 | 11.77691 | NONE | 28.00000 | . |
| 8 | CARB | EQ | 8100.00000 | . | 8100.00000 | 8100.00000 | 6.66667- |
| 9 | ARMOR | EQ | 1938.00000 | . | 1938.00000 | 1938.00000 | 7.50000- |
| 10 | ALLOY | EQ | 2128.00000 | . | 2128.00000 | 2128.00000 | 10.71429- |
| 11 | STNLS | EQ | 1020.00000 | . | 1020.00000 | 1020.00000 | 9.82327- |

SECTION 2 - COLUMNS

| NUMBER | .COLUMN. | AT | ...ACTIVITY... | ..INPUT COST.. | ..LOWER LIMIT. | ..UPPER LIMIT. | .REDUCED COST. |
|---|---|---|---|---|---|---|---|
| 12 | OH1-C | BS | 30.00000 | 400.00000 | . | NONE | . |
| 13 | OH1-A | LL | . | 440.00000 | . | NONE | 60.00000 |
| 14 | OH1-S | LL | . | 480.00000 | . | NONE | 270.95729 |
| 15 | OH2-C | BS | 29.00000 | 440.00000 | . | NONE | . |
| 16 | OH2-A | LL | . | 484.00000 | . | NONE | 2.33333 |
| 17 | OH2-S | LL | . | 528.00000 | . | NONE | 333.70447 |
| 18 | OH3-C | BS | 2.77500 | 360.00000 | . | NONE | . |
| 19 | OH3-A | BS | 24.22500 | 380.00000 | . | NONE | . |
| 20 | OH3-S | LL | . | 410.00000 | . | NONE | 89.72018 |
| 21 | BO-C | LL | . | 380.00000 | . | NONE | 220.19048 |
| 22 | BO-A | LL | . | 406.00000 | . | NONE | 227.85714 |
| 23 | BO-L | BS | 19.48454 | 416.00000 | . | NONE | . |
| 24 | BO-S | BS | 10.51546 | 426.00000 | . | NONE | . |
| 25 | ELECC | BS | 4.41278 | 300.00000 | . | NONE | . |
| 26 | ELECA | LL | . | 350.00000 | . | NONE | 35.00000 |
| 27 | ELECL | BS | 11.81031 | 375.00000 | . | NONE | . |
| 28 | ELECS | LL | . | 400.00000 | . | NONE | 36.53903 |

**Fig. 7-8** Solution printout by MPS system—IBM System/360 computer.

mathematical development of matrix inversion procedures has been so streamlined that matrices representing more than 1,000 simultaneous equations have been inverted in less than 1 minute of high speed computer time. The normal iteration procedure, without a prespecified starting point for such a problem, can take anywhere from 20 minutes to 1 hour on a similar computer.

Especially when large size problems (300 or more constraints) are being developed, it is wise to frequently punch out the BASIS or otherwise save the current solution, because this procedure will greatly aid in reducing the computer time required to eliminate inconsistencies that invariably appear in a newly developed large-scale linear programming model.

In the normal course of solving a linear programming problem, the computer code will itself frequently call upon the reinversion procedure. This happens because in the normal solution method, an activity frequently gets elected as being promising, and at a later time this same activity is dropped from the schedule because a more promising activity has been discovered. Especially in large scale problems, it frequently happens that a single activity jumps in and out of the solution several times. The example in Fig. 7-4 has two such occurrences—the variables BO-A and BO-C are introduced in iterations 5 and 3 and removed in iterations 7 and 10. This type of "ping-pong" activity will not only increase the computer solution times, which is inevitable, but in addition it will slow down subsequent pricing and solution activities, and it will increase the possibility of rounding errors creeping into the solution. Because of this, all of the modern linear programming solution codes will periodically "reinvert," i.e., they will recalculate the current solution starting from an absolutely clean slate. Generally, these reinversions take place after about 1.25 to 1.40$m$ iterations, where $m$ represents the number of rows in the matrix. For example, if there are 300 rows in the matrix, the first reinversion will generally take place after 375 to 520 iterations have been carried out. Subsequent reinversions will tend to become more frequent because, as the solution proceeds, rounding errors and numerical difficulties will naturally accrue, and reinversion is the most straightforward way to reduce this difficulty.

### Heading

Another very useful command available in most linear programming solutions codes is HEADING or TITLE. This command will let the originator introduce the heading or page title that he wishes on his output reports. Headings are generally not limited to the beginning of a run; they can also be used at later solution stages. Especially if a number of trial runs are made with a single model, it is frequently very desirable to indicate the date, time, originator, and model name or number in the heading on the title page, so that at a later review the results will clearly display what the actual model parameters were at the time of solution. This is especially important when the input data are not reproduced along with the log of operations of the linear programming solution. In such cases, it is difficult to reconstruct at a later time the results obtained from a solution if adequate documentation regarding originator, problem, and data are not readily available. Especially during the early stages of model development, the heading or title feature should be used to the utmost. In addition, when long and complicated runs with sensitivity analyses, parametric procedures, etc., are used, resetting of the heading or title is feasible and advisable.

## Other Commands

Besides the mandatory commands to READ DATA and to SOLVE the problem, a number of other commands generally exist. Some of these additional commands will extract additional data from the problem, or the computer program will explore a number of solutions adjacent to the optimum solution. The additional data that can be extracted from the problem are the reduced costs or the marginal prices. These are also known as the shadow prices or $\pi$ values. Usage of these shadow prices is described in detail in Chapter 8. The most frequently used command to extract these marginal prices from the solution are DO.D/J or REDCST. When such a command is given, the computer program will extract and print all the reduced costs from the optimum solution. Figure 7-9 gives two examples of such special printouts. It should be noted that in the

```
DO.D/J                  MULTIPRODUCT MANUFACT. MODEL

                   VARIABLE          D/J
                   +  OH1         400.000
                      OH1-A        59.999
                      OH1-S       270.957
                   +  OH2         493.333
                      OH2-A         2.333
                      OH2-S       333.704
                   +  OH3         220.000
                      OH3-S        89.720
                   +  BO          526.857
                      BO  -A      227.857
                      BO  -C      220.190
                      ELECA        34.999
                      ELECS        36.539
                   R    1       -53302.354


                MULTIPRODUCT MANUFACTURING MODEL

                          REDCST OUTPUT

   CASE              ITERATION    10 OBJECTIVE VALUE ************

      LABEL      COST      REDUCED COST          LABEL      COST      REDUCED COST
      OH1       .000000    399.999990            OH2       .000000    493.333320
      BO        .000000    526.857130       Z    CARB      .000000     -6.666667
   Z  ALLOY     .000000    -10.714286       Z    STNLS     .000000     -9.823269
      OH1-S  -480.000000   270.957300            OH2-A  -484.000000     2.333321
      OH3-S  -410.000000    89.720184            BO  -C -380.000000   220.190470
      ELECA  -349.999990    34.999999            ELECS  -400.000000    36.539035

   END REDCST OUTPUT


                                              LABEL      COST      REDUCED COST
                                              OH3        .000000    219.999990
                                        Z     ARMOR      .000000     -7.500000
                                              OH1-A  -440.000000    59.999992
                                              OH2-S  -528.000000   333.704460
                                              BO  -A -406.000000   227.857130
                                        Z     B1         .000000   ************
```

**Fig. 7-9** Printout of shadow prices or reduced costs.

MULTIPRODUCT MANUFACT. MODEL

| RANGES | | COST RANGES | | | |
|---|---|---|---|---|---|
| VARIABLE | LEVEL | MINIMUM | C/J INIT. | MAXIMUM |
| OH1-C | 30.000 | UNLIMITED | 400.000 | 460.000 |
| OH2-C | 29.000 | UNLIMITED | 440.000 | 442.333 |
| OH3-C | 2.775 | 358.564 | 360.000 | 449.720 |
| OH3-A | 24.225 | UNLIMITED | 380.000 | 381.435 |
| BO -L | 19.484 | 320.208 | 416.000 | 636.190 |
| BO -S | 10.515 | UNLIMITED | 426.000 | 521.791 |
| ELECC | 4.412 | 253.592 | 300.000 | 334.482 |
| ELECL | 11.810 | 287.424 | 375.000 | 413.098 |
| + ELEC | 11.776 | - 76.362 | | 113.793 |

MULTIPRODUCT MANUFACTURING MODEL

PRIMAL RANGE OUTPUT

CASE                ITERATION    10 OBJECTIVE VALUE ************

```
                  - - - - - - LIMITS OF RANGE - - - - - -
LABEL     COST       LABEL   INCREMENT    LABEL   INCREMENT
DCOST     .000000            -9999.000000 ELECA    34.999999
FUNCT     .000000    ELECA   -1.000000            9999.000000
ELEC      .000000    OH3     -113.793100  OH2-A    76.363090
OH1-C    -400.000000 OH1-A   -59.999992            9999.000000
OH2-C    -440.000000 OH2-A   -2.333321            3999.000000
OH3-C    -360.000000 OH3-S   -89.720186   OH2-A    1.435890
OH3-A    -380.000000 OH2-A   -1.435890            9999.000000
BO -L    -416.000000 BO -C   -220.190470  ELECS    95.791526
BO -S    -426.000000 ELECS   -95.791526           9999.000000
ELECC    -300.000000 ELECA   -34.482758   OH3-S    46.406992
ELECL    -375.000000 ELECS   -38.098902   BO -C    87.575758
```

FND PRIMAL RANGE OUTPUT

**Fig. 7-10** Primal ranges of the multiproduct manufacturing model.

output shown in Figs. 7-7 and 7-8, the reduced costs and shadow prices were directly presented without the necessity of a special output request.

Frequently it is also interesting to observe the RANGE over which costs or requirements can vary without changing the optimum solution. In this case, the request is to display for each variable in the solution the lowest and the highest costs for which the solution remains optimal. This feature is useful mostly for model sensitivity analysis. Ranges can also be requested for the requirements vector, which is also known as the right-hand side vector. In this case, there will be indicated for each original constraint the smallest and the largest value for which the current optimal solution will remain the same. The normal mode for requesting these ranges is to specify RANGES, COST, RANGES, or RHS. RANGES. Figure 7-10 gives an example of a printout of cost or primal ranges, as prepared by two different computer codes. Note that one code minimizes and the other maximizes. Also, one code shows the primal solution and the absolute value of the cost ranges, while the other one gives only the differences that represent the ranges. In addition, it indicates the name of the variable that would enter the solution if the cost range were exceeded. Figure 7-11 gives the RHS or dual ranges for the same problem, again indicating the name of the variable that would enter the solution if the RHS range were exceeded.

MULTIPRODUCT MANUFACTURING MODEL

DUAL RANGE OUTPUT

CASE                ITERATION    10 OBJECTIVE VALUE ************

- - - - - - LIMITS OF RANGE - - - - - -

| LABEL | ORIG. ACT. | LABEL | INCREMENT | LABEL | INCREMENT |
|-------|-----------|-------|-----------|-------|-----------|
| OH1 | 30.000000 | ELECC | -1.654792 | ELEC | 4.416342 |
| OH2 | 29.000000 | ELECC | -1.418393 | ELEC | 3.785436 |
| OH3 | 27.000000 | ELECC | -2.282471 | OH3-C | 2.775000 |
| RO | 30.000000 | ELECC | -4.697282 | ELEC | 4.683999 |
| OH1-A | .000000 | OH3-C | -2.134615 | OH3-A | 18.634614 |
| OH1-S | .000000 | ELECC | -1.654792 | ELECL | 7.348973 |
| OH2-A | .000000 | OH3-C | -1.707692 | OH3-A | 14.907692 |
| OH2-S | .000000 | ELECC | -1.418393 | ELECL | 6.509091 |
| OH3-S | .000000 | ELECC | -2.282471 | OH3-C | 2.775000 |
| RO -C | .000000 | ELECL | -4.697282 | ELECC | 1.927913 |
| RO -A | .000000 | OH3-C | -2.361702 | ELECC | 1.942529 |
| ELECA | .000000 | OH3-C | -5.285714 | ELECC | 4.347565 |
| ELECS | .000000 | RO -L | -51.081081 | ELECL | 12.314496 |

END DUAL RANGE OUTPUT

Fig. 7-11 Dual ranges of the multiproduct manufacturing model.

TWO STAGE MANUFACTURING MODEL                    11/21/68 AT 22 13 PAGE 3 VARIABLE SUMMARY    PAGE-1
                                                 1* COST                  1*RHS001

| F | VARBLE | VALUE | CJ | EXT COST | DJ | RANGE LOWER | VEAL | RANGE UPPER | VEAU |
|---|--------|-------|-----|----------|-----|-------------|------|-------------|------|
| ✦ | MINEG | .3433333+05 | .000000 | .000000 | .000000 | -1.925807 | A-B | 4.223419 | RED-A |
| ✦ | MINES | | .000000 | | 6.600000 | -6.600000 | MINES | UNBNDED | |
| ✦ | MINEA | 8000.000000 | .000000 | .000000 | .000000 | -4.364200 | RED-A | 1.990000 | A-B |
| ✦ | RED-S | | .000000 | | 1.964000 | -1.964000 | RED-S | UNBNDED | |
| ✦ | RED-B | .1633333+05 | .000000 | .000000 | .000000 | -4.164581 | A-K | 1.964000 | RED-S |
| ✦ | RED-A | | .000000 | | 4.364200 | -4.364200 | RED-A | UNBNDED | |
| ✦ | RED-K | .8000000+05 | .000000 | .000000 | .000000 | UNBNDED | | 4.303400 | A-K |
| ✦ | SCAPB | 1500.000000 | .000000 | .000000 | .000000 | UNBNDED | | UNBNDED | |
| ✦ | SCAPK | 4000.000000 | .000000 | .000000 | .000000 | UNBNDED | | UNBNDED | |
| | G-S | | 8.200000 | | .966000 | 7.234000 | G-S | UNBNDED | |
| | G-B | 1666.666660 | 9.300000 | .1549999+05 | .000000 | 5.076581 | RED-A | 10.266000 | G-S |
| | G-A | | 24.300000 | | 19.118200 | 5.181800 | G-A | UNBNDED | |
| | G-K | | 23.400000 | | 13.242000 | 10.158000 | G-K | UNBNDED | |
| | S-S | .4000000+05 | 3.700000 | .1480000+06 | .000000 | UNBNDED | | 4.666000 | G-S |
| | S-B | .1200000+05 | 5.800000 | .6960000+05 | .000000 | 4.834000 | G-S | 12.400000 | MINES |
| | S-A | | 19.900000 | | 18.136200 | 1.763800 | S-A | UNBNDED | |
| | S-K | | 18.700000 | | 11.756000 | 6.944000 | S-K | UNBNDED | |
| | A-S | | 21.700000 | | 14.159400 | 7.540600 | A-S | UNBNDED | |
| | A-B | | 11.600000 | | 1.990000 | 9.610000 | A-B | UNBNDED | |
| | A-A | .2000000+05 | 5.500000 | .1100000+06 | .000000 | UNBNDED | | 9.864200 | RED-A |
| | A-K | | 14.800000 | | 4.303400 | 10.496600 | A-K | UNBNDED | |
| | R.S | 3200.000000 | 3.300000 | .1056000+05 | .000000 | UNBNDED | | 27.850000 | RED-S |
| | R.B | 1060.000000 | 3.800000 | 4027.999999 | .000000 | -20.750000 | RED-S | 73.209678 | A-K |
| | R.A | 1240.000000 | 3.200000 | 3968.000000 | .000000 | -1004.366667 | S-A | 73.590323 | RED-A |
| | R.K | .000000 | 2.400000 | .000000 | .000000 | -67.009678 | A-K | UNBNDED | |
| | S*B | 1440.000000 | 2.200000 | 3168.000001 | .000000 | -1.050000 | B*K | 11.900000 | A*B |
| | S*K | 1760.000000 | 15.100000 | .2657599+05 | .000000 | 5.400000 | A*B | 18.350000 | B*K |
| | B*B | 1060.000000 | .000000 | .000000 | .000000 | -24.550000 | RED-S | 3.250000 | B*K |
| | B*K | | 16.150000 | | 3.250000 | 12.900000 | B*K | UNBNDED | |
| | A*B | | 6.200000 | | 9.700000 | -3.500000 | A*B | UNBNDED | |
| | A*K | 1240.000000 | 9.400000 | .1165600+05 | .000000 | -998.166667 | S-A | 19.100000 | A*B |
| | K*B | | 14.650000 | | 27.550000 | -12.900000 | K*B | UNBNDED | |
| | K*K | .000000 | .000000 | .000000 | .000000 | -69.409678 | A-K | 27.550000 | K*B |
| | SMB | 2500.000000 | 85.000000 | .2124999+06 | .000000 | UNBNDED | | UNBNDED | |
| | SMK | 3000.000000 | 52.000000 | .1559999+06 | .000000 | UNBNDED | | UNBNDED | |

Fig. 7-12 Solution of two-stage manufacturing model—variable order.

In the newer linear programming codes, the option frequently exists to have the entire solution presented together, and in the order in which the problem was presented. Figures 7-12 and 7-13 contain examples of such complete solution printouts for the two-stage manufacturing problem given in Chapter 5. Figure 7-12 shows the variable summary, with the solution value, the original input cost, the extended cost, the reduced cost for the variables not in the solution, and the ranges of the variables

TWO STAGE MANUFACTURING MODEL                    11/21/68 AT 22 13 PAGE 4 CONSTRAINT SUMMARY   PAGE-1
                                                 1* COST                    1*RHS001

| VARBLE | VALUE | CJ | EXT COST | ROW NM | DUAL | RHS VALUE | RANGE LOWER | VLAL | RANGE UPPER | VLAU |
|---|---|---|---|---|---|---|---|---|---|---|
| COST | -.7715559+06 | .000000 | .000000 | COST | 1.000000 | .000000 | | | | |
| MINEG | .3433333+05 | .000000 | .000000 | MINEG | .000000 | .3599999+05 | 1666.666660 | MINEG | UNBNDED | |
| S-B | .1200000+05 | 5.800000 | .6960000+05 | MINES | 6.400000 | .5200000+05 | .4000000+05 | S-B | .5324999+05 | G-B |
| MINEA | 8000.000000 | .000000 | .000000 | MINEA | .000000 | .2800000+05 | .2000000+05 | MINEA | UNBNDED | |
| R.S | 3200.000000 | 3.300000 | .1056000+05 | BBALS | -153.300000 | .000000 | -100.000000 | G-B | 980.000000 | RED-B |
| G-B | 1666.666660 | 9.300000 | .1549999+05 | BBALB | -155.000000 | .000000 | -100.000000 | G-B | 980.000000 | RED-B |
| R.A | 1240.000000 | 3.200000 | 3968.000000 | BBALA | -159.100000 | .000000 | -100.000000 | G-B | 980.000000 | RED-B |
| R.K | .000000 | 2.400000 | .000000 | BBALK | -169.300000 | .000000 | -100.000000 | G-B | .000000 | R.K |
| S-S | .4000000+05 | 3.700000 | .1480000+06 | RED-S | 1.964000 | .4000000+05 | .2366666+05 | RED-B | .5200000+05 | S-B |
| RED-B | .1633333+05 | .000000 | .000000 | RED-B | .000000 | .3000000+05 | .1366666+05 | RED-B | UNBNDED | |
| A-A | .2000000+05 | 5.500000 | .1100000+06 | RED-A | 4.364200 | .2000000+05 | 4193.548381 | RED-B | .2161290+05 | G-B |
| RED-K | .8000000+05 | .000000 | .000000 | RED-K | .000000 | .8000000+05 | .000000 | RED-K | UNBNDED | |
| S*B | 1440.000000 | 2.200000 | 3168.000001 | ABALS | -156.600000 | .000000 | -100.000000 | G-B | 980.000000 | RED-B |
| R.B | 1060.000000 | 3.800000 | 4027.999999 | ABALB | -158.800000 | .000000 | -100.000000 | G-B | 980.000000 | RED-B |
| A*K | 1240.000000 | 9.400000 | .1165600+05 | ABALA | -162.300000 | .000000 | -100.000000 | G-B | 980.000000 | RED-B |
| K*K | .000000 | .000000 | .000000 | ABALK | -171.700000 | .000000 | -100.000000 | G-B | .000000 | K*K |
| B*B | 1060.000000 | .000000 | .000000 | SMLTB | -158.800000 | .000000 | -100.000000 | G-B | 950.000000 | RED-B |
| S*K | 1760.000000 | 15.100000 | .2657599+05 | SMLTK | -171.700000 | .000000 | -100.000000 | G-B | 980.000000 | RED-B |
| SCAPB | 1500.000000 | .000000 | .000000 | SCAPB | .000000 | 4000.000000 | 2500.000000 | SCAPB | UNBNDED | |
| SCAPK | 4000.000000 | .000000 | .000000 | SCAPK | .000000 | 7000.000000 | 3000.000000 | SCAPK | UNBNDED | |
| SMB | 2500.000000 | 85.000000 | .2124999+06 | DEM-B | -609.500000 | 1000.000000 | 960.000000 | G-B | 1392.000000 | RED-B |
| SMK | 3000.000000 | 52.000000 | .1559999+06 | DEM-K | -559.250000 | 1200.000000 | 1160.000000 | G-B | 1592.000000 | RED-B |

**Fig. 7-13** Solution of two-stage manufacturing model—row order.

along with the names of the incoming variables when the ranges are exceeded. Figure 7-13 gives a similar summary for the original model constraints.

Other commands that exist in all good linear programming solution codes are the parametric action commands, i.e., requests to investigate a series of solutions when a given parameter or set of parameters changes continuously. The parameters that can change are the costs associated with the variables in the problem or they can represent some of the elements in the requirements vector. Parametric programming procedures are especially important when linear programming models are used in a simulation mode and when in fact one requests that the model develop optimum operating strategies under varying conditions. Chapter 9 contains a detailed description of simulation procedures that use linear programming models. The commands for the execution of a parametric procedure are generally given as PARA. COSTS, PARA. RHS, or their respective equivalents DO.PCR and DO.PLP. It can easily be seen that the RANGE commands are actually the first steps in the parametric program procedures if one realizes that the parametric procedures continually jump from one solution to the next when the range for the specific parameters is exceeded. We should note here though, that RANGES will provide data for *all* the variables in the problems, i.e., they indicate the possible range for each individual variable, while parametric procedures apply when only a selected set of variables is changing.

## Model Analysis

Many of the available computer codes also have extensive model review procedures. Their prime purpose is to aid in model development and model testing. In these cases, the computer displays and comments on the structure of the model that is presented. Some of these routines are MATRIX PRINTOUT, in which a full printout of the entire matrix is presented. A single sheet of computer output paper can contain a subset of the matrix consisting of 12 to 15 variables and up to 50 constraints. For large models, with more than 200 constraints or variables, the amount of paper produced by a full matrix printout is so large as to be useless. For smaller models, full matrix printouts are oftentimes helpful. A more condensed version of the matrix

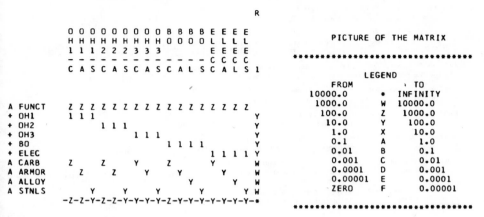

**Fig. 7-14** Picture of the multiproduct manufacturing model matrix.

printout can frequently be obtained with the commands AMATRIX, PICTURE, or MATRIXMAP. Such a picture of the matrix portrays each matrix element in an alphabetically or numerically coded form, indicating the order of magnitude and the sign of the matrix element. Such pictorial representations of matrices are extremely useful in ascertaining that individual matrix elements have been placed correctly in the matrix, especially since the great majority of the matrix elements are zero. A picture of a multiplant-multitime period model will quickly point out the matrix elements that are wrongly placed, because the great majority of the off-diagonal elements should be zero. A single page of computer output paper can contain up to 60 variables in pictorial form and it can cover up to 50 constraint rows. Pictures of matrices are useful model review procedures so long as the models contain less than 300 equations and 1000 variables. Figure 7-14 contains an example of a matrix PICTURE printout of the multiproduct manufacturing model.

Another aid in model review is the request EQ.LIST which stands for "equations listing." This procedure will, for each constraint equation, list all the variables and their coefficients. Since the original input data is generally presented in a column format, the EQ.LIST often serves a useful purpose in the review of linear programming models, since it presents the matrix in the other direction. Figure 7-15 contains an example of an equation listing. Also frequently available are counts of nonzero elements by column as well as by row.

Some of the more powerful linear programming computer codes will, besides printing out the model in pictorial matrix form, also do a logical analysis of the model. Such a logical analysis is aimed at finding inconsistencies and infeasibilities in the model. Besides being an aid in model review, the procedure is also useful in reducing actual solution times, because the logical analysis will frequently indicate that a certain variable must logically be part of the solution, while others cannot be a part of the solution. Subsequent to a logical analysis, therefore, an inversion to a then specified solution can greatly reduce computer time.

```
OR MAY 68              MULTIPRODUCT MANUFACTURING MODEL                           .000.003.001

   CASE                          EQLIST OUTPUT
   EQUATION    1 LABEL  DCOST COST =      .000000 ORIGINAL BI =     .000000
   +  1.00000( DCOST) -  1.00000( ELECA)

   EQUATION    2 LABEL  FUNCT COST =      .000000 ORIGINAL BI =     .000000
   +    1.00000( FUNCT) + 400.00000( OH1-C) + 440.00000( OH1-A) + 480.00000( OH1-S) + 4   .00000( OH2-C) + 484.00000( OH2-A)
   +  528.00000( OH2-S) + 360.00000( OH3-C) + 380.00000( OH3-A) + 410.00000( OH3-S) + 3   .00000( BO -C) + 406.00000( BO -A)
   +  416.00000( BO -L) + 426.00000( BO -S) + 300.00000( ELECC) + 349.99999( ELECA) + 3   .00000( ELECL) + 400.00000( ELECS)

   EQUATION    3 LABEL  OH1   COST =      .000000 ORIGINAL BI =    30.000000
   +  1.00000( OH1  ) +  1.00000( OH1-C) +  1.00000( OH1-A) +  1.00000( OH1-S) +   .00000(*B1   )

   EQUATION    4 LABEL  OH2   COST =      .000000 ORIGINAL BI =    29.000000
   +  1.00000( OH2  ) +  1.00000( OH2-C) +  1.00000( OH2-A) +  1.00000( OH2-S) +   .00000(*B1   )

   EQUATION    5 LABEL  OH3   COST =      .000000 ORIGINAL BI =    27.000000
   +  1.00000( OH3  ) +  1.00000( OH3-C) +  1.00000( OH3-A) +  1.00000( OH3-S) +   .00000(*B1   )

   EQUATION    6 LABEL  BO    COST =      .000000 ORIGINAL BI =    30.000000
   +  1.00000( BO   ) +  1.00000( BO -C) +  1.00000( BO -A) +  1.00000( BO -L) +   .00000( BO -S) + 30.00000(*B1   )

   EQUATION    7 LABEL  ELEC  COST =      .000000 ORIGINAL BI =    27.999999
   +  1.00000( ELEC ) +  1.00000( ELECC) +  1.00000( ELECA) +  1.00000( ELECL) +   .00000( ELECS) + 28.00000(*B1   )

   EQUATION    8 LABEL  CARB  COST =      .000000 ORIGINAL BI =  8099.999900
   +    1.00000( CARB ) + 120.00000( OH1-C) + 139.99999( OH2-C) +  87.00000( OH3-C) + 1  .00000( BO -C) +  45.00000( ELECC)
   +8099.99990(*B1   )

   EQUATION    9 LABEL  ARMOR COST =      .000000 ORIGINAL BI =  1937.999900
   +    1.00000( ARMOR) + 104.00000( OH1-A) + 130.00000( OH2-A) +  80.00000( OH3-A) +   .00000( BO -A) +  42.00000( ELECA)
   +1937.99990(*B1   )

   EQUATION   10 LABEL  ALLOY COST =      .000000 ORIGINAL BI =  2128.000000
   +  1.00000( ALLOY) +  88.00000( BO -L) +  35.00000( ELECL) +2128.00000(*B1   )

   EQUATION   11 LABEL  STNLS COST =      .000000 ORIGINAL BI =  1020.000000
   +    1.00000( STNLS) +  62.00000( OH1-S) +  70.00000( OH2-S) +  55.00000( OH3-S) +   .00000( BO -S) +  37.00000( ELECS)
   +1020.00000(*B1   )
   END EQLIST OUTPUT
```

**Fig. 7-15** Equation listing of the multiproduct manufacturing model matrix.

### Instructing the Computer

In the older linear programming codes, the operating commands were almost always presented to the computer in the form of punched cards. In certain codes, the commands could be submitted with the data cards, while in others, input data and the operating commands had to be submitted separately to the computation center. The newer linear programming codes have a much greater flexibility than the older codes; operating commands and data can be submitted apart, together, or split up in almost any conceivable fashion. The actual control languages, or the commands available to the user, have become quite flexible. They have started to resemble common English more closely, and they are now far less restricted in the way that the commands must appear on the punched cards.

The newer program control procedures are further distinguished by the fact that before solution is started, all the control commands can be scanned, checked for correctness, accuracy, and consistency, and only after the full set of commands has been found to be error free will solution begin. With the older codes, and on the small computer systems, the control commands are read in, one at a time, and executed upon reading by the computer. When there are inconsistencies or errors in the command string, the program often will be at a loss to decide what is required of it, and its only recourses are to query the computer operator for further guidance or to abort the run. Since many computer operators are at best only slightly familiar with linear programming methods and solution procedures, quite a few runs were aborted

```
'  997 B
'  RUN CO7300,ADL005,10,200
'  MSG TAPE 45E05=0 INPUT
'  MSG TAPE 3 AND 4 ARE SCRATCH
'  XQT CUR
TRW A,D
 IN A
 TRI A
'Q XQT LP1108
TITLE
CONDENSED PIERCE CONTAINER MODEL FOR A.HAX
SET LINMAX TO 40
SET OBJECT TO (MIN    )
LOAD 2
ROW ID
•                                          HEADING,   MULTIPRODUCT MANUFACTURING MODEL
•                                          INPUT,1
•                                          ROW ID
•                                          •
EOF                                        •
MTXMAP                                     •
PRESLV,INVERT STATED                       •
GOGOGO                                     FOF
PRIMAL                                     PICTURE
REDCST                                     NORMAL,1,1
BASISO                                     DO.D/J
ENDJOB                                     RANGES
' '                                        GETOFF
```

|            (a)            |            (b)            |

**Fig. 7-16** (a) Sample Univac Exec II system and LP1108 controls; (b) sample IBM 1401 LP/11 controls.

prematurely, often because of only a small keypunch error. This, therefore, prompted the approach for checking the entire command string before embarking on a linear programming solution and not wasting computer time when subsequent control card errors would cause a run abortion. In all fairness, we should state that with the old control card procedure, very few runs on large models were ever satisfactorily completed on the first try. Examples of various command sequences are shown in Figs. 7-16 and 7-17.

## COMPUTER SYSTEM OPERATION

Besides instructing a given linear programming computer program on the actions it should take, it is also necessary to instruct the data processing center on the task that it should carry out. In very small data processing centers it is often enough to ask the computer operator to: "Please run this linear programming job." This simple communication quickly gives way to more formal procedures as the size and complexity of the data processing center grow. In most cases, a charge account for the job must be specified as well as an expected and a maximum duration for calculation. In addition, essentially all medium and large scale computers are operated under control of a so-called operating, executive, or monitor system. Such a system is itself a computer program that initiates, schedules, controls, and monitors the calculations under way. The prime task of such an operating system is to schedule the individual jobs through the computer, making sure that all the desired peripheral devices such as tapes, disks, and other memory units are available and operating. An operating system may even elect or be instructed to have the computer carry out two or more jobs simultaneously, with one of the jobs at a higher priority. Frequently, an operating system will log and present an accounting of the amount of time and equipment

```
''GG
//TED1   JOB  MSGLEVEL=1
//JOBLIB    DD   DSNAME=MPSLMOD,DISP=OLD
//COMPILE  EXEC PGM=COMPILER
//SYSMLCP  DD   UNIT=SYSDA,VOLUME=SER=HUD008,SPACE=(TRK,(5,2)),
//              DISP=(NEW,PASS)
//SCRATCH1 DD   DSNAME=MPS.SCRTCH1,DISP=OLD
//SCRATCH2 DD   DSNAME=MPS.SCRTCH2,DISP=OLD
//SCRATCH3 DD   DSNAME=MPS.SCRTCH3,DISP=OLD
//SCRATCH4 DD   DSNAME=MPS.SCRTCH4,DISP=OLD
//SCRATCH5 DD   DSNAME=MPS.SCRTCH5,DISP=OLD
//SYSABEND DD   SYSOUT=A
//SYSPRINT DD   SYSOUT=A
//SYSIN    DD   *
              PROGRAM
              INITIALZ
              TITLE('MULTIPRODUCT MANUFACTURING MODEL')
              MOVE(XDATA,'PROBFILE')
              MOVE(XPBNAME,'PBFILE')
              MOVE(XOBJ,'FUNCT')
              MOVE(XRHS,'RHS1    ')
              CONVERT('SUMMARY')
              SETUP
              PRIMAL
              SOLUTION
              PUNCH
              PICTURE
              RANGE
              STATUS
              EXIT
              PEND
//FXECUTE  EXEC PGM=EXECUTOR,COND=(COND=(0,NE,COMPILE)
//ETA1     DD   DSNAME=MPS.ETA1,DISP=OLD
//MATRIX DD  DSNAME=MPS.MATRIX1,DISP=OLD
//SCRATCH1 DD   DSNAME=MPS.SCRATCH1,DISP=OLD
//SCRATCH2 DD   DSNAME=MPS.SCRATCH2,DISP=OLD
//PROBFILE DD   DSNAME=MPS.PROBFILE,DISP=OLD
//SYSMLCP  DD   UNIT=SYSDA,VOLUME=SER=HUD008,DSNAME=*.COMPILE.SYSMLCP,
//              DISP=(OLD,DELETE)
//SYSABEND DD   SYSOUT=A
//SYSPRINT DD   SYSOUT=A
//SYSIN  DD   *
```

(a)

```
'JOB,11171,ADL,75,4444
'EQUIP,1=**,SV
'EQUIP,30=(NDRIEBEEK,25,1,999),SV
'EQUIP,32=**,SV
'EQUIP,33=(TPS4,1,1,999)
'LOADMAIN,33,75,10000
TITLE,TWO STAGE MANUFACTURING MODEL
INPUT,INPTAPE=60
ROW ID
  .
  .
  .
  .
EOF
PRIMAL
PREPARE,RANGECON,RANGEVAR
RPG,ALL
PUNCH
EXITLP
'
  '
```

(b)

**Fig. 7-17** (a) Sample IBM OS and MPS commands; (b) sample CDC-3600 Scope and Allegro commands.

used and the corresponding charge. These all are desirable features; the only drawback is that these operating systems themselves often require an intricate set of commands describing the job priority, job type, the amounts and types of memory devices that are to be made available, the location of the input data and the control card deck, etc. Obviously the request: "Please run this linear programming job" would be much simpler, but with the bigger and more sophisticated computer systems this option no longer exists. Most routine users of linear programming solution procedures will, once they have developed or otherwise obtained an appropriate set of operating system instructions or job control cards, reuse this same set from one run to the next, changing only the actual linear programming code controls as required for each specific calculation. Figures 7-16 and 7-17 contain examples of monitor system controls and linear programming code controls for selected computer systems. A full description of the operating commands for the monitor systems and the linear programming codes available for various makes and models of computers is beyond the scope of this work. The interested reader is urged to consult the specific manuals pertaining to each individual computer system and linear programming code.

### Matrix Generation Programs

When linear programming problems were small, e.g., less than 40 constraints and 80 variables, it was entirely feasible to construct the linear programming matrices manually. However, as model sizes grew, it became rapidly apparent that the development of larger linear programming matrices could best be done in a computer-aided manner. The specification of a matrix element is generally performed by indicating the constraint row name, the variable name, and the matrix element value. Each one of these three fields must be filled out exactly right. A matrix with 300 rows, 1000 variables, and 10% dense (10% nonzero elements) will have 30,000 matrix elements. The chances that $30,000 \times 3$ fields $= 90,000$ fields are filled out and keypunched without a single error are extremely small. Because of this volume of input data preparation, matrix generation programs have become indispensable.

Two types of matrix generation programs have been developed and used. The first of these types are general purpose matrix generation programs or matrix manipulation procedures. The MARVEL and MAGEN languages are examples of such procedures. In general purpose matrix generator programs, the following items must be specified:

1. The original input data including all the costs, and all technical coefficients that apply.
2. The structure of the model that is to be generated.

Tabular formats are generally used for input of the data. The mode or procedure for specifying the structure for the linear programming model, however, is not easy, especially if the matrix generation program is to be a truly general purpose program. The matrix generation program then becomes a procedure that translates the data from a tabular form into an appropriate model input form as specified for the selected linear programming code. Consider for example the product mixing model described in Chapter 4. All the pertinent data for this model was contained in Tables 4-1 and

4-2. Then, in a narrative form, it was stated that all five components could be blended to the final product so long as the product specifications were observed. This last sentence completely describes how the model should be constructed, but unfortunately a computer system requires a much more precise statement of the actions to be carried out. As can be seen from the blending model in matrix format, there is a certain "structure" to the model, and it is this structure that must be specified unambiguously. We should observe initially that each of the components that can be blended (each variable) has six coefficients:

- One cost coefficient.
- Two volume coefficients, one for demand balance, the other for supply balance.
- Three quality coefficients.

We can thus describe the "format" or structure of each variable by the following procedure which refers to Table 4-1:

1. Variable name = Code name column entry
2. Row name 1 = OBJECTIVE
3. Coefficient in row 1 = Value in Cost column
4. Row name 2 = TOTAL VOLUME
5. Coefficient in row 2 = 1.0
6. Row name 3 = Code name + VOLUME
7. Coefficient in Row 3 = 1.0
8. Row name 4 = OCTANE SPEC
9. Coefficient in row 4 = Value in Research Octane number column
10. Row name 5 = VAPOR PRESSURE
11. Coefficient in row 5 = Value in Vapor pressure column
12. Row name 6 = VOLATILITY
13. Coefficient in row 6 = Value in Volatility index column
14. Go back to procedure 1 until all variables have been constructed.

We leave it to the reader to specify the procedure for the requirements vector for this problem.

For a problem as small as the one shown, it appears hardly worth while to use a matrix generation program. However, consider the possibility of having 20 components available for this blend, or to have these five components available for four different products. Quickly it becomes clear that with the large models, a matrix generation procedure can become quite necessary because it greatly facilitates the conversion from tabular input data into a format acceptable by a specific linear programming code.

In the general purpose matrix generation programs, the specific "structure" of each variable must be specified similar to the example above.

The second type of matrix generation program consists of special purpose procedures in which the structure of the model is an integral part of the matrix generation program, and only the varying inputs need be specified. In fact, most of the special purpose matrix generation programs are written in the FORTRAN language, and they will closely resemble the example given above. Especially when a linear programming model is used for routine operations or scheduling, the special purpose matrix generation programs are to be preferred over general purpose matrix generation programs, because they tend to be more efficient of computer usage. For experimental models, however, it is frequently inconceivable to develop a special purpose matrix generation program, because the development costs can outweigh the advantages.

Matrix generation programs of either type are especially useful in the development of multitime period models, because the subsections of the model representing each individual time period are duplicates of one another except for the corresponding elements in the right-hand side vector. A manual construction of a multitime period model is often tedious, and an automated procedure can both speed up the process and improve the accuracy.

## MATRIX REVISIONS

A completely different mode of manipulating large linear programming matrices is by revisions or by editing procedures. In this mode of operation, a standard model is stored in its original form on a computer peripheral device such as a magnetic tape or disk unit. This standard model is then used as a base model, and revisions or modifications are inserted into the model to create the actual model that is to be solved at this time. When this mode of operation is used, the structure of the linear programming model is entirely incorporated into the standard model; changes are incorporated by a merging operation. The revise mode of operation was used extensively on the second-generation computing equipment, but it has been losing favor to the straightforward matrix generation programs because the revise procedures require intricate understanding of the method by which the original matrix was stored. In addition, the amount of computer time involved in revising a large matrix frequently exceeds the time required to generate a new matrix entirely from original data. This occurs because in a revise operation, a full old model must be read in and appropriate adjustments made when the model is read in. In a regenerate mode, only the compact mode data tables need be read in, and appropriately exploded to the full model. This requires less data input, which is frequently the most time-consuming task of the entire operation. Another advantage to regeneration over revision is that the tabular form data can easily be printed and preserved in their entirety for later reference, while revision data is generally only useful to indicate the changes or modifications in the model. When such changes are stacked one after the other, it is difficult to trace later on what was the actual problem that was solved. Sophisticated linear programming users will generally employ both matrix generation and matrix revision as is most appropriate for each individual calculation.

## OUTPUT ANALYSES PROGRAMS

The volumes of output produced from the solution of a large linear programming model are such that output writer programs, or programs that interpret and reformat the solution, are as necessary as the matrix generation programs used to develop the appropriate matrix. General purpose report writing programs have existed for some time, and they are widely used because they present the output from a linear programming solution in a readable and analyzable fashion. The majority of these output writer programs will take instructions from the originator regarding the desired format of the output reports.

In a manner similar to the matrix generation programs, there exist various output writer programs. While the matrix generation programs are used to convert model data into a matrix format, output writers are useful in converting the volumes of data available from a linear programming solution to a summarized report that is more condensed, and especially more easily interpretable than a raw linear programming solution output. A problem with 200 variables and 100 constraints generally gets printed on six full computer sheets. The problem originator, however, is often interested only in selected portions plus some summaries, occupying at most two or three pages of readable report. Output writer or report programs, therefore, must "know" the format of the linear programming solution output and they must be instructed on how to move, sum, or otherwise manipulate this data into a specified report format to be used directly by managers and others not intimately acquainted with linear programming. General purpose output writer programs do greatly assist linear programming operations and many standard report writing programs are quite good. They do, however, require detailed specifications on the actions they have to take.

Figures 7-12 and 7-13 contained the standard linear programming results for the two-stage manufacturing model example. The pertinent results could also have been shown as:

| Mining | Tons Bauxite | % |
|---|---|---|
| Guinea | 1,666.67 | 22.7 |
| Surinam | 52,000.0 | 71.0 |
| Arkansas | 20,000.0 | 27.3 |
| Total | 73,166.67 | 100.0 |

| Bauxite Conversion | Tons Alumina | % |
|---|---|---|
| Surinam | 3,200 | 58.1 |
| Baltimore | 1,060 | 19.3 |
| Arkansas | 1,240 | 22.6 |
| Kitimat | 0 | 0.0 |
| Total | 5,500 | 100.0 |

| Smelting | Tons Alumina | % |
|---|---|---|
| Baltimore | 2,500 | 45.5 |
| Kitimat | 3,000 | 54.5 |
| Total | 5,500 | 100.0 |

| Transportation | Route | Tons |
|---|---|---|
| Bauxite | Guinea to Baltimore | 1,666.67 |
| Bauxite | Surinam to Baltimore | 12,000.0 |
| Alumina | Surinam to Baltimore | 1,440.0 |
| Alumina | Surinam to Kitimat | 1,760.0 |
| Alumina | Arkansas to Kitimat | 1,240.0 |

It should be obvious that a report presented in this form is infinitely more legible than the standard linear programming output results.

The report writing programs thus merely move, accumulate, and summarize the pertinent data. In order to do so, they must know the format of the linear programming solution and the format of the desired report, along with appropriate keys to extract the necessary information. Report writing programs are extra valuable when many routine linear programming solutions are to be analyzed or tabulated. This occurs especially during studies involving parametric programming procedures as described in Chapter 9, because during such studies a whole set of linear programming solutions is examined when one or more parameters vary over a prespecified range. Oftentimes, 10 to 25 solutions are so developed, and if the model contains 100 equations and 300 variables, it is easy to see that all these linear programming solutions represent an enormous amount of paper that has to be analyzed. In this case, it often is even advisable to use special plotting techniques to reduce the volume of answers to meaningful proportions.

Also, when a single linear programming model contains more than 200 equations and it is used more than a few times, it is almost mandatory that report writing programs are used, because of the sheer bulk of straight linear programming output that must be analyzed *and* tabulated in order to be meaningful for a manager.

When linear programming models are used for routine operations scheduling, it is frequently more desirable to devise one's own special purpose report writing programs. The advantage in special purpose report writing programs is again that the structure of the report becomes an integral part of the program and hence the program can be economical of computer time. Input data to such a program is of course the normal output data from the linear programming solution procedure. The format of the reports is entirely embedded in the report writing program.

The great majority of the *special purpose* matrix generation programs and output writer programs have been developed in the FORTRAN language. Other high level computer languages such as COBOL, ALGOL, or PL/1 can be used, but traditionally FORTRAN has been the favored language.

## DISCUSSION TOPICS AND PROBLEMS

1. Construct a set of control cards to solve a linear program with two objective functions and two right-hand sides, and to print all four solutions.

2. Construct a set of control cards for a problem for which a BASIS is supplied, assuming that there is only one objective row and one right-hand side.

3. When a problem is submitted with a BASIS and an inversion to the desired basis is carried out, will the so obtained solution be feasible, optimal, neither, or both? Explain your views.

4. How can an equation listing be helpful in model review?

5. How would you construct the matrix generation portion for the right-hand side vector of the sample blending model?

6. How would you construct a matrix generator for a time phased model? Would you have the matrix generator construct every variable, or would you use it only to expand a manually constructed one-period model to cover the other time periods?

7. How would you construct or use a report writing program on a multitime period model?

8. How would you run a sample linear programming problem? Who would make up the linear programming system control cards? Who would make up the appropriate computer operating system control cards? Who would run the job?

# Model
# Sensitivity
# Analysis                                                     8

The prime motivation for constructing a linear programming model is to determine an optimum operating strategy for the process under consideration. Such a best strategy is represented by the optimum solution to the linear programming problem. Finding such a best strategy is obviously important, but frequently one would wish to know more; especially one would like to know why the suggested solution is the best solution. In addition, planning managers and others who use linear programming procedures would like to know to which parameter variations the solution is most sensitive. For example, future variable operating costs are bound to be somewhat inaccurate. If the linear programming model suggests entirely different strategies for small variations in the future variable manufacturing cost of a product, then the solution is highly sensitive to this cost, and it may be wise to develop a more precise estimate of such a cost element. If the model indicates that a solution remains constant for wide variations in most cost factors, then we consider that the operation is relatively insensitive to those cost factors, and further refinement of these costs is unwarranted.

Similar conditions apply to the availability of limited resources. In some cases, it may be found that what was expected to be a limited resource actually turns out to be not limiting. In such a case, one may be interested to know how much of this resource is "not needed." Also, having more than the initially specified quantity available will not alter either the suggested strategy or the cost or profit of the total operation because increasing the availability of a resource that is already surplus will only increase the surplus, and not the use of the resource. An example of this may be the availability in machine hours of a rock crusher. As long as the demand for crushed rock is less than the crusher capacity, there is little justification for speeding up the maintenance on the crusher because the additional capacity hours will undoubtedly be left unused anyway. We see thus that relaxing a nonbinding constraint will have little or zero value.

The simplex linear programming procedure continually strives to find a better operating strategy than the one currently at hand. It does so by reviewing at each step of the solution process the marginal cost reduction or profit potential of all the activities that are not in the current solution. The simplex procedure determines what activities to include to improve solutions and ultimately to find the optimum solution to the problem. The procedure not only determines which activities appear to be promising for further cost reduction or profit improvement, but it automatically determines the rate at which costs will increase or profit decrease if it were to introduce unprofitable activities into the solution. It is on the basis of this activity selection criterion that the procedure finally stops and determines that an optimum solution has been found, because when there are no more promising activities to introduce into the solution, the optimum solution has been found. Obviously, at this point it should be possible to display the amount of "unprofitableness" of each of the activities that are not part of the solution. This unprofitableness is also known as the marginal cost or shadow price. Still other names that have been used are: opportunity costs, multipliers, $\pi$ values, and dual variables.

## MULTIPRODUCT MANUFACTURING MODEL EXAMPLE

In order to show the effects of the various sensitivity analyses that can be carried out as an extension to linear programming procedures, we will use the multiproduct manufacturing model from Chapter 4. For completeness sake, this problem is reproduced here. The pertinent operating data are shown in Table 8-1.

**Table 8-1**

**Steel Production (Tons Per Day) with Five Furnaces**

| Steel type | OH1 | OH2 | OH3 | BO | ELEC | Requirement, tons |
|---|---|---|---|---|---|---|
| Carbon | 120 | 140 | 87 | 103 | 45 | 8100 |
| Armor | 104 | 130 | 80 | 94 | 42 | 1938 |
| Alloy | — | — | — | 97 | 35 | 2128 |
| Stainless | 62 | 70 | 55 | 88 | 37 | 1020 |
| Days available | 30 | 29 | 27 | 30 | 28 | |

Standard production rates: tons per day
Availability: stream days per month
Requirement: total tonnage forecast

MULTIPRODUCT MANUFACTURING MODEL                 11/21/68 AT 22 13 PAGE 3 VARIABLE SUMMARY    PAGE-1
                                                 1* FUNCT                        1*RHS001

| F VARBLE | VALUE | CJ | EXT COST | DJ | RANGE LOWER | VEAL | RANGE UPPER | VEAU |
|---|---|---|---|---|---|---|---|---|
| * OH1 | | .000000 | | 400.000000 | -400.000000 | OH1 | UNBNDED | |
| * OH2 | | .000000 | | 493.333333 | -493.333333 | OH2 | UNBNDED | |
| * OH3 | | .000000 | | 220.000000 | -220.000000 | OH3 | UNBNDED | |
| * BO | | .000000 | | 526.857143 | -526.857143 | BO | UNBNDED | |
| * ELEC | 11.776913 | .000000 | .000000 | .000000 | -76.363637 | OH2-A | 113.793104 | OH3 |
| OH1-C | 30.000000 | 400.000000 | .1200000+05 | .000000 | UNBNDED | | 460.000000 | OH1-A |
| OH1-A | | 440.000000 | | 60.000000 | 380.000000 | OH1-A | UNBNDED | |
| OH1-S | | 480.000000 | | 270.957290 | 209.042710 | OH1-S | UNBNDED | |
| OH2-C | 29.000000 | 440.000000 | .1276000+05 | .000000 | UNBNDED | | 442.333333 | OH2-A |
| OH2-A | | 484.000000 | | 2.333333 | 481.666667 | OH2-A | UNBNDED | |
| OH2-S | | 528.000000 | | 333.704467 | 194.295533 | OH2-S | UNBNDED | |
| OH3-C | 2.775000 | 360.000000 | 999.000000 | .000000 | 358.564103 | OH2-A | 449.720177 | OH3-S |
| OH3-A | 24.225000 | 380.000000 | 9205.500000 | .000000 | UNBNDED | | 381.435898 | OH2-A |
| OH3-S | | 410.000000 | | 89.720177 | 320.279823 | OH3-S | UNBNDED | |
| BO -C | | 380.000000 | | 220.190476 | 159.809524 | BO -C | UNBNDED | |
| BO -A | | 406.000000 | | 227.857143 | 178.142857 | BO -A | UNBNDED | |
| BO -L | 19.484536 | 416.000000 | 8105.567010 | .000000 | 320.208494 | ELECS | 636.190476 | BO -C |
| BO -S | 10.515464 | 426.000000 | 4479.587629 | .000000 | UNBNDED | | 521.791506 | ELECS |
| ELECC | 4.412778 | 300.000000 | 1323.833334 | .000000 | 253.593012 | OH3-S | 334.482759 | ELECA |
| ELECA | | 350.000000 | | 35.000000 | 315.000000 | ELECA | UNBNDED | |
| ELECL | 11.810309 | 375.000000 | 4428.865980 | .000000 | 287.424243 | BO -C | 413.098894 | ELECS |
| ELECS | | 400.000000 | | 36.539028 | 363.460972 | ELECS | UNBNDED | |

MULTIPRODUCT MANUFACTURING MODEL                 11/21/68 AT 22 13 PAGE 4 CONSTRAINT SUMMARY   PAGE-1
                                                 1* FUNCT                        1*RHS001

| VARBLE | VALUE | CJ | EXT COST | ROW NM | DUAL | RHS VALUE | RANGE LOWER | VLAL | RANGE UPPER | VLAU |
|---|---|---|---|---|---|---|---|---|---|---|
| FUNCT | -.5330235+05 | .000000 | .000000 | FUNCT | 1.000000 | .000000 | | | | |
| OH1-C | 30.000000 | 400.000000 | .1200000+05 | OH1 | 400.000000 | 30.000000 | 25.583658 | ELEC | 31.654792 | ELECC |
| OH2-C | 29.000000 | 440.000000 | .1276000+05 | OH2 | 493.333333 | 29.000000 | 25.214564 | ELEC | 30.418393 | ELECC |
| ELEC | 11.776913 | .000000 | .000000 | OH3 | 220.000000 | 27.000000 | 24.225000 | OH3-C | 29.282471 | ELECS |
| BO -L | 19.484536 | 416.000000 | 8105.567010 | BO | 526.857143 | 30.000000 | 25.316001 | ELEC | 34.697282 | ELECL |
| ELECC | 4.412778 | 300.000000 | 1323.833334 | ELEC | .000000 | 28.000000 | 16.223087 | ELEC | UNBNDED | |
| BO -S | 10.515464 | 426.000000 | 4479.587629 | CARB | -6.666667 | 8100.000000 | 7901.425000 | ELECC | 8629.961082 | ELEC |
| ELECL | 11.810309 | 375.000000 | 4428.865980 | ARMOR | -7.500000 | 1938.000000 | 1755.402299 | ELECC | 2160.000000 | OH3-C |
| OH3-A | 24.225000 | 380.000000 | 9205.500000 | ALLOY | -10.714286 | 2128.000000 | 1714.639175 | ELECL | 2540.191953 | ELEC |
| OH3-C | 2.775000 | 360.000000 | 999.000000 | STNLS | -9.823270 | 1020.000000 | 564.363636 | ELECL | 1474.347948 | ELEC |

**Fig. 8-1** Sample computer output—Allegro code, CDC-3600 computer.

SECTION 1 - ROWS

| NUMBER | ...ROW.. | AT | ...ACTIVITY... | SLACK ACTIVITY | ..LOWER LIMIT. | ..UPPER LIMIT. | .DUAL ACTIVITY |
|---|---|---|---|---|---|---|---|
| 1 | FUNCT | BS | 53302.35395 | 53302.35395- | NONE | NONE | 1.00000 |
| 2 | DCOST | BS | . | . | NONE | NONE | . |
| 3 | OH1 | UL | 30.00000 | . | NONE | 30.00000 | 400.00000 |
| 4 | OH2 | UL | 29.00000 | . | NONE | 29.00000 | 493.33333 |
| 5 | OH3 | UL | 27.00000 | . | NONE | 27.00000 | 220.00000 |
| 6 | BO | UL | 30.00000 | . | NONE | 30.00000 | 526.85714 |
| 7 | ELEC | BS | 16.22309 | 11.77691 | NONE | 28.00000 | . |
| 8 | CARB | EQ | 8100.00000 | . | 8100.00000 | 8100.00000 | 6.66667- |
| 9 | ARMOR | EQ | 1938.00000 | . | 1938.00000 | 1938.00000 | 7.50000- |
| 10 | ALLOY | EQ | 2128.00000 | . | 2128.00000 | 2128.00000 | 10.71429- |
| 11 | STNLS | EQ | 1020.00000 | . | 1020.00000 | 1020.00000 | 9.82327- |

SECTION 2 - COLUMNS

| NUMBER | .COLUMN. | AT | ...ACTIVITY... | ..INPUT COST.. | ..LOWER LIMIT. | ..UPPER LIMIT. | .REDUCED COST. |
|---|---|---|---|---|---|---|---|
| 12 | OH1-C | BS | 30.00000 | 400.00000 | . | NONE | . |
| 13 | OH1-A | LL | . | 440.00000 | . | NONE | 60.00000 |
| 14 | OH1-S | LL | . | 480.00000 | . | NONE | 270.95729 |
| 15 | OH2-C | BS | 29.00000 | 440.00000 | . | NONE | . |
| 16 | OH2-A | LL | . | 484.00000 | . | NONE | 2.33333 |
| 17 | OH2-S | LL | . | 528.00000 | . | NONE | 333.70447 |
| 18 | OH3-C | BS | 2.77500 | 360.00000 | . | NONE | . |
| 19 | OH3-A | BS | 24.22500 | 380.00000 | . | NONE | . |
| 20 | OH3-S | LL | . | 410.00000 | . | NONE | 89.72018 |
| 21 | BO-C | LL | . | 380.00000 | . | NONE | 220.19048 |
| 22 | BO-A | LL | . | 406.00000 | . | NONE | 227.85714 |
| 23 | BO-L | BS | 19.48454 | 416.00000 | . | NONE | . |
| 24 | BO-S | BS | 10.51546 | 426.00000 | . | NONE | . |
| 25 | ELECC | BS | 4.41278 | 300.00000 | . | NONE | . |
| 26 | ELECA | LL | . | 350.00000 | . | NONE | 35.00000 |
| 27 | ELECL | BS | 11.81031 | 375.00000 | . | NONE | . |
| 28 | ELECS | LL | . | 400.00000 | . | NONE | 36.53903 |

**Fig. 8-2** Solution printout by MPS system—IBM System/360 computer.

Table 8-2

**Linear Programming Calculated Operating Plan**

| Steel type | Days of operation | | | | |
|---|---|---|---|---|---|
| | OH1 | OH2 | OH3 | BO | ELEC |
| Carbon | 30.0 | 29.0 | 2.775 | | 4.41 |
| Armor | | | 24.225 | | |
| Alloy | | | | 19.48 | 11.81 |
| Stainless | | | | 10.52 | |
| Idle time | | | | | 11.78 |
| Total available | 30.0 | 29.0 | 27.0 | 30.0 | 28.00 |

When this problem was submitted for solution to two up-to-date linear programming solution procedures, the results were as shown in Fig. 8-1 and 8-2. The actual outputs shown are in standard compact format as prepared, respectively, by the Allegro code (CDC-3600 computer) and MPS (IBM System/360 computer).

In a formal report for management review, the calculated plan of operations could be as shown in Table 8-2, and the sensitivity of the operating plan could be reported as shown in Table 8-3. With this understanding, let us see how to interpret the marginal cost analysis.

## MARGINAL COSTS

The marginal costs fall into two major categories:

1. The first category comprises those costs that describe the rate of change in the value of the objective of the problem if an activity that is not part of the best solution is introduced into the solution anyway. In this case, the marginal cost represents the amount by which that activity is "too expensive" to be included in the schedule of operations. For example, in the multiproduct manufacturing model as described above, the optimum schedule of operation is to use open hearth furnace 1 to make carbon steel for all 30 days of the time period. If we would insist on using open hearth furnace 1 for 1 day to manufacture armor steel, the total cost of operation would increase by $60 (see Table 8-3). The $60 figure reflects all the other necessary changes in the manufacturing process to continue meeting the other requirements under such a changed operating plan. The marginal cost for the activity to use open hearth furnace 1 in the manufacture of armor steel can also be interpreted as stating that the activity is not selected in the operating plan because it is $60 per day too expensive. If, for example, the daily operating cost for making armor steel on that furnace could be reduced from $440 to $380, then that particular activity could be selected without

**Table 8-3**

**Operating Plan Sensitivity**

| Extra furnace capacity | | Penalties for deviating from plan, $/day | | | |
|---|---|---|---|---|---|
| Furnace | $/day | Carbon | Armor | Alloy | Stainless |
| OH1 | 400.00 | 0.0 | 60.0 | N.A.* | 270.96 |
| OH2 | 493.33 | 0.0 | 2.33 | N.A. | 333.70 |
| OH3 | 220.00 | 0.0 | 0.0 | N.A. | 89.72 |
| BO | 526.86 | 220.19 | 227.86 | 0.0 | 0.0 |
| ELEC | 0.0 | 0.0 | 35.0 | 0.0 | 36.54 |
| Marginal production cost, $/ton | $\pi$ values | 6.67 | 7.50 | 10.71 | 9.82 |

* N.A. = not allowed.

altering the total cost of the operation. A $380 operating cost represents a point at which more than one equally attractive operating plan exists. If the operating cost could be further reduced from $380 to, for example, $370 per day, it would become attractive to manufacture some armor steel in open hearth furnace 1 and to make further adjustments in the operating schedule to arrive at a new optimal solution.

For another example, the *actual* cost of making armor steel on the electrical furnace is $350 per day. The *marginal* cost of making armor steel on the electrical furnace is $35. (Again see Table 8-3.) From this we can deduce that only when the cost of operating the electrical furnace reduces to $315 will it become economically attractive to do so. At any cost above $315, this is not an attractive mode of operation and hence undesirable.

2. The shadow prices associated with the original slack, surplus, and artificial variables are indicative of the rate of change of the value of the objective function when the product requirements or the resource availabilities change. The shadow prices pertaining to the slack, surplus, and artificial variables indicate the rate of change in the objective function value in a positive as well as in a negative direction.

In the multiproduct manufacturing model described in Chapters 4 and 7, we found that the furnace capacities of the three open hearth furnaces as well as the basic oxygen furnace were all consumed entirely. From Figs. 8-1 and 8-2, and as reconstructed in Table 8-3, we can observe that the shadow price associated with the slack variable representing the unused capacity on open hearth furnace 1 (+OH1) is $400. This implies that if there were one less day of capacity on furnace 1 available, the total cost of operation would increase by $400, due to necessary modifications in operations of the other furnaces. Conversely, if an additional day of capacity would have been available for this furnace, the total cost of operation could have been decreased by $400. We see thus that the shadow price or $\pi$ value represents the *rate of change* of the objective function for variations in resource availability. In mathematical terms, the shadow price is the partial derivative of the objective function with respect to changes in resource availability or requirements. These changes generally apply over at least a small range of availability of the resource.

The difference between the pure margial costs associated with the initial structural variables and the shadow prices associated with the initial slack, surplus, and artificial factors is that the marginal costs indicate how much overpriced an activity is to be considered in the operating plan, while the shadow prices or $\pi$ values indicate the rate of change of the objective if requirements or availabilities vary up or down. The shadow prices are of interest to the user of linear programming because they indicate how a limiting constraint can affect the cost of the operation. In the same example, open hearth furnace 3 was available for only 27 days in the month. Figure 8-1 shows that the shadow price for this furnace capacity (+OH3) is $220. This means that the operating cost could be reduced by $220 if furnace 3 could be made available an additional day. Initially, the furnace was scheduled for preventive maintenance for 3 days; if maintenance could be speeded up through overtime to take only 2 days, an additional day of capacity could be made available. This thus indicates what a manager may wish to spend for overtime maintenance.

Another useful interpretation of the shadow prices concerns marginal product manufacturing costs. In Fig. 8-1 we can note that the marginal manufacturing cost for carbon steel (see constraint summary − ROW NM = CARB) is $6.666, and it is $10.714 for alloy steel (row name = ALLOY). If the profit margin on the last ton of carbon steel is less than $6.666, it will be better not to sell this last unit. Conversely, if an additional sale of alloy steel can be made with the marginal profit exceeding $10.714 per ton, then the transaction will be profitable to the firm.

Great care should be taken in the interpretation of shadow prices because they imply only the rate of change in the objective function for a small change in resource availability or requirement. There is no immediate indication available about the range over which such an availability can vary and produce the indicated change in the objective value.

## TRANSFER PRICES

One very important use of shadow prices as developed by a linear programming solution is in setting transfer prices. Let us assume that the linear programming model of the two-stage manufacturing operation of Chapter 5 has been developed as reproduced in Fig. 8-3. The objective of this model is to minimize the firm's total variable operating cost. When the linear programming solution has been reached, we will find certain quantities of materials transferred from the bauxite conversion to the smelting operations. These quantities are shown as R.S., R.B., R.A., and R.K., the outputs from the various conversion units. These outputs become inputs to the smelters as the variables S*B, S*K, B*B, etc. and inputs and outputs are equalized through the balance equations known as ABALS, ABALB, ABALA, and ABALK.

When obtaining the linear programming solution now, shadow prices will be indicated for the artificial vectors associated with these balance equations. These

TWO STAGE MODEL

```
                                                                    R

        G G G G S S S S A A A A R R R R S S B B A A K K S S
        - - - - - - - - - - - - . . . . * * * * * * * * M M
        S B A K S B A K S B A K S B A K B K B K B K B K B K

                                                                    1


A COST  X X Y Y X X Y Y Y Y X Y X X X X X Y   Y X X Y   Y Y  .
+ MINEG 1 1 1 1                                               *
+ MINES         1 1 1 1                                       *
+ MINEA                 1 1 1 1                               *
A BBALS B       B       B       -1
A BBALB   B       B       B       -1
A BBALA     B       B       B       -1
A BBALK       B       B       B       -1
+ RED-S 1       1       1                                     *
+ RED-B   1       1       1                                   *
+ RED-A     1       1       1                                 *
+ RED-K       1       1       1                               *
A ABALS                         1   -1-1
A ABALB                           1     -1-1
A ABALA                         1           -1-1
A ABALK                         1               -1-1
A SMLTB                             1   1   1   1   -1
A SMLTK                               1   1   1   1   -1
+ SCAPB                                             1   W
+ SCAPK                                             1   W
A DEM-B                                             A   W
A DEM-K                                             A   W
    -B-B-B-B-B-B-B-B-B-B-B-B-B                      A   A-W
```

TWO STAGE MODEL

PICTURE                              PICTURE OF THE MATRIX

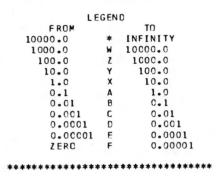

Fig. 8-3 Picture of a two-stage manufacturing model matrix.

| VARBLE | VALUE | CJ | EXT COST | ROW NM | DUAL | RHS VALUE | RANGE LOWER | VLAL | RANGE UPPER | VLAU |
|---|---|---|---|---|---|---|---|---|---|---|
| COST | -.7715559+06 | .000000 | .000000 | COST | 1.000000 | .000000 | | | | |
| MINEG | .3433333+05 | .000000 | .000000 | MINEG | .000000 | .3599999+05 | 1666.666660 | MINEG | UNBNDED | |
| S-B | .1200000+05 | 5.800000 | .6960000+05 | MINES | 6.600000 | .5200000+05 | .4000000+05 | S-B | .5324999+05 | G-B |
| MINEA | 8000.000000 | .000000 | .000000 | MINEA | .000000 | .2800000+05 | .2000000+05 | MINEA | UNBNDED | |
| R.S | 3200.000000 | 3.300000 | .1056000+05 | BBALS | -153.300000 | .000000 | -100.000000 | G-B | 980.000000 | RED-B |
| G-B | 1666.666660 | 9.300000 | .1549999+05 | BBALB | -155.000000 | .000000 | -100.000000 | G-B | 980.000000 | RED-B |
| R.A | 1240.000000 | 3.200000 | 3968.000000 | BBALA | -159.100000 | .000000 | -100.000000 | G-B | 980.000000 | RED-B |
| R.K | .000000 | 2.400000 | .000000 | BBALK | -169.300000 | .000000 | -100.000000 | G-B | .000000 | R.K |
| S-S | .4000000+05 | 3.700000 | .1480000+06 | RED-S | 1.964000 | .4000000+05 | .2366666+05 | RED-B | .5200000+05 | S-B |
| RED-B | .1633333+05 | .000000 | .000000 | RED-B | .000000 | .3000000+05 | .1366666+05 | RED-B | UNBNDED | |
| A-A | .2000000+05 | 5.500000 | .1100000+06 | RED-A | 4.364200 | .2000000+05 | 4193.548381 | RED-B | .2161290+05 | G-B |
| RED-K | .8000000+05 | .000000 | .000000 | RED-K | .000000 | .8000000+05 | .000000 | RED-K | UNBNDED | |
| S*B | 1440.000000 | 2.200000 | 3168.000001 | ABALS | -156.600000 | .000000 | -100.000000 | G-B | 980.000000 | RED-B |
| R.B | 1060.000000 | 3.800000 | 4027.999999 | ABALB | -158.800000 | .000000 | -100.000000 | G-B | 980.000000 | RED-B |
| A*K | 1240.000000 | 9.400000 | .1165600+05 | ABALA | -162.300000 | .000000 | -100.000000 | G-B | 980.000000 | RED-B |
| K*K | .000000 | .000000 | .000000 | ABALK | -171.700000 | .000000 | -100.000000 | G-B | .000000 | K*K |
| B*B | 1060.000000 | .000000 | .000000 | SMLTB | -158.800000 | .000000 | -100.000000 | G-B | 980.000000 | RED-B |
| S*K | 1760.000000 | 15.100000 | .2657599+05 | SMLTK | -171.700000 | .000000 | -100.000000 | G-B | 980.000000 | RED-B |
| SCAPB | 1500.000000 | .000000 | .000000 | SCAPB | .000000 | 4000.000000 | 2500.000000 | SCAPB | UNBNDED | |
| SCAPK | 4000.000000 | .000000 | .000000 | SCAPK | .000000 | 7000.000000 | 3000.000000 | SCAPK | UNBNDED | |
| SMB | 2500.000000 | 85.000000 | .2124999+06 | DEM-B | -609.500000 | 1000.000000 | 960.000000 | G-B | 1392.000000 | RED-B |
| SMK | 3000.000000 | 52.000000 | .1559999+06 | DEM-K | -559.250000 | 1200.000000 | 1160.000000 | G-B | 1592.000000 | RED-B |

Fig. 8-4 Solution of a two-stage manufacturing model matrix.

### Table 8-4

### Shadow Price Analysis for Two-Stage Manufacturing Model

Equipment and operations capacity limitations, $/ton

| Location | Mining | Bauxite conversion | Smelting |
|---|---|---|---|
| Guinea | 0.0 | N.A.* | N.A. |
| Surinam | 6.6 | 1.96 | N.A. |
| Arkansas | 0.0 | 4.36 | N.A. |
| Baltimore | N.A. | 0.0 | 0.0 |
| Kitimat | N.A. | 0.0 | 0.0 |

Product transfer prices, $/ton

| Location | Bauxite | Alumina | Final product |
|---|---|---|---|
| Surinam | 153.30 | 156.60 | N.A. |
| Arkansas | 159.10 | 162.30 | N.A. |
| Baltimore | 155.00 | 158.80 | 609.50 |
| Kitimat | 169.30 | 171.70 | 559.25 |

* N.A. = Not Applicable.

shadow prices indicate the rate of change in the objective value if slightly more or slightly less of that commodity were available. Or in other words, the $\pi$ values or shadow prices indicate the marginal value of the transferred material. Figure 8-4 shows these shadow prices in the column headed DUAL, and the variable names are in the column ROW NM.

Are these $\pi$ values the appropriate transfer price for the goods moving between the two manufacturing stages? Yes, indeed they are, because if these shadow prices had been used in the objective function, each stage of the operation could have been optimized by itself and a solution identical to the overall solution would have been obtained. With different transfer prices, each of the two stages would most likely have been scheduled differently, and hence not optimally for the overall operation. The shadow prices therefore are the appropriate transfer prices for total corporate maximization; they are the values that allow for each submodule to be optimized independently and at the same time give a total corporate optimum operating plan. A complete shadow price analysis for this model is contained in Table 8-4.

We can see here that some knowledge about an operation can be gained by reviewing the shadow prices of the balance equations. This often is an argument for constructing a model in a more general way and not as compact as has been discussed in Chapter 5. Adding some additional balance equations to a model may slightly increase computer solution time, but the benefits often outweigh this. Again, the versatility of the model builder gets tested under these conditions. Figures 8-3 through 8-9 show the matrix printouts, solution logs, and the full solution printouts of both the fully expanded two-stage model and its compact equivalent.

TWO STAGE MODEL

| TOTAL ITERS | ROW IDENT. | SUM OF INFEAS. | CHOSEN VECTOR | VECTOR REMOVD | NEG D/J |
|---|---|---|---|---|---|
| 1 | COST | − 2200.000 | S−K | A BBALK | 24 |
| 2 | COST | − 2200.000 | S−A | A BBALA | 21 |
| 3 | COST | − 2200.000 | S−B | A BBALB | 18 |
| 4 | COST | − 2200.000 | S−S | A BBALS | 15 |
| 5 | COST | − 2200.000 | R.K | A ABALK | 12 |
| 6 | COST | − 2200.000 | K*K | A SMLTK | 11 |
| 7 | COST | − 2200.000 | K*B | A SMLTB | 8 |
| 8 | COST | − 2200.000 | R.A | A ABALA | 5 |
| 9 | COST | − 22C0.000 | R.B | A ABALB | 4 |
| 10 | COST | − 2200.000 | R.S | A ABALS | 3 |
| 11 | COST | − 1000.000 | SMK | A DEM−K | 2 |
| 12 | COST | − 536.000 | SMB | + MINES | 1 |
| 13 | COST | 0.0 | A−K | A DEM−B | 8 |

SOLUTION FEASIBLE

TWO STAGE MODEL

| TOTAL ITERS | ROW IDENT. | SUM OF INFEAS. | CHOSEN VECTOR | VECTOR REMOVD | NEG D/J |
|---|---|---|---|---|---|
| 14 | COST | −121297+ 6 | S*B | K*B | 5 |
| 15 | COST | −109292+ 6 | S*K | + RED−S | 3 |
| 16 | COST | −954969+ 5 | B*K | S−K | 3 |
| 17 | COST | −954969+ 5 | A−A | S−A | 5 |
| 18 | COST | −781617+ 5 | A*K | + RED−A | 6 |
| 19 | COST | −778497+ 5 | B*B | B*K | 4 |
| 20 | COST | −771556+ 5 | G−B | A−K | 3 |

PRIMAL SOLUTION

Fig. 8-5 Iteration log of a two-stage manufacturing model solution.

TWO STAGE MODEL

SOLUTICN PRINT — FUNCTION ROW  COST  −771556+ 5  RHS       1

| VARIABLE | LEVEL | C/J |
|---|---|---|
| G−B | 1666.666 | 9.300 |
| S−S | 40000.000 | 3.7C0 |
| S−B | 12000.000 | 5.8CC |
| A−A | 200C0.000 | 5.50C |
| R.S | 32CC.000 | 3.3CC |
| R.B | 1059.999 | 3.8C0 |
| R.A | 124C.000 | 3.20C |
| R.K | 0.0 | 2.4C0 |
| S*B | 1440.000 | 2.2CC |
| S*K | 1760.000 | 15.10C |
| B*B | 105S.999 | C.C |
| A*K | 1240.000 | 9.4C0 |
| K*K | 0.0 | 0.C |
| SMB | 25CC.000 | 85.0CC |
| SMK | 3000.000 | 52.CC0 |

| VARIABLE | LEVEL |
|---|---|
| A COST | −771556+ 5 |
| + MINEG | 34333.334 |
| + MINEA | 8000.000 |
| + RED−B | 16333.334 |
| + RED−K | 80000.000 |
| + SCAPB | 1500.000 |
| + SCAPK | 40C0.000 |

**Fig. 8-6** Solution of a two-stage manufacturing model.

From Fig. 8-8 it can readily be seen that the compact model was solved in 11 iterations, 9 less than the full model. But the increased number of iterations occurred in phase 1, establishing feasibility. Since the full model has 10 balance equations (which are strict equalities) and the compact model has none (see Fig. 8-7), it should not be surprising that it requires more iterations in the full model to attain feasibility. The additional information available from the full model makes it very well worth while, especially since with clever usage of the INVERT mode of operation much of the additional

COMPACT FORMULATION OF TWO STAGE MANUF. MODEL

```
                                                        R

      G G G G G G G G S S S S S S S S A A A A A A A A
      S S A A B B K K S S A A B B K K S S A A B B K K
      B K B K B K B K B K B K B K B K B K B K B K B K

                                                        1

A COST      Z Z Z Z Z Z Z Z Z Z Z Z Z Z Z Z Z Z Z Z Z Z Z Z
+ MINEG     1 1 1 1 1 1 1 1                                   W
+ MINES                     1 1 1 1 1 1 1 1                   W
+ MINEA                                   1 1 1 1 1 1 1 1 W
+ RED-S     Y Y             Y Y             Y Y             *
+ RED-A       Y Y             Y Y             Y Y           *
+ RED-B         Y Y             Y Y             Y Y         *
+ RED-K           Y Y             Y Y             Y Y *
+ SMLTB     1   1   1   1   1   1   1   1   1   1   1   1   W
+ SMLTK       1   1   1   1   1   1   1   1   1   1   1   1 W
A DEM-B     A   A   A   A   A   A   A   A   A   A   A   A   W
A DEM-K       A   A   A   A   A   A   A   A   A   A   A   A W
          -A-A-A-A-A-A-A-A-A-A-A-A-A-A-A-A-A-A-A-A-A-A-A-A-W
```

COMPACT FORMULATION OF TWO STAGE MANUF. MODEL

PICTURE                          PICTURE OF THE MATRIX

****************************************

LEGEND

| FROM | | TO |
|---|---|---|
| 10000.0 | * | INFINITY |
| 1000.0 | W | 10000.0 |
| 100.0 | Z | 1000.0 |
| 10.0 | Y | 100.0 |
| 1.0 | X | 10.0 |
| 0.1 | A | 1.0 |
| 0.01 | B | 0.1 |
| 0.001 | C | 0.01 |
| 0.0001 | D | 0.001 |
| 0.00001 | E | 0.0001 |
| ZERO | F | 0.00001 |

****************************************

Fig. 8-7 Picture of the compact formulation of a two-stage manufacturing model.

computer time can be saved anyhow. One final note: the solution strategies suggested by both models are identical, as they should be, of course, but the final objective value differs slightly ($13), which is due only to rounding errors introduced in the construction of the compact model.

There are often major organizational difficulties in trying to implement such a transfer price scheme in an actual on-going corporation. First of all, when demands and supplies vary from one time period to another, the transfer prices are quite

COMPACT FORMULATION OF TWO STAGE MANUF. MODEL

| TOTAL ITERS | ROW IDENT. | SUM OF INFEAS. | CHOSEN VECTOR | VECTOR REMOVD | NEG D/J |
|---|---|---|---|---|---|
| 1 | COST | − 1505.600 | AKK | + MINEA | 24 |
| 2 | COST | − 1000.000 | SKK | A DEM-K | 16 |
| 3 | COST | 0.0 | SKB | A DEM-B | 12 |
| SOLUTION FEASIBLE | | | | | |

COMPACT FORMULATION OF TWO STAGE MANUF. MODEL

| TOTAL ITERS | ROW IDENT. | SUM OF INFEAS. | CHOSEN VECTOR | VECTOR REMOVD | NEG D/J |
|---|---|---|---|---|---|
| 4 | COST | −121485+ 6 | SSB | SKB | 13 |
| 5 | COST | −109484+ 6 | SSK | + RED-S | 7 |
| 6 | COST | −101382+ 6 | SBK | SKK | 9 |
| 7 | COST | −954956+ 5 | + MINEA | + MINES | 6 |
| 8 | COST | −781603+ 5 | AAK | + RED-A | 9 |
| 9 | COST | −774988+ 5 | GBK | AKK | 7 |
| 10 | COST | −771868+ 5 | SBB | SBK | 2 |
| 11 | COST | −771543+ 5 | GBB | GBK | 1 |
| PRIMAL SOLUTION | | | | | |

**Fig. 8-8** Solution log of the compact formulation of a two-stage manufacturing model.

COMPACT FORMULATION OF TWO STAGE MANUF. MODEL

SOLUTION PRINT − FUNCTION ROW   COST   −771543+ 5   RHS        1

| VARIABLE | LEVEL | C/J |
|---|---|---|
| GBB | 99.997 | 243.800 |
| SSB | 1440.002 | 136.750 |
| SSK | 1759.997 | 116.650 |
| SBB | 960.000 | 161.300 |
| AAK | 1240.002 | 153.300 |

| A COST | −771543+ 5 |
|---|---|
| + MINEG | 2060.002 |
| + MINEA | 495.997 |
| + RED-B | 16333.042 |
| + RED-K | 80000.000 |
| + SMLTB | 1500.000 |
| + SMLTK | 4000.000 |

NO MORE CONTROL CARDS

**Fig. 8-9** Solution of the compact formulation of a two-stage manufacturing model.

likely to vary. A manager of an operating module, whose reward partially depends on operating profits will be quite loath to have to plan his operations against a varying price for his products and/or his raw materials. Even though total corporate rewards can be so maximized, his own rewards are apt to suffer.

A possible approach is to set fixed transfer prices for reward purposes, but to schedule the volumes of each manufacturing unit through a central linear program. This is often more acceptable to the individual plant managers even though it can affect each plant's operating revenue. So long as these variations are within reasonable limits they can be accepted. But with fixed transfer prices for reward purposes, the variable manufacturing costs are affected, which can in turn influence the total corporate operating strategy again.

The whole problem is actually the result of a conflict between central planning for maximum profit and decentralized reward systems aimed at optimizing the individual operating modules. It can readily be seen that total corporate models frequently involve extensive reviews of company policies if not organization as a whole. The problem is most severe in multistage manufacturing operations, and less difficult in single-stage operations such as wholesaling and retailing.

## COST RANGES

Users of linear programming generally have a further interest in the stability of a solution as indicated by the range over which the cost factors can vary without upsetting the optimal solution. In the example of Chapter 1, we saw that if the resource availabilities were kept constant, and if the profit margin on product R remained constant at $3, then the solution would remain optimal for profit margins on B ranging all the way from $1.50 to $3 per carload. If the profit margin for B went below $1.50 per carload, it became more attractive to produce only type R insulation. On the other hand, if the profit margin of B were to exceed $3.00, it became more attractive to produce only type B insulation and none at all of R. We note thus that such a cost range is indicative of stability of the solution for variations in the cost of a single activity, keeping all other costs, technical coefficients, resource availabilities, and product requirements constant. Figure 8-10 shows this graphically.

Figure 8-1 shows the cost ranges for the multiproduct manufacture model. We see there that open hearth furnace 1 is used to manufacture carbon steel for 30 days, at a daily initial cost of $400 (OH1-C). Further inspection of this same line indicates that the linear programming solution will remain optimal so long as the operating cost for this activity stays between $-\infty$ and $460$. For open hearth furnace 2 we note that the activity is selected for 29 days of manufacturing carbon steel at an initial cost of $440 per day, but that the optimum operating strategy will change when the operating cost increases to only $442.33. A comparison of these two factors indicates that the suggested operating schedule is relatively insensitive to the cost of manufacturing carbon steel on furnace 1 but that a slight variation in the manufacturing cost of furnace 2 would suggest a different operating strategy. If the actual costs of operation of furnaces 1 and 2 are lower than, respectively, $400 and $440 per day, the linear programming solution remains constant. In fact, reducing the operating cost

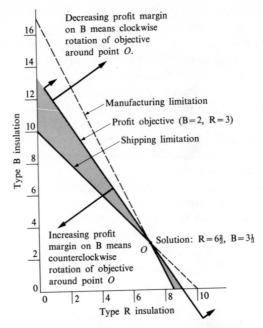

Decreasing profit margin on B means clockwise rotation of objective around point $O$.

Manufacturing limitation

Profit objective $(B=2, R=3)$

Shipping limitation

Increasing profit margin on B means counterclockwise rotation of objective around point $O$

Solution: $R=6\frac{2}{3}$, $B=3\frac{1}{3}$

Type B insulation

Type R insulation

**Fig. 8-10** Graphical representation of the cost range.

does not suggest a different *operating strategy* even though the total operating cost of the firm decreases with the reductions in manufacturing costs. We must remember here that the solution obtained indicates the best operating plan, in terms of the selected processes or activities, and the objective value is the cost of the total operation. Altering selected cost factors in the operation can cause alterations in the total operation cost, even if the operating plan remains constant.

The optimum solution also suggests the manufacture of carbon steel on open hearth furnace 3 for 2.775 days at an initial cost of \$360 per day. If this cost decreases to \$358.564, a different operating strategy or a different solution will become optimal. Also, if the cost increases to \$449.72, a different operating strategy will prevail. We conclude here that the manufacturing cost of carbon steel on furnace 3 is quite sensitive on the low side but insensitive on the high side.

The cost ranges of the other activities in the optimal solution should be self-explanatory except for the cost range on the slack capacity of the electrical furnace (+ELEC). As indicated, 11.77 days of furnace capacity are left unused. The initial cost of not using this capacity was 0. The ranges here imply that if the operating cost of this furnace could be credited with \$76.36 or if it were increased by \$113.79, different optimum solutions to the problem would prevail.

The linear programming computer program used in this example also indicates what other or new activities would be selected at either the minimum or maximum cost. Many of the newer and more sophisticated linear programming solution codes provide this type of information. Thus, if the cost of manufacturing carbon steel on

OH2 rose above $442.33, it would become attractive to start making armor steel on this unit (OH2-A).

It should be clear that cost ranges apply only to those variables or activities that form a part of the optimum solution, because if they were not part of the optimum solution, they would be "overpriced" and their marginal value would indicate by what amount their cost would have to be reduced in order to become a candidate for inclusion in the solution.

Cost ranges have one very important use during model development i.e., they indicate to which costs the overall model is most sensitive. If, for example, it is learned that a given cost can range 20% up or down before the solution changes, and another can range only 3% up or down, then it is clear that in the next cost data review, more attention should be paid to the latter cost factor. In actual practice, many model builders will initially use rough estimates of costs, subsequently refining only those to which the operation is most sensitive. This tends to speed up model development, checkout, and implementation and it can reduce overall model and system development costs.

## RIGHT-HAND SIDE RANGES

Right-hand side ranges indicate the amount over which the resource requirements or availabilities can vary without making the optimum solution infeasible. Cost ranging is equivalent in a graphical sense to altering the slope of the objective line, but right-hand side ranging is equivalent to moving a constraint line parallel to itself, either inward or outward. Such a parallel move can continue until the intersection representing the optimum solution meets a new constraint, and a change in basis is required.

In Fig. 8-1, in the constraint summary, under ROW NM, we can see that the availability of furnace 3 (OH3) can range between 24.225 and 29.282 days and the current optimal solution will remain feasible. Similarly, the availability of the basic oxygen furnace (BO) can range between 25.316 and 34.697 days for the solution to remain feasible. We see here that the selected operating strategy is relatively insensitive to the actual availability of furnace capacity. For the carbon steel product requirements, at 8100 tons, we see that the solution is not overly sensitive. The requirement for this steel can vary from 7901.4 to 8630.0 and the suggested solution will remain optimal. At either of these two extremes, a different operating schedule will become necessary. The same thing applies to alloy steel where the range is between 1714.6 and 2540.2 tons, with an initial value of 2128. The solution procedure appears to be somewhat sensitive (less than 10%) on either side for armor and stainless steel. In view of such small ranges, it may well be advisable to investigate a whole set of solutions covering variations in demand for the several products. The parametric programming procedures described in Chapter 9 are useful in this regard.

It should be clear that ranges in availabilities in requirements or right-hand side ranges apply only to the initial constraints in the program, while cost ranges apply only to those variables that are part of the optimum solution.

## SENSITIVITY TO MATRIX COEFFICIENTS

In addition to sensitivity to costs and resource availabilities, the linear programming user is often interested in the sensitivity of technical coefficients in the matrix. For example, the multiproduct manufacturing model contains the information that open hearth furnace 1 can manufacture 120 tons of carbon steel per day. One may be interested in finding the range over which this coefficient can vary before the current solution becomes nonoptimal or infeasible. Very few of the commercially available linear programming codes have a capability for establishing such sensitivity analysis. A possible mode of carrying out such an investigation is to solve a set of linear programming problems each of which differs only by the previous one through a small change in the coefficient under question. Such an investigation can be carried out through parametric programming procedures as described in Chapter 9.

## DISCUSSION TOPICS AND PROBLEMS

1. How can cost ranges be useful in model development and testout?
2. What is the exact meaning of right-hand side ranges?
3. What is indicated when, after an optimum solution has been reached, a variable has a reduced cost of 32¢?
4. What does it mean when an artificial variable has a shadow price of $-4$¢, 0, or $+6$¢?

# Parametric
# Programming
# Procedures                                                    9

Frequently, an operations or planning manager is not satisfied with finding only a best operating plan for a given set of costs and resource availabilities, because neither the costs nor the availabilities are known with adequate precision. In such cases, one is interested in finding a set of solutions or a set of best operating practices as the parameters under consideration vary from a lower extreme to a higher extreme condition. All good linear programming codes have the capability to investigate sets of solutions when either the cost or the availabilities vary beyond the ranges indicated in Chapter 8. Some of the more sophisticated linear programming codes will also trace a set of solutions when both costs and availabilities range simultaneously or when some coefficients inside the main matrix vary.

There are three types of questions that can be answered by parametric programming methods:

1. How does optimum operating strategy vary when one or more problem parameters change?

2. How does the total operating cost or the total profit of the operation under study vary with the changes in parameters?

3. How do the marginal costs and shadow prices vary with the changes in the parameters?

We will examine these further with the aid of some examples.

### CHANGE VECTORS

The user of a parametric programming procedure must specify, besides the original model, the rate of change of the various parameters and the total range over which the parametric programming procedure is to be carried out. The specification of the rates of change is accomplished by constructing a *change vector* that describes the various rates of change. For a parametric cost study, such a change vector is normally an additional function row, and for a parametric study on resources and availabilities, the change vector is an additional right-hand side vector. These change vectors are generally best introduced with the initial submission of the problem. Later introduction, after an optimal solution has been reached, is possible, but this frequently requires quite intimate understanding of the computer program. Introduction of the change data right along with the entire model inputs is simpler and less subject to error.

A change vector must have a minimum of one entry, specifying the desired rate of change of a single parameter. As a maximum, a cost change vector can contain as many entries as there are structural variables in the problem, and a right-hand side change vector can contain as many entries as there are constraint rows in the matrix. Nonspecified elements are considered to be zero, so only nonzero elements need be introduced.

Most parametric programming uses begin by examining the various linear programming solutions that result from a change in a single parameter; after several such single parameter investigations have been carried out, it can become practical to study the effects of simultaneous changes in two, three, four, or more parameters. Of course, in time-phased models, a change to a single parameter, like a change in cost in one time period, will generally produce a similar change in the other time periods. In such cases, the change vector will often have as many entries as there are time periods in the model.

### CONTROL PROCEDURE

The control procedure for parametric programming commences only after an initial optimum linear programming solution has been found. At such a time, the user specifies that he wishes to examine a series of optimal solutions starting from the initial optimal solution, and extending throughout the range indicated by the change vector multiplied by a control variable. In parametric cost procedures, the control variable is known as phi or $\phi$; in parametric right-hand side procedures, the multiplier is known as theta or $\theta$. The range of the solutions desired extends from $\phi$ or $\theta = 0$ to $\phi$ or $\theta = $ maximum and the general command is: "Do parametric cost (or right-hand side) procedure for $\phi$ (or $\theta$) ranging from 0 to $\phi_{max}$ (or $\theta_{max}$)."

Special additional commands may be to print solutions at specified intervals of $\phi$ or $\theta$, to print only when basis changes occur, or to print when either an unbounded or infeasible solution is encountered. The special commands vary from one computer program to another; for specific details it is best to consult the users' manual for the particular linear programming code to be used.

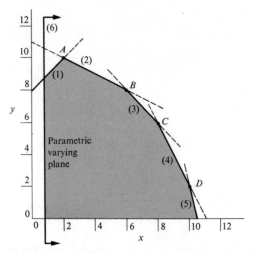

**Fig. 9-1** Graphical description of the parametric linear programming procedure.

## SIMPLE EXAMPLE

A simple example, employing two structural variables and five constraints may be useful for a graphical presentation of the parametric linear programming procedure.

Two variables $x$ and $y$ are constrained as follows:

$$-x + y \le 8, \tag{9-1}$$

$$x + 2y \le 22, \tag{9-2}$$

$$x + y \le 14, \tag{9-3}$$

$$x + 1/2y \le 11, \tag{9-4}$$

$$x + 1/4y \le 10.5. \tag{9-5}$$

The objective is to maximize $y$. Figure 9-1 depicts the feasible solution space for this problem. Simple inspection will show that the optimum solution to this problem is at point $A$, with an objective function value of 10. We now add a new constraint:

$$x \ge c, \tag{9-6}$$

and we let $c$ increase from 0 to 12. This is equivalent to driving a vertical line through the solution space in an easterly direction. This movement shrinks the solution space, since feasible solutions can exist only to the right of the (9-6) line.

When increasing $c$ from 0 upward, nothing happens until $c$ reaches 2, because the optimum solution is $y = 10$, $x = 2$. Expression (9-6) is not limiting for $c$ between 0 and 2.

At the original optimal solution, (9-1) and (9-2) were limiting; when $c$ reaches 2, (9-2) and (9-6) become limiting. When $c$ further increases to 6, (9-3) and (9-6) become limiting, etc. Figure 9-2 shows the value of the objective function and two of the

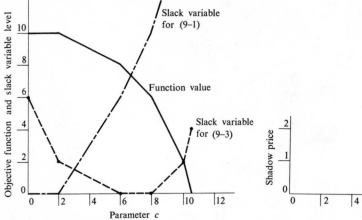

**Fig. 9-2** The function value and magnitude of slack variables as parameter c ranges from 0 to 12.

**Fig. 9-3** The shadow price for slack 3 as parameter c ranges from 0 to 12.

slack variables as the parameter $c$ ranges from 0 to 12. We should observe here that as the parameter $c$ increases, different constraints become binding, and when a constraint becomes binding, the magnitude of the associated slack variable becomes 0. At each vertex, therefore, a basis change occurs. The parametric procedure thus jumps from one vertex to another, assuring that each subsequent solution stays feasible and optimal for the current set of constraints. The value of the objective function varies linearly between adjacent vertices, and so does the magnitude of all the problem variables. For example, when $c = 4$, $x = 4$, $y = 9$. The value of the objective is also 9 and the amount of slack for (9-3) is $14 - 9 - 4 = 1$.

While the magnitude of the variables and the objective value vary linearly between adjacent basis changes, the shadow prices are constant for the same variation in parameter. This is so because the shadow prices indicate the rate of change in the objective value if a constraint were raised or lowered. Shadow prices are nonzero only for limiting constraints, and the *rate of change* in the objective remains constant whether the constraint is just barely binding or doing so severely. In the example, (9-3) is binding when the change parameter $c$ ranges from 6 to 8. At the same time, (9-6), the changing plane, is binding. The optimum solution exists at the intersection of the lines representing (9-3) and (9-6). A small positive variation $e$ in (9-3) causes the intersection of (9-3) and (9-6) to slide upward on the (9-6) line, increasing $y$ and the value of the objective. We note that the rate of change in the objective value is proportional to the rate of change of the constraint for (9-3). During the parametric linear programming run, therefore, the shadow price for slack variable 3 is as shown in Fig. 9-3.

In a similar manner, the shadow price for slack variable 1, when (9-1) and (9-2) are binding is 0.333. If the constraint value of (9-1) were raised from 8 to 9, the intersection of (9-1) and (9-2) lines would shift from $x = 2$, $y = 10$ to $x = 1.333$,

|  | $\dfrac{K}{P}$ | $\dfrac{K}{Q}$ | $\dfrac{L}{P}$ | $\dfrac{L}{Q}$ | $T_{P_{12}}$ | $T_{P_{21}}$ | $T_{Q_{12}}$ | $T_{Q_{21}}$ | $\dfrac{M}{P}$ | $\dfrac{M}{Q}$ | $\dfrac{N}{P}$ | $\dfrac{N}{Q}$ | $\dfrac{O}{P}$ | $\dfrac{O}{Q}$ | |
|---|---|---|---|---|---|---|---|---|---|---|---|---|---|---|---|
| Operating cost | 100 | 102 | 105 | 108 | 10 | 10 | 12 | 12 | 92 | 94 | 104 | 107 | 110 | 113 | |
| P1 balance | 40 | | 50 | | −1 | +1 | | | | | | | | | = 1400 units |
| Q1 balance | | 35 | | 42 | | | −1 | +1 | | | | | | | = 1020 units |
| K upper bound | 1 | 1 | | | | | | | | | | | | | ≤ 30 days |
| L upper bound | | | 1 | 1 | | | | | | | | | | | ≤ 24 days |
| P2 balance | | | | | +1 | −1 | | | 35 | | 50 | | 60 | | = 1350 units |
| Q2 balance | | | | | | | +1 | −1 | | 32 | | 45 | | 58 | = 1820 units |
| M upper bound | | | | | | | | | 1 | 1 | | | | | ≤ 30 days |
| N upper bound | | | | | | | | | | | 1 | 1 | | | ≤ 28 days |
| O upper bound | | | | | | | | | | | | | 1 | 1 | ≤ 30 days |

Plant 1 model    Transportation model    Plant 2 model

**Fig. 9-4** A two-plant, two-product model for a single time period.

TWO PLANT TWO PRODUCT MODEL

SOLUTION PRINT — FUNCTION ROW   COST   −14076.594   RHS

| VARIABLE | LEVEL | C/J |
|---|---|---|
| K-P | .857 | 100.000 |
| K-Q | 29.142 | 102.000 |
| L-P | 24.000 | 105.000 |
| TP21 | 165.714 | 10.000 |
| M-P | 3.306 | 92.000 |
| M-Q | 2.499 | 94.000 |
| N-P | 28.C00 | 104.000 |
| O-Q | 30.C00 | 113.000 |

A COST   −14076.594

+ M      24.193

**Fig. 9-5** Solution printout of two-plant, two-product model.

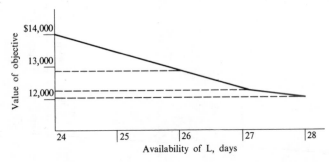

**Fig. 9-6** Value of the objective as the availability of machine $L$ increases from 24 to 28 days.

$y = 10.333$ and the objective value would be 10.333. Thus a change of 1 unit in the constraint causes 0.333 unit difference in the objective value, and hence the shadow price for the slack variable associated with (9-1) is 0.333 when the optimum solutions lie at the intersection of the (9-1) and (9-2) lines. Also, this value is a constant so long as the same set of equations is binding.

## EXAMPLE WITH THE MULTIPLANT MODEL

The two-plant, two-product model described in Chapter 5 is shown in matrix form as Fig. 9-4. This problem has an optimum solution as shown in Fig. 9-5. In the original problem, the manufacturing unit $L$ was available for 24 days. We will examine the set

Table 9-1

Results of Parametric Linear Programming Run Two-Plant, Two-Product Model

| Variable | Availability of machine $L$, days | | | |
|---|---|---|---|---|
| | 24.000 | 26.314 | 27.314 | 28.000 |
| K producing P | 0.857 | 0.857 | 0.857 | 0.0 |
| K producing Q | 29.142 | 29.142 | 29.142 | 29.142 |
| L producing P | 24.000 | 26.314 | 27.314 | 28.000 |
| Transport P − 2 → 1 | 165.714 | 50.000 | 0.0 | 0.0 |
| M producing P | 3.306 | 0.0 | 0.0 | 0.0 |
| M producing Q | 2.499 | 2.499 | 1.093 | 1.093 |
| N producing P | 28.000 | 28.000 | 27.000 | 27.000 |
| O producing Q | 30.000 | 30.000 | 30.000 | 30.000 |
| Unused capacity M | 24.193 | 27.500 | 28.906 | 28.906 |
| N producing Q | 0.0 | 0.0 | 1.000 | 1.000 |
| Value of objective | $14,076.594 | $12,858.288 | $12,334.101 | $12,320.387 |

of optimal solutions as the availability of machine L ranges from 24 to 30 days. The results are tabulated in Table 9-1. From this we should note that as more manufacturing capacity becomes available for machine L, up to 26.314 days, the initial step is to manufacture more P on L, to reduce the amount of P made on M to zero, and to reduce the transportation of product P from plant 2 to 1. The next step then, when the availability of L increases to 27.314 days, is to reduce the manufacture of P on machine N, to start manufacturing Q on N, to reduce the production of Q on M, and to eliminate transportation of P from plant 2 to 1. Finally, the last step is to reduce the manufacture of P on K to zero, and to manufacture all of the requirements for P at plant 1 using machine L only.

The value of the objective throughout this range of operations is shown graphically in Fig. 9-6. The rate reduction in cost is greater between 24 days and 27.314 days than it is between 27.314 days and 28 days, because differences in manufacturing costs *and* a transportation charge were being eliminated at first, and only differences in manufacturing costs applied when the availability of machine L approached 28 days.

## PARAMETRIC COST RANGING

Parametric cost ranging is similar to parametric linear programming, with the difference that the right-hand side vector remains constant as one or more costs or profit margins vary. Again, the procedure commences from an optimal solution and examines the set of solutions as selected cost elements vary over a specified range. Basis changes occur when the change in slope of the objective function is so large that a new solution becomes more attractive. Marginal costs, shadow prices, and the value

MULTIPRODUCT MANUFACTURING MODEL                    11/21/68 AT 22 13 PAGE 3 VARIABLE SUMMARY    PAGE-1
                                                    1* FUNCT                        1*RHS001

| F | VARBLE | VALUE | CJ | EXT COST | DJ | RANGE LOWER | VEAL | RANGE UPPER | VEAU |
|---|--------|-------|----|----------|----|-------------|------|-------------|------|
| + | OH1 | | .000000 | | 400.000000 | -400.000000 | OH1 | UNBNDED | |
| + | OH2 | | .000000 | | 493.333333 | -493.333333 | OH2 | UNBNDED | |
| + | OH3 | | .000000 | | 220.000000 | -220.000000 | OH3 | UNBNDED | |
| + | BO | | .000000 | | 526.857143 | -526.857143 | BO | UNBNDED | |
| + | ELEC | 11.776913 | .000000 | .000000 | .000000 | -76.363637 | OH2-A | 113.793104 | OH3 |
| | OH1-C | 30.000000 | 400.000000 | .1200000+05 | .000000 | UNBNDED | | 460.000000 | OH1-A |
| | OH1-A | | 440.000000 | | 60.000000 | 380.000000 | OH1-A | UNBNDED | |
| | OH1-S | | 480.000000 | | 270.957290 | 209.042710 | OH1-S | UNBNDED | |
| | OH2-C | 29.000000 | 440.000000 | .1276000+05 | .000000 | UNBNDED | | 442.333333 | OH2-A |
| | OH2-A | | 484.000000 | | 2.333333 | 481.666667 | OH2-A | UNBNDED | |
| | OH2-S | | 528.000000 | | 333.704467 | 194.295533 | OH2-S | UNBNDED | |
| | OH3-C | 2.775000 | 360.000000 | 999.000000 | .000000 | 358.564103 | OH2-A | 449.720177 | OH3-S |
| | OH3-A | 24.225000 | 380.000000 | 9205.500000 | .000000 | UNBNDED | | 381.435898 | OH2-A |
| | OH3-S | | 410.000000 | | 89.720177 | 320.279823 | OH3-S | UNBNDED | |
| | BO -C | | 380.000000 | | 220.190476 | 159.809524 | BO -C | UNBNDED | |
| | BO -A | | 406.000000 | | 227.857143 | 178.142857 | BO -A | UNBNDED | |
| | BO -L | 19.484536 | 416.000000 | 8105.567010 | .000000 | 320.208494 | ELECS | 636.190476 | BO -C |
| | BO -S | 10.515464 | 426.000000 | 4479.587629 | .000000 | UNBNDED | | 521.791506 | ELECS |
| | ELECC | 4.412778 | 300.000000 | 1323.833334 | .000000 | 253.593012 | OH3-S | 334.482759 | ELECA |
| | ELECA | | 350.000000 | | 35.000000 | 315.000000 | ELECA | UNBNDED | |
| | ELECL | 11.810309 | 375.000000 | 4428.865980 | .000000 | 287.424243 | BO -C | 413.098894 | ELECS |
| | ELECS | | 400.000000 | | 36.539028 | 363.460972 | ELECS | UNBNDED | |

MULTIPRODUCT MANUFACTURING MODEL                    11/21/68 AT 22 13 PAGE 4 CONSTRAINT SUMMARY  PAGE-1
                                                    1* FUNCT                        1*RHS001

| VARBLE | VALUE | CJ | EXT COST | ROW NM | DUAL | RHS VALUE | RANGE LOWER | VLAL | RANGE UPPER | VLAU |
|--------|-------|----|----------|--------|------|-----------|-------------|------|-------------|------|
| FUNCT | -.5330235+05 | .000000 | .000000 | FUNCT | 1.000000 | .000000 | | | | |
| OH1-C | 30.000000 | 400.000000 | .1200000+05 | OH1 | 400.000000 | 30.000000 | 25.583658 | ELEC | 31.654792 | ELECC |
| OH2-C | 29.000000 | 440.000000 | .1276000+05 | OH2 | 493.333333 | 29.000000 | 25.214564 | ELEC | 30.418393 | ELECC |
| ELEC | 11.776913 | .000000 | .000000 | OH3 | 220.000000 | 27.000000 | 24.225000 | OH3-C | 29.282471 | ELECC |
| BO -L | 19.484536 | 416.000000 | 8105.567010 | BO | 526.857143 | 30.000000 | 25.316001 | ELEC | 34.697282 | ELECL |
| ELECC | 4.412778 | 300.000000 | 1323.833334 | ELEC | .000000 | 28.000000 | 16.223087 | ELEC | UNBNDED | |
| BO -S | 10.515464 | 426.000000 | 4479.587629 | CARB | -6.666667 | 8100.000000 | 7901.425000 | ELECC | 8629.961082 | ELEC |
| ELECL | 11.810309 | 375.000000 | 4428.865980 | ARMOR | -7.500000 | 1938.000000 | 1755.402299 | ELECC | 2160.000000 | OH3-C |
| OH3-A | 24.225000 | 380.000000 | 9205.500000 | ALLOY | -10.714286 | 2128.000000 | 1714.639175 | ELECL | 2540.191953 | ELEC |
| OH3-C | 2.775000 | 360.000000 | 999.000000 | STNLS | -9.823270 | 1020.000000 | 564.363636 | ELECL | 1474.347948 | ELEC |

**Fig. 9-7** Multiproduct model computer solution.

of the objective vary continuously between adjacent basis changes, but the actual solution remains constant between adjacent basis changes.

In the multiproduct manufacturing model discussed in Chapters 4 and 8, the marginal cost of producing armor steel on the electrical furnace (ELECA) was $35.00, while the actual cost of operation is $350. See Fig. 9-7. We will examine how the operating strategy varies when the manufacturing cost for armor steel on the electrical furnace ranges from $350.00 down to $82.00. Table 9-2 contains the results. We can note that the initial solution remains optimal until the manufacturing cost of armor (ELECA) on the electrical furnace drops to $315.00. At this point, it becomes attractive to use the electrical furnace for the manufacture of armor steel instead of carbon steel. Appropriate adjustments are made on furnace OH3 to compensate. Note that the total cost of operation has not changed; at $315 for ELECA, there is a standoff in the two operating plans. When the cost further reduces to $233.00 it becomes attractive to discontinue the manufacture of alloy steel on the electrical furnace. More alloy steel must then be made on the basic oxygen furnace and stainless must be produced on open hearth furnace 3, and there must be an offsetting reduction of the amount of armor made on open hearth furnace 3. Finally, when the manufacturing cost drops all the way to $82, it becomes attractive to use all of the available electrical furnace capacity in the manufacture of armor steel and idle open hearth furnace 3 for 4.133 days.

**Table 9-2**

**Parametric Cost Ranging for Multiproduct Manufacturing Model**

| Variable | Cost of ELECA | | | |
|---|---|---|---|---|
| | $350.000 | $315.000 | $233.000 | $82.000 |
| OH1-C | 30.000 | 30.000 | 30.000 | 30.000 |
| OH2-C | 29.000 | 29.000 | 29.000 | 29.000 |
| OH3-C | 2.775 | 5.057 | 5.057 | 5.057 |
| OH3-A | 24.225 | 21.942 | 13.658 | 9.524 |
| OH3-S | 0.0 | 0.0 | 8.284 | 8.284 |
| BO-L | 19.484 | 19.484 | 24.181 | 24.181 |
| BO-S | 10.515 | 10.515 | 5.818 | 5.818 |
| ELECC | 4.412 | 0.0 | 0.0 | 0.0 |
| ELECL | 11.810 | 11.810 | 0.0 | 0.0 |
| +ELEC | 11.776 | 11.842 | 7.872 | 0.0 |
| +OH3 | 0.0 | 0.0 | 0.0 | 4.133 |
| ELECA | 0.0 | 4.347 | 20.127 | 28.000 |
| Value of objective | $53,302 | $53,302 | $52,393 | $48,442 |

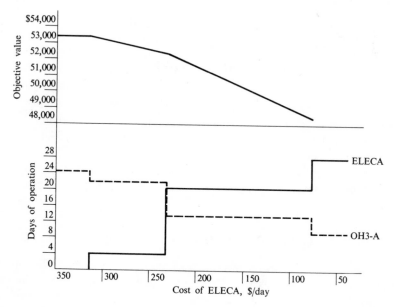

**Fig. 9-8** Variation in objective function value and operating strategy as the cost of ELECA varies.

Note again that the optimum solution, i.e., the schedule of operations, remains constant between basis changes, but that the objective value varies continuously as shown in Fig. 9-8.

## VARIATIONS IN MATRIX COEFFICIENTS

Only a very few commercially available linear programming codes are capable of directly carrying out studies of variations in matrix coefficients. There often is a genuine interest in such studies, and luckily, they can be carried out in an indirect but entirely adequate manner. In this procedure, the variable containing the coefficient to be studied is frozen at the level in the optimum solution, and a parametric linear program is carried out with a change vector that contains a single change element in the row containing the coefficient under study.

*Example.* Light naphtha has an octane rating of 84.5 RON. It is being blended into regular motor gasoline, and the optimum solution is to use 12 barrels of light naphtha (LN-MO). So we see that $(12 \times 84.5)$ + other octane barrel supplies (OOBS) = total octane barrel requirements (TOBR). We wish to investigate how the marginal cost and the objective function value change with a change in the octane quality of light naphtha. Begin by specifying that LN-MO must be equal to 12.0, as shown in the optimum solution. Now

$$12 \times 84.5 + OOBS = TOBR.$$

If the octane quality would improve to 85.5, we could simulate that by stating

$$(12 \times 84.5) + (12 \times 1.0) + OOBS = TOBR$$

or

$$(12 \times 84.5) + OOBS = TOBR - (12 \times 1.0).$$

In the change vector, we thus have a coefficient representing, in octane barrels, the variation induced by the matrix coefficient change. In this case, the change coefficient is $-(12 \times 1.0)$. A normal parametric programming procedure is then carried out to study how marginal costs and the objective value change for the variation in octane quality of the naphtha.

Other matrix coefficient variations can be studied in a similar manner. The sophisticated user of linear programming should be able to construct his own examples.

## SIMULATION WITH LINEAR PROGRAMMING MODELS

The ready availability of good parametric programming procedures has opened the way to performing simulations with linear programming models, where in fact, the linear programming program assumes the role of a "perfect decision maker" while a number of parameters range or vary. The net result of such simulations is that different operating strategies are suggested by the linear programming procedure for variations in resource availability and/or costs. Various industries use this mode of operation to evaluate major capital investments. Two cases are so set up, one without the new facility and one with, and the increased profit or reduction in operating cost is used as the economic justification for the new investment.

When using this approach, a true measurement of the value of the new investment is made because optimum operating conditions are established both with and without the new facility. This type of linear programming usage is especially valuable when total corporate models exist, with many interactions between plants, manufacturing units, and multiple time periods. Manually developing a good operating plan with and without a new facility is extremely complex and time consuming, and while a good plan for the existing facilities can be constructed based on prior operating experience, no such basis exists for operations with the new facility. Incorporating a new hypothetical facility in a corporate model thus turns out to be a most powerful approach, because future operations can be so simulated before the new facility exists or even before a commitment for the new facility is made.

Another use of simulation with linear programming models has been to establish future price trends in raw materials and finished goods. Under such a changing environment, it is attractive to be able to simulate future optimum operating strategies, because actual future operations will likely be quite near optimum. The linear programming model then is viewed as representing the future decision maker and the assumption is made that he will attempt to maximize profits. For examples of such uses of linear programming, see Chapters 15 and 17.

In carrying out parametric studies with large (300 rows or more) linear programming models, one generally finds that the procedure must trace through hundreds and even thousands of solutions. This occurs because the large models generally describe operations with a large amount of flexibility, just as much as an overall company frequently has a large amount of latitude in its operating plans. Tracing through such a large set of solutions becomes a herculean task if every solution is printed out. In this case it is preferable to use the options available in the good linear programming codes to print out the current best solution at predescribed intervals. For example, $\theta$, the parametric control variable, is allowed to range between 0 and 1.0. Often it is advisable to print the current solution for every 0.1 increment of $\theta$, thus giving a total of only 11 solutions that must be examined and analyzed. If drastic changes occur between two adjacent printouts, one can always return to the problem for a closer examination of the region in question, especially if restart positions (BASIS) are saved concurrent with each solution printout.

## DISCUSSION TOPICS AND PROBLEMS

1. In a parametric study of variations in right-hand side values, do the variables in the basis vary continuously or discretely between adjacent iterations? Why?

2. The steel manufacturing operation discussed in Chapters 4 and 8, and which was used as an example for parametric cost ranging in this chapter, is facing labor

negotiations for its open hearth furnace crews only. In simulating wage adjustments, how many coefficients should be contained in the change vector for this evaluation?

3. In a parametric cost range study, is it possible that the value of the objective first increases and subsequently decreases? Why? Would this be possible in a parametric right-hand side study?

4. In a parametric right-hand side study, is it possible for the level of a variable to first decrease and then increase?

# Integer
# Programming                                                        10

One of the basic assumptions of conventional linear programming procedures is that all the variables are continuous, or in other words, they are allowed to take on fractional values as well as whole numbers. In the small example of Chapter 1 we saw that the optimum solution was to produce $6\frac{2}{3}$ carloads of type R and $3\frac{1}{3}$ carloads of type B insulation. In many industrial situations, such fractional answers are entirely appropriate and useful. For example, it is quite possible to use manufacturing machine P to produce a product A for 1.3 days. Similarly, it is completely correct to blend 3.74 barrels of naphtha into a regular motor gasoline blending pool. Also, it can be appropriate to operate a catalytic reforming unit in a high severity mode for 0.21 of the time available, and to operate it in a low severity mode for 0.79 of the total time available. We see thus that fractional answers are completely correct in many situations; yet, there are instances when only answers in integers or whole numbers are acceptable.

When all of the variables in a problem are restricted to take only integer or whole number values, we speak of an all-integer or just plainly an integer programming problem. In other problems, only a certain set of the variables is restricted to integer values, and the remaining variables are allowed to take on fractional or integer answers. Problems of this nature are termed *mixed integer programming problems* because there is a mixture of variables restricted to integer values and there are some variables that are continuous.

## TYPICAL PROBLEMS

There are a number of typical operational problems that require that either all or some of the variables in the problem be restricted to integer values. Some examples are discussed below.

### Fixed Charge Problems

Many operations involve a fixed charge or fixed cost along with a unit rate. Manufacturing unit operations frequently have such a cost relationship because there is a certain time requirement to set up for the operation. The fixed charge in such cases is equivalent to the machine hours made unavailable for setting up the new operation, along with some production losses during the initial startup of the production cycle. The unavailability of the machine, the labor, and losses together form the setup cost, which is unrelated to the quantity produced once the setup has been made.

Investment type problems also fall into the fixed charge category. If a manufacturer finds that he is becoming capacity limited, he will be able to produce more goods by making an investment in new facilities. Such an investment is a fixed charge. After this charge has been incurred, more goods can be manufactured with the remaining manufacturing cost representing only the variable cost of the operation. The manager has two choices in this respect: he can make the investment and avail himself of additional manufacturing capacity or he can forego the investment and continue to operate with only the existing equipment. This is a discrete event that can be expressed as an integer programming problem, with the decision for the new investment expressed as a variable that can assume only the values 0 and 1. When the variable is at 0, no investment is made, and when it is at 1, a full investment cost is incurred. Obviously, a fractional answer for this variable is not tolerated because a half investment is not an acceptable answer to the problem.

Minimum payment clauses are another example of problems that may need to be expressed in the form of integer programming problems. Such rate schedules do exist extensively in the transportation industry where there is a minimum charge for a fractional truck or carload and an additional charge once the minimum has been exceeded.

Still another example of fixed charges are landing or port fees, i.e., whenever a plane lands or a ship enters a port, there is a charge for the landing or the entering of the port. This charge is related to the carrier entering or leaving and is not dependent upon the number of persons or the amount of tonnage carried during the landing or port entering operation. In this sense, the landing fees or port fees are fixed charges and they must be dealt with explicitly.

### Multiple Choice Problems

Oftentimes there is a necessity to choose one of a number of possible alternatives. Orange juice is normally packaged in 6-ounce or 12-ounce cans, and a choice must be made whether to purchase a small or a large can. In an industrial situation, it may be possible to build a 20,000-, a 30,000-, or a 40,000-barrel-per-day catalytic cracking unit. Standard engineering designs are available for these specific sizes, and a special design and fabrication of a unit of an in-between size would be prohibitively expensive. The decision must therefore be reached among the three possible choices of equipment size.

Conventional utility rate schedules can also be expressed as a multiple choice programming problem. The multiple choices here refer to the possibility of operating with a low volume at a high rate, with a medium volume at a medium rate, or with a high volume of consumption at an incrementally low rate. The choice among these alternatives is, of course, predicated on other operational considerations; we wish only to note here that a stepwise arranged rate schedule can be expressed in a multiple choice integer programming format.

### Knapsack Problems

The knapsack problem is so named because when the problem was first proposed, it was described as the problem faced by a hiker who could carry only a single knapsack of a given size on his hike. The hiker was trying to choose from among the many items that he could carry, those that would give him maximum utility for minimum weight, and not exceed the size of the knapsack. The integer aspect of the problem is, of course, that the hiker must take along complete units of equipment since a fractional pot or a fractional cooking stove is meaningless. When expressed as a knapsack problem, the problem poses merely an interesting intellectual exercise. But in industrial situations, an entirely similar situation exists. This is the paper trim problem. In paper-making operations, paper rolls are made in a given width and length. These large rolls of paper are further subdivided into individual customer requirements for shorter and narrower rolls. The problem then becomes one of making sure that each one of the orders is satisfied in terms of length and width while minimizing the amount of trim losses, the amount of wastage from the roll. Intuitively it may not be difficult to see that this kind of paper trim problem is mathematically identical to the knapsack problem, since both the paper maker and the hiker want to minimize their excess material or space. This specific problem occurs not only in the paper industry, but it also applies to roofing felt, carpeting, and other operations dealing with production units of large, flat materials that have to be divided into specific size rectangles. Consider, for example, a carpeting firm that has a piece of material 13 ft by 24 ft = 312 sq ft. A customer wants to install wall to wall carpeting in portions of his home. The necessary sizes are:

| | |
|---|---|
| 1 piece 12 ft by 11 ft | = 132 |
| 1 piece 9 ft by 3 ft | = 27 |
| 1 piece 10 ft by 8 ft 6 in. | = 85 |
| 1 piece 9 ft by 4 ft | = 36 |
| Total | 280 sq ft |

This is well within the total area available. The question is whether it is possible to cut the desired pieces from the available material. Figure 10-1 gives a possible solution. The problem becomes more complex if the carpet firm has several pieces of material available. The question would be how much to cut from each available piece. A

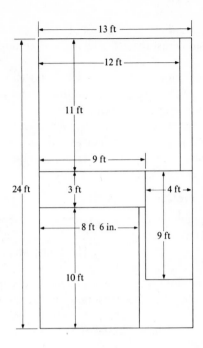

**Fig. 10-1** Possible cutting pattern for carpeting.

still more complex problem would have several purchasers order materials from a supplier who has many pieces available. This is usually the paper company's problem. In any event, the integer aspect should be clear; only whole pieces are salable.

**Traveling Salesman Problems**

This is another problem that can be formulated as an integer programming problem. It concerns itself with a salesman that must travel around various cities, and he should visit every city at least once while minimizing the total travel time involved. In its formulation for optimum route development, the problem is usable in industrial situations. However, of more importance has been the development of production sequences on manufacturing machines for short-term operational scheduling. For example, a single machine must be used to produce ten products named *A, B, C*, etc. Each specific product manufacturing operation requires a certain machine setup that depends on the product being manufactured, as well as the product that was manufactured before. In mathematical terms, this is equivalent to the traveling salesman problem, because the setup times are equivalent to the travel from one city to the next. Obviously, the travel time depends on both the origin and destination cities, just as setup depends on the initial product made and the subsequent product made. Furthermore, each product must be manufactured at least once (each city must be visited at least once). The object, of course, is to minimize total setup cost (total travel cost or time). One minor point of note is that travel time or expenses are generally equal in both directions. In industrial situations, shifting from product A to B can be much different costwise than shifting from B to A!

Another application of the traveling salesman problem exists in computer manufacturing operations. Here, wiring schedules must be made up in such a way that a single wire will meet various posts in its travels through the computer frame. Each selected post must be touched at least once and the objective is to minimize the amount of wire involved in connecting the posts.

The above examples highlight some situations in which it is necessary that some or all of the variables in the problem assume only integer or whole number answers. Many more examples of problems requiring integer considerations are readily available; in industrial operations, however, the above specified categories are of prime interest. We shall examine the actual formulation of models that fall into these various categories of integer programming problems. We should note here though that problems in which the variables are restricted to many integer values, i.e., 0 to 60, can often be rounded to the nearest integer solution without much danger; rounding a solution to 0 or 1, however, is often dangerous.

## MODEL FORMULATION

### Fixed Charge Problems

A manufacturer can install a new manufacturing unit. With normal financing, taxes, and depreciation, the annual cost for this unit is $300,000. The unit is capable of producing 11 tons per day at a variable manufacturing cost of $85. Total annual production capacity for a 365-day year equals 4015 tons at a total variable manufacturing cost of $341,275 (see Fig. 10-2). This manufacturing operation is best described by two variables, one that constitutes the investment portion of the activity and the other representing the actual level of manufacturing of the unit. If we let the investment variable be named $I_a$ and the manufacturing activity $M_a$, we can express our problem with a single constraint:

$$I_a \geq M_a/4015. \tag{10-1}$$

The unit cost associated with $I_a$ is $300,000, and with $M_a$ is $85. If we now further restrict $I_a$ to assume only the values 0 or 1, the entire problem is correctly formulated. Note that as soon as $M_a$ begins to exceed 0, $I_a$ must jump from 0 to 1 because of

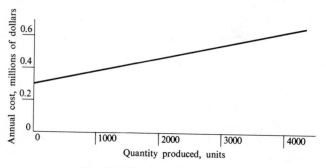

Fig. 10-2 Total annual cost versus quantity produced.

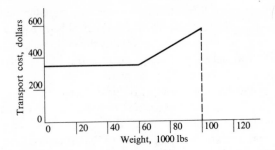

**Fig. 10-3** Transport cost versus weight of a given commodity.

constraint (10-1). In addition, the manufacturing capacity of $M_a$ for the entire year is limited to 4015 because $I_a$ is restricted from becoming larger than 1.0. Here we see how a fixed cost and a variable cost operation can be formulated in a mathematical programming format using only two variables, one representing the investment decision, which is either 0 or 1, and the other one representing the manufacturing activity.

A minimum cost rate schedule, as depicted in Fig. 10-3, can be described in a similar manner. The fixed charge will be noted as $I_b$, and the variable cost charge as $T_b$. Let us assume that there is a minimum charge for shipping a carload of materials from Chicago to New York and that this minimum charge is $342. Now let us assume that there is an additional charge when the weight of the goods shipped exceeds 60,000 pounds, and this additional charge amounts to 5 cents per pound. Figure 10-3 depicts such a typical minimum rate schedule in transportation. The minimum cost of shipping a given commodity between two points is $342. This minimum applies as long as the total weight of the shipment is less than 60,000 pounds. The excess weight surcharge is 5 cents per pound up to a maximum of 100,000 pounds total. This minimum rate of transportation cost schedule can be described with an integer variable and a continuous variable, where the integer variable carries the fixed cost of $342 and where the excess weight cost is described by the continuous variable as shown in the following:

$$60,000I_b + T_b \geq \text{total weight,} \tag{10-2}$$

$$I_b - \frac{T_b}{40,000} \geq 0, \tag{10-3}$$

$$I_b = 0 \quad \text{or} \quad 1.$$

Then

$$\text{cost of } I_b = \$342.0,$$

$$\text{cost of } T_b = \$0.05.$$

We define $I_b$ here as the existence of a load and $T_b$ as the part of the load exceeding 60,000 pounds.

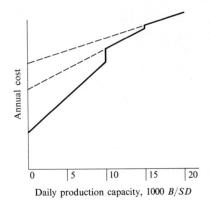

Fig. 10-4 Total operating cost as a function of unit size.

## Multiple Choice Models

Integer programming problems of the multiple choice variety are most easily represented as a set of 0-1 variables in which each variable describes one of the possible choices. In addition, then, there must be an equation that enforces the condition that only one variable can be chosen out of the set, and that the others must be 0. This is easily accomplished:

$$\text{Production:} \qquad 12V_1 + 16V_2 + 20V_3 \geq \text{demand}, \qquad (10\text{-}4)$$

$$\text{Multiple choice:} \qquad V_1 + V_2 + V_3 \leq 1.0, \qquad (10\text{-}5)$$

where $V_1$, $V_2$, and $V_3$ are restricted to 0 or 1.

Some examples of model construction that include multiple choice conditions may be helpful. For the first example, let us examine an existing petroleum refining operation that is contemplating the installation of a new catalytic reforming unit. Standard designs for such a unit exist for 10,000 barrels per stream day (B/SD), 15,000 B/SD, and 20,000 B/SD. Figure 10-4 describes this model graphically.

Let $R_{10}$, $R_{15}$, and $R_{20}$ be the investment components of the three possible sizes of new catalytic reformers. Let $P_{10}$, $P_{15}$, and $P_{20}$ be the production from these three units. If we now let $P_0$ be the production from the existing reforming unit, we have

$$P_0 + P_{10} + P_{15} + P_{20} = \text{demand}, \qquad (10\text{-}6)$$

$$R_{10} \qquad - \frac{P_{10}}{10,000} \qquad \geq 0, \qquad (10\text{-}7)$$

$$R_{15} \qquad - \frac{P_{15}}{15,000} \qquad \geq 0, \qquad (10\text{-}8)$$

$$R_{20} \qquad - \frac{P_{20}}{20,000} \geq 0, \qquad (10\text{-}9)$$

$$R_{10} + R_{15} + R_{20} \qquad \leq 1.0, \qquad (10\text{-}10)$$

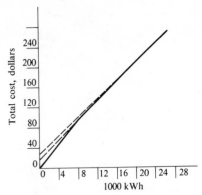

**Fig. 10-5** Power cost versus quantity for an industrial concern.

where $R_{10}$, $R_{15}$, and $R_{20}$ are limited to 0 or 1. This along with (10-10) clearly shows that only one new unit $R$ is tolerated. The total appropriate model consists of (10-6) to (10-10) plus the integer constraint.

Another example of a multiple choice set exists in a declining rate schedule for electric power consumption. An industrial power consumer must pay 1.2 cents per kilowatt hour ($\cent$/kWh) for the first 8,000 kWh consumed during a month. The next 10,000 kWh costs 1.0 $\cent$/kWh, and all consumption above 18,000 is provided at 0.85 $\cent$/kWh. Figure 10-5 shows this relation graphically and (10-11) through (10-15) shows this relationship mathematically:

$$\text{Cost:} \qquad 0.012P_a + 0.01P_b + 0.0085P_c \qquad + 16F_b + 31F_c, \qquad (10\text{-}11)$$

$$\begin{aligned} \text{Power} \\ \text{equipment:} \qquad P_a + \quad P_b \qquad \quad P_c \qquad\qquad\qquad\qquad = \text{demand,} \quad (10\text{-}12) \end{aligned}$$

$$\frac{-P_a}{8{,}000} \qquad\qquad\qquad + F_a \qquad\qquad\qquad \geq 0, \qquad (10\text{-}13)$$

$$\frac{-P_b}{18{,}000} \qquad\qquad\qquad + \quad F_b \qquad\qquad \geq 0, \qquad (10\text{-}14)$$

$$\frac{-P_c}{100{,}000} \qquad\qquad\qquad + \quad F_c \geq 0, \qquad (10\text{-}15)$$

$$F_a + \quad F_b + \quad F_c \leq 0 \qquad (10\text{-}16)$$

where $P_a$ is power consumed at rate $a = 1.2\cent/\text{kWh}$, $P_b$ is power consumed at rate $b = 1.0\cent/\text{kWh}$, $P_c$ is power consumed at rate $c = 0.85\cent/\text{kWh}$, $F_b$ is the fixed charge incurred due to the difference between rates $a$ and $b$ for the first 8,000 kWh, $F_c$ is the fixed charge incurred due to the difference between rates $a$, $b$, and $c$ for the first 18,000 kWh. Total power consumption is arbitrarily limited to 100,000 kWh; this figure should be so large as to never be a limiting condition.

In these multiple choice problems, the desired level of production or the desired level of consumption of power depends of course on the many other factors of the total operation. Actually, the optimum amount of power to be used, or the optimum size of the equipment, will result from an investigation of these other factors. The model structures that are shown here are only indicative of the process that one has to go through to describe discrete nonlinear problems, i.e., problems that are piecewise linear but are not convex. (For a detailed discussion on convex and concave non-linearities, see Chapter 11.)

## SOLUTION PROCEDURES

Good general purpose solution procedures for integer linear programming problems are still somewhat scarce. Although many talented individuals have actively researched the field, and although a great many algorithms for the solution of integer linear programming problems have been proposed, only a handful has been transformed into actual working computer programs and of this handful, a still smaller set has been proven useful for the solution of practical problems. Historically, the solution of discrete problems has always been difficult, and the actual development of solution procedures for integer linear programming problems has again borne this out. Research and development of algorithms and computer programs for the solution of integer problems continues, and with the advent of especially large drum and disk memories and large core storage memories on electronic computers, we fully expect that reliable general purpose integer linear programming codes will become readily available in the near future.

Actual experience to date has indicated that it may well develop that computer programs will be augmented with a variety of different algorithms to solve integer linear programming problems. This is so because certain algorithms appear to work better on certain kinds of problems and hence it is desirable to select the most appropriate algorithm for the problem at hand. For initial experimentation, of course, it is highly desirable to have general purpose algorithms available that will solve most problems quite well. Once such problems do become operational, it may be well to devise special purpose algorithms to make the computational effort more efficient and less costly. An example of a special purpose algorithm is the solution of the knapsack problem as presented by Gomory and Gilmore. This solution method lends itself quite well to the knapsack type problem, but it has been of less use in other types of problems.

The solution procedures used by integer linear programming algorithms fall into two major categories: (1) purely algorithmic and (2) trial and error. In purely algorithmic procedures, an optimal solution to an integer linear programming problem is found by elaborate but straightforward mathematical means with the process converging onto the answer in a similar sense as the simplex algorithm converges on an ordinary linear programming answer. The major contribution in this area has been made by Dr. R. O. Gomory; others have extended and implemented his work.

In trial and error or branch and bound approaches, the procedure is to investigate a series of partial or full linear programming solutions, and on the basis of these solutions develop a search strategy for investigating other solutions. Finally, through clever logical analysis, it is determined that one solution is preferable to all others even though full enumeration has not been carried out.

In both of these classes of algorithms, there have been attempts to solve integer linear programming problems with due recognition at the outset of the integer constraints. These "primal" algorithms begin attacking the problem right away by taking account of all the constraints in the problem including those that specify that certain or all of the variables of the problem are restricted to only integer values. These algorithms are mathematically entirely correct, but computationally they have not fared well. Another class of algorithm begins by solving an ordinary linear programming problem without consideration that certain or all of the variables can take on only integer values. At the close of the initial calculation, when a continuous noninteger constrained problem has been solved, the integer constraints are appended to the model, and new solutions are calculated from this hypothetically "ideal" solution. We imply here that an ideal solution is one that could be obtained if one were to ignore the integer constraints.

These solution procedures depend heavily on the dual linear programming procedure discussed later in this chapter. The algorithms of this variety have been much more successful and are the only truly operational algorithms available to date. The trial and error type algorithms have been quite successful using this initial approach. This is so because after starting from an "ideal" solution, it is often quite easy to arrive at a feasible integer solution, i.e., a solution that satisfies all the normal linear programming constraints and in addition satisfies the integer constraints. The one aspect that is not known is whether the solution so found is the optimal solution. But as soon as a feasible integer solution has been found, a *bound* has been established and it should intuitively be easy to see that if a better integer solution exists, it must lie between the actual solution at hand and the ideal solution. If the relative difference between the ideal and the actual solution is very small, it may not even be advisable to search for additional solutions, because additional search time may be more expensive than the potential benefit gained from finding an optimal solution. It is on this premise that some of the trial and error or branch and bound algorithms have proven to be useful even though mathematically they are not as sophisticated as the pure algorithmic type procedures. In the bibliography there are listed a large number of papers dealing with integer linear programming algorithms.

At present, the integer programming field is still being researched by many individuals and groups throughout the world. The result of these research efforts will undoubtedly produce some algorithms that are quite useful for general purpose type of problems. At the present time, the algorithms that have shown the best actual performance to date are the Balas type algorithms for all integer 0-1 type problems and conventional branch and bound algorithms for mixed integer programming type problems. There are many variations of such algorithms, and some work better in selected cases than others.

The current algorithms are capable of solving with great confidence problems containing from 20 to 40 integer variables. Experimentally, some problems involving up to 200 integer variables have been solved successfully, but these generally have been specific types of problems that lend themselves to solution by selected specific algorithms. With all the research in the area, it should be expected that reasonable and reliable solution procedures for all mixed integer programming problems will be quite readily available before 1972.

## INTEGER PROGRAMMING VERSUS CASE STUDIES

When the number of integer variables in a problem are small, say three or four 0-1 variables, it is frequently possible to solve the entire problem by means of case studies. In such an approach, a series of linear programs is solved, each representing a different combination of the integer variables. For a three 0-1 variable problem this means $2^3 = 8$ specific case as shown in Table 10-1.

**Table 10-1**

| Case | $V_1$ | $V_2$ | $V_3$ |
|------|-------|-------|-------|
| 1 | 0 | 0 | 0 |
| 2 | 0 | 0 | 1 |
| 3 | 0 | 1 | 0 |
| 4 | 0 | 1 | 1 |
| 5 | 1 | 0 | 0 |
| 6 | 1 | 0 | 1 |
| 7 | 1 | 1 | 0 |
| 8 | 1 | 1 | 1 |

Carrying out such a study is, of course, entirely feasible. However, as the number of integer variables increases to 10, there are 1024 potential cases and for 20 integer variables there are more than 1,000,000 cases. Obviously, a case study approach is inconceivable for such problems, and this is where integer programming approaches become attractive. But one should realize that these approaches frequently are only an extension of case study methods.

## DUAL LINEAR PROGRAMMING

In earlier sections we have alluded to dual variables and dual linear programming without explaining this concept. The basic premise is that to any linear programming problem there exists a dual or shadow problem. This may be easiest to explain by way of a very simple example, as shown in Fig. 10-6. Assume that we have the problem to find the highest point in a pyramid, as shown. Obviously this point is at the simplex or top of the pyramid. In a physical sense, this is where the space ends. In mathematical terms, however, the planes that make up the sides of the pyramid are not

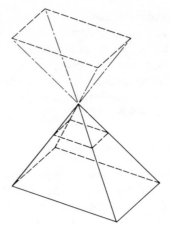

**Fig. 10-6** Primal and dual space.

limited by the tip, but rather, they continue as shown by the dashed lines. If we can now consider the base pyramid as being representative of primal solution space, then we can clearly see that there exists an inverted pyramid that connects with the primal one at the simplex or highest point. This we now call the dual or shadow model.

The practical uses of this concept are considerable. As can easily be seen, primal and dual space meet at the optimum solution; so we should be able to ascend via the primal or descend via the dual and reach the tip or optimal solution by either process. Many good linear programming codes recognize this and solve a problem by what appears to be the easiest route.

In the dual solution procedure, the objective is to attain primal feasibility while minimizing the reduction in profit. The primal problem of course was to maximize profit while maintaining feasibility. The two procedures thus work as depicted in Table 10-2.

Mathematically, the two procedures are quite similar. The real advantage of the dual procedure emerges when there are changes to the original solution space. These can occur due to the integrality constraints added to the problem at a later stage or to any other modifications to the solution space *after* an initial solution has been found.

**Table 10-2**
**Solution Procedures**

| Step | Primal | Dual |
|------|--------|------|
| 1 | Find most profitable new activity. If none left, you are finished. | Find the most infeasible activity. If none left, you are finished. |
| 2 | Select the limiting activity to maintain feasibility. | Select an activity to minimize the reduction in profit. |
| 3 | Solve for new solution | Solve for new solution |

This includes parametric right-hand side procedures. If, for example, the pyramid of Fig. 10-6 had a maximum height of $3\frac{1}{3}$ inches, but we wanted to find the maximum integral height, it may be best to solve the problem without the integrality constraint, to find the solution at $3\frac{1}{3}$ inches, and then to *back off* to the appropriate solution via the dual method.

This discussion of dual linear programming is intended only to convey the concepts involved. The interested reader should refer to the material contained in references 21, 40, 54, and 58 to obtain a full mathematical treatment of these concepts.

## DISCUSSION TOPICS AND PROBLEMS

1. Describe in mathematical form a data processing center's operation when there exists a minimum computer rental charge of $20,000 per month that entitles the user to 176 hours of usage. All extra time usage of the computer will be charged at $15.00 per hour.

2. Describe in mixed integer programming form a capital budget evaluation project for a new machine tool. Two sizes are commercially available:

|  | Small | Large |
|---|---|---|
| Purchase cost | $15,000 | $25,000 |
| Annual capacity | 1000 tons | 2000 tons |
| Variable operating cost | $5/ton | $4/ton |

3. Describe in mixed integer format a traveling salesman problem involving four cities.

4. How many case studies would have to be carried out to evaluate a problem in which there are three possible new alternatives for one investment and two new alternatives for another investment possibility?

5. In a primal-dual model, what is the geometric representation of two alternative solutions? What is it for three alternative solutions?

6. Would it be possible in a linear system for the primal and dual solution spaces not to meet at the optimum for both?

# Nonlinear
# Conditions

11

Actual industrial operations contain a great many truly linear relationships.  These are conditions where an activity or variable has linear responses to all its constraints, and in addition, has a linear cost factor, one that does not vary with the quantity of the activity.  An example of such a purely linear activity exists in transportation variables, because for most practical purposes transportation costs are linear (e.g., $17.00 per ton), and the relationship to its constraints is purely linear, because the amount of withdrawal of goods is equal to the amount of the activity and is also equal to the amount of goods delivered at the destination.

Another example of a strictly linear problem is the animal feed mix problem.  A number of different components can be blended together to produce an appropriate animal feed.  The specifications are that the ultimate product contain a minimum amount of carbohydrates, vitamins, and proteins.  Each of the components that can be blended into this mix has known amounts of carbohydrates, vitamins, and proteins. The contribution to the mix is therefore strictly defined by the qualities of the component introduced into the batch and these qualities remain constant over a wide range of volume.  If now its cost is also linear, then blending this component into the mix batch is a purely linear problem.

Many examples can also be cited for purely linear response situations in industrial problems.  However, there also exist many situations in which variables or activities do not produce linear responses or do not have linear costs associated with the level of the activity. Obvious ones are quantity discounts, where the first few units incur higher costs than later units. This phenomenon exists in many purchasing operations, where the unit cost decreases as the volume increases. Another example of a nonlinear response is the use of fertilizer on a lawn. The first few bags of fertilizer will stimulate growth tremendously, but as more fertilizer is applied, the additional growth is not equal to that of the initial volume. Another example of a nonlinear response is in chemical processes. As the severity of the processes increases by raising temperature or pressure, for example, an additional yield of desirable product can be obtained but generally at greatly increased cost.

We see thus that in many industrial situations, there exist nonlinear relationships, and they are of great importance to the optimization process. How do we now deal with such nonlinearity in a linear programming environment?

## PIECEWISE LINEAR APPROXIMATIONS

Many of the nonlinear response curves are relatively smooth curves that do not contain sharp curves or even S-curve shapes. When the responses to an activity are of a relatively smooth but nonlinear relationship, it is frequently possible to approximate the nonlinear curve with a series of a piecewise linear segments. Figure 11-1 gives an example of such piecewise linearization. In making linear approximations to nonlinear responses, the main criterion to use is to minimize the error introduced by the simplifying linearization. For example, in Fig. 11-2 there is shown a nonlinear response, with three piecewise linear approximations. Line $A$ connects two extreme points on the curve which are equivalent to the lowest and highest level of activity that has ever been observed. Line $C$ is tangential at the point of greatest deflection. Line $B$ represents an averaging condition.

If the actual expected response is in between the two extremes, using line $C$ will introduce a positive error, or in other words, line $C$ will averagely indicate too high a cost. The errors introduced by the simplifying assumption of linearization when using line $C$ are always in one direction, namely positive. On the other hand, line $A$ will generally introduce a negative error or too low a cost for the operation. Only at the point of contact will line $A$ present an accurate cost relationship. Using line $B$,

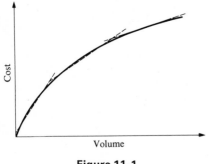

Figure 11-1

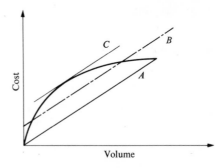

Figure 11-2

however, will provide an exact answer only at the two points where $B$ intersects the two response curves. If the desired activity is between the two intersections of line $B$, then the error introduced by using line $B$ is negative; the cost used by the linear assumption is too low. If, however, the actual desired response is outside of the two intersections, the errors introduced by the linear approximation is on the positive side. The most important thing, however, for using line $B$ is not that the errors can be positive or negative, but rather that the average error introduced by the linear approximation represented by line $B$ is much smaller, and hence less error is introduced into the model by making a simplifying assumption of this type.

It should, of course, be realized that piecewise linearization is a simplifying assumption that will introduce errors, and the main effort is to minimize the errors so introduced. One way, of course, is to use an error averaging procedure as has just been described. Another way in which to reduce the size of the errors introduced by the simplifications is to make each one of the segments under consideration smaller. Figure 11-1 typifies this. However, introducing more linear approximations does increase the size of the model, and hence increases computation time. A tradeoff, therefore, is to approximate a nonlinear response in such a way that the errors introduced by the simplifying assumptions are not excessive, and yet not cause computer solution times to be excessive.

A large number of industrial relationships have actually been reduced to linear forms even before the introduction of linear programming methods. This has occurred because manual calculation procedures are also much more difficult when they involve nonlinear relationships, and computer solution routines are not at all foreign to this concept. With such linear approximations there frequently have been developed a series of "indices," numbers that describe the linear approximations in a nonlinear curve. For example, fuel oil viscosities do not blend linearly. Long before the advent of linear programming, however, blending specialists had developed a set of viscosity blending numbers that represent a linear response. We must note, therefore, that linearization is not a simplification only to allow us to use linear programming solution procedures, but also because once problems have been presented in a linear form, they are just easier to solve by any procedure, manual or by computer.

Piecewise linear approximations may exist in two distinct curve linear relationships, concave and convex. When used in a linear programming problem, they must be treated differently.

**Table 11-1**

**Typical Residential Power Rate Schedule (Rate B :
Without electric water heater or general space heating)**

| Consumption, kWh/month | Cost, $/kWh |
|---|---|
| 0 to 14 | 1.44 (minimum charge) |
| 15 to 76 | 0.05 |
| 76 to 186 | 0.03 |
| 186 to ∞ | 0.026 |

**Table 11-2**

**Typical Industrial Power Rate, Monthly Rates**

| Demand charge | | Energy charge | |
|---|---|---|---|
| Consumption, kW | Cost, $/kW | Consumption, kWh | Cost, ¢/kWh |
| 0 to 50 | 142 (minimum charge) | 0 to 4000 | 2.75 |
| 51 to 300 | 2.35 | 4000 to 20,000 | 1.60 |
| 301 to 800 | 2.15 | 20,000 to 120,000 | 1.20 |
| 801 to 3000 | 2.00 | 120,000 to ∞ | 0.97 |
| 3001 to ∞ | 1.80 | | |

## CONCAVE RELATIONSHIPS

Concave nonlinear relationships occur throughout industry, and consumer products. A concave relationship is one in which the unit price of the product decreases as the volume increases. Typical examples are the rate schedule that applies to conventional power consumption. A typical residential rate schedule is portrayed in Table 11-1. An equivalent industrial rate schedule is shown in Table 11-2. The residential power rates cover only the energy consumed, while the industrial rate has separate charges for energy consumed and for the demand or peak consumption. For example, with 720 hours in a month and a consumption of 43,200 kWh, the average demand is 60 kW, but the peak may well be 100 to 120 kW. Here we see that, as the consumption increases, the unit rate decreases. This is an entirely common occurrence in industrial operations.

Manufacturers realize that there is a certain minimum cost involved in the processing of an order, the development of paperwork, the supply of basic facilities, etc. Because of this, they expect to recover such order handling or setup costs on the basis of units sold, and when the quantity sold is small, the factor representing the overhead cost of order handling is relatively large. As the volume of the order increases, however, the prorated costs of the overhead expenses become smaller. It may well be that the true cost relationship to the manufacturer is as shown in Fig. 11-3.

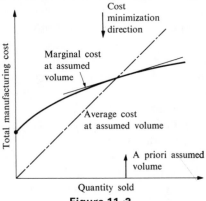

**Figure 11-3**

**Table 11-3**

**Duplication Cost Per Page of Original Material**

| Number of copies | Cost, ¢/page |
|---|---|
| 1 to 3 | 10 |
| 4 to 10 | 5 + 30¢ |
| 11 and up | 2 + 65¢ |

However, many a manufacturer is reluctant to put the full order processing burden on the small consumer of a given product, because he may well be a large consumer of other products and it would be senseless to steer him away. On the other hand, the manufacturer does like to promote large orders, because his fixed expenses are smaller on a unit basis. This allows him to sell at a lower unit cost, and yet show a profit. A typical price quotation representing such a distribution of setup costs is shown in Table 11-3; the example is drawn from a large volume duplication shop.

Concave nonlinear relationships can cause difficulties if they are incorporated into a linear programming model without any special precautions. The result can be that the optimum solution suggests to use all the "low cost units" and none of the "high cost ones." This, of course, is not acceptable to the supplier. There are two possible ways out of this dilemma. The first and frequently simpler procedure is to estimate before solving the linear program, how much of the material that has the concave cost structure will be consumed and to apply the appropriate rate for this volume of consumption. Note here that incremental consumption will be available at the marginal cost for that level, and not at an "average" rate. Figure 11-3 depicts this graphically. The marginal cost relationship provides by far the best approximation for small variations from the originally assumed volume. When this procedure is employed, it behooves the problem formulator to recheck his basic assumption(s) after a linear programming solution has been obtained. Normal sensitivity analysis procedures frequently suffice in this case.

If the overall problem is very sensitive to the concave nonlinear relationship, or if it is difficult or impossible to "guess" at the level of consumption, it may be necessary to treat the concave nonlinear relationship explicitly. One way is to express the mathematical program formulation of a declining cost relationship in a multiple choice type of environment as explained in Chapter 10. The model structure then will present each of the individual quoted rates as a single activity, and the question is asked of the mathematical programming model to apply the appropriate rate/cost relationship. Chapter 10 contained an example of such a problem. We should note here, however, that general purpose, mixed integer programming procedures are still somewhat unsophisticated, and that a careful user should try to minimize the development of models that use extensive integer or mixed integer programming formulations.

Another and more frequently used approach is to estimate the quantity that the linear programming solution will select, and then initially use the tangential response (line *C* in Fig. 11-2) at the estimated consumption level. Upon conclusion of the linear programming solution, a check is made of the actual quantity used, and now a new response is used, and another linear program is solved. With a few such cycles, a solution representing a very close approximation to the nonlinear response can be found. In some cases, the actual cycling between linear programming solutions is done by hand, but in the more routine uses, such as by the chemical and petroleum industries the cycling is actually done with a computer program that calls the linear programming solution procedure as if it were a subroutine. Another procedure that works on a similar principle is "separable programming" as described in Chapter 12.

## CONVEX RELATIONSHIPS

Not all industrial relationships are concave nonlinear. There are a great many relationships in which the cost of unit production increases as the volume increases. This is especially so whenever stimulants are applied. For example, fertilizer applied to a lawn represents a convex relationship, because the first 100 pounds of fertilizer spread evenly across the lawn tends to produce a larger growth increase than the next 100 pounds, and hence, the additional growth increase is more costly on a unit basis. Another example of convex nonlinear relationships exists in the blending of tetraethyl lead (TEL) or tetramethyl lead (TML) into motor gasoline to increase octane. Both TEL and TML are stimulants, and their initial octane improvements are much greater than those obtained from additional amounts of TEL or TML. See Fig. 11-4 for an example. Other examples of such convex relationships are operating severity in chemical processes. In this case, the product yield may increase linearly as the severity of the processing increases, but the cost associated with an increase in yield grows even faster.

The introduction of linear approximations to convex nonlinear problems is quite straightforward, and it does not incur the computational burden involved in the

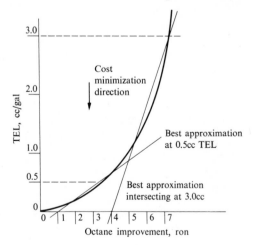

**Fig. 11-4** Typical octane improvement as the result of TEL blended into gasoline.

concave linear programming that may require integer programming procedures or repeated linear programming solutions. This is so because in any convex linear programming approximation, the normal simplex method will try to select the lowest unit cost alternative available to the total problem, and hence it is not necessary to introduce integer programming concepts into the model. It should be obvious that a computer routine when asked to search for a lowest cost operation, will always pick out that segment of the operation for the current level of activity that represents the lowest cost. Convex nonlinear programming problems, when described by piecewise linear segments do satisfy these conditions. Equations (11-1), (11-2), and (11-3) describe a very common convex nonlinear programming problem encountered in gasoline blending. The model formulation described here is due to Dr. W. C. Healy and this particular procedure is in use by many of the leading petroleum companies in the world. In this particular aspect, Healy proposed to use only two linear approximations, and the relationship is convex. In actuality, the errors introduced by this simplifying assumption of only two linear segments to the total response curve of tetraethyl lead blending are quite small, oftentimes, they are as small as or smaller than the measuring error that exists in sampling actual octane numbers in a finished blend. Because of this, it has been felt that approximating the TEL response curve with more than two linear approximations is somewhat superfluous.

In the formulation of the octane blending section of the model, an initial assumption is made of the octane response of the final blend, or in other words, the expected TEL versus octane improvement curve of the finished blend is "guessed." These curves can be steeper or shallower depending on the components used in the blend, but generally the curve falls into an average shape. Next, linear approximating lines are drawn through the 0.5 and 3.0 cc/gal (frequently the legal limit of TEL) points. The slope of these two lines is measured, and introduced into the linear programming model as shown below. Let the blending components be $B_1$, $B_2$, $B_3$, and $B_4$. Their octane qualities have been measured as:

|  | $B_1$ | $B_2$ | $B_3$ | $B_4$ |
|---|---|---|---|---|
| At 0.5 cc TEL | 90 | 76 | 92 | 94 |
| At 3.0 cc TEL | 96 | 86 | 97 | 98 |

After assuming the TEL response curve and producing the linear approximations, they are found to have slopes for 0.5 cc TEL of 6.0, and for 3.0 cc TEL of 1.2. With these linear approximations, the *apparent* octane quality of the blending components is:

|  | $B_1$ | $B_2$ | $B_3$ | $B_4$ |
|---|---|---|---|---|
| For 0.5 cc line | 87.0 | 73.0 | 89.0 | 91.0 |
| For 3.0 cc line | 92.4 | 82.4 | 93.4 | 94.4 |

These pseudo blend numbers are, of course, the actual measured quality minus the TEL induced improvement. For component $B_1$, they are

$$90.0 - (6.0 \times 0.5) = 87.0$$

and

$$96.0 - (1.2 \times 3.0) = 92.4.$$

These pseudo blend numbers are also the intersections of the linear approximations and the x-axis.

The blending problem now resolves to two equations and five variables:

$$87.0B_1 + 73.0B_2 + 89.0B_3 + 91.0B_4 + 6.0TEL \geq BOG^*, \qquad (11\text{-}1)$$

$$92.4B_1 + 82.4B_2 + 93.4B_3 + 94.4B_4 + 1.2TEL \geq BOG. \qquad (11\text{-}2)$$

In addition, there frequently is a limitation that the total amount of TEL must be less than or equal to 3.0 cc/gal. This is expressed as

$$B_1 + B_2 + B_3 + B_4 - \tfrac{1}{3}TEL \geq 0. \qquad (11\text{-}3)$$

This now formulates the entire nonlinear blending problem. Let us see what happens in various cases.

If the final blend is made up of 25% of each of the four components $B_i$ (TEL has essentially zero volume), we find that the non-TEL blend has a base octane of

$$(\tfrac{1}{4})(87 + 73 + 89 + 91) = 85$$

for the 0.5 cc response line and

$$(\tfrac{1}{4})(92.4 + 82.4 + 93.4 + 94.4) = 90.65$$

for the 3.0 cc response line.

If the final octane requirement is 90.0, then for the 0.5 cc line

$$\frac{90.0 - 85.0}{6.0} = 0.833 \text{ cc TEL/gal}$$

is required, and for the 3.0 cc line

$$\frac{90.0 - 90.65}{1.2} = \text{negative,}$$

and therefore is not binding. In this case, therefore, 0.833 cc TEL/gal is required and the 0.5 cc line is controlling. However, if the final blend octane requirement is 94.0, then

$$\frac{94.0 - 85.0}{6.0} = 1.5 \text{ cc TEL/gal}$$

---

\* BOG = blend octane gallons.

would satisfy the 0.5 cc line, but also,

$$\frac{94.0 - 90.65}{1.2} = 2.79 \text{ cc TEL/gal}$$

will be required to satisfy the 3.0 cc line. So now, the 3 cc line is controlling and 2.79 cc TEL/gal must be used. Since the model always tries to minimize cost, it will follow the high response initially, and only later the low response, just as it should be. Of course, after the linear programming is solved, it may be wise to recheck if the final blend matches the initially assumed response curve!

## COMPLETE NONLINEAR SYSTEMS

The treatment of complete nonlinear systems is outside the scope of this work. However, the bibliography at the end of this book will provide the interested user with appropriate insight into the descriptive material available to him.

## DISCUSSION TOPICS AND PROBLEMS

1. How can you easily establish if a nonlinear relationship is concave or convex?
2. Can you describe a set of logic rules to be employed to solve a mathematical programming problem with a concave nonlinear relationship for a key variable, such as power purchases. We refer here to a cycling procedure between several linear programming solutions.
3. Would the convex nonlinear relationships in a problem have to be treated differently if the model also contained some concave nonlinear relationships?
4. What is the conceptual difference between a multiple linear programming cycling procedure and an integer programming solution to a problem containing several concave nonlinear relationships?

# Special
# Algorithms

12

Most useful linear programming applications have in the past been obtained through use of general purpose linear programming algorithms, and general purpose computer programs employing these algorithms. In a way, linear programming technology has matured through the stages of initial conception and experimentation with alternative solution methods, and it has standardized on "the product form of the inverse simplex algorithm" as the industry standard. Part of the justification for the selection of this algorithm is that it most closely matches the characteristics of modern high-speed computers. The product form of the inverse algorithm minimizes the amount of input and output to secondary computer memory during the solution at the expense of possibly slightly increased computation. But since electronic computers are more adapt at computation than they are at data transfer to or from secondary memory devices, the product form of the inverse algorithm matches the computer characteristics as well as or better than most other general purpose linear programming algorithms. In earlier parts of this book we have suggested that the routinely available linear programming codes are both quite mature and also quite similar; they all have evolved from many years of extensive experimentation, and a more or less common ground has been obtained.

An extensive survey of the operations research and management science literature, however, would indicate that a great many varieties of linear programming solution algorithms have been suggested. This is not surprising, because linear programming and its many extensions has represented a new area of interest in mathematics, and as such the entire field has been a fertile area for detailed mathematical research, often carried out as partial fulfillments of an academic degree. Through this extensive research, a number of meaningful improvements has been incorporated into the general purpose linear programming technology, but the large majority of the suggested algorithms as described in the scientific literature has never been translated into reliable computer codes, and hence the actual applied worth of many of these special algorithms has never been tested. It has been our experience that general purpose linear programming solution codes are seldom fully reliable within the first year after their initial release. Even after that, additional program malfunctions are corrected, and program speed improvements are incorporated. Through extensive use, the general purpose linear programming codes tend to become both more reliable and more efficient, but it is only through extensive use that this development occurs.

Another aspect worth noting is that throughout the development of linear programming technology, the available linear programming algorithms and solution codes have generally exceeded in capacity the size of meaningful problems that could be constructed, analyzed, and whose results could be put to good use in industrial applications. This is partly due to the fact that linear programming technology grew very fast and many potential users had to be trained in its methodology, application, and consequences. Even more important, though, is that after the initial wave and enthusiasm in late 1950's, it was quickly established that linear programming solution procedures formed only a small segment of a much larger system that includes data gathering, input data validation, model construction, and linear programming solution, followed by solution analysis and implementation. In this overall sequence of operations, it can readily be seen that the linear programming solution procedure is only a small segment of the overall system. Even though much of the total system's performance depends on the availability of a good general purpose linear programming system, the solution procedure by itself does not really occupy more than a major subroutine status in the overall system. While initially, many linear programming practitioners were overly enthused by the beauty and sophistication of the optimization process, many have come to realize the importance of the surrounding and supporting systems without which the linear programming solution procedure is relatively useless. This observation, of course, includes the areas of matrix generation and output analysis programs, but it is not limited only to those. In general, it should be said that both mathematical and computer technology have been somewhat ahead of the human capabilities needed to make sophisticated linear programming systems fully operational and useful to industrial operations. Despite all this, a large number of mathematical programming uses has been suggested to the managements of operating companies on the basis of using experimental algorithms and experimental computer codes. Many of these suggested applications have failed because oftentimes the system planners were not mature enough to realize that the overall system implementation entailed much more than the development of a linear programming solution, by whatever algorithm was to be selected or used.

We should note here especially that the only advantages accruing to special purpose algorithms, as compared to general purpose algorithms, are the possibilities of reduction in computer time or possibly to solve linear programming problems on inhouse computers rather than equipment at a service bureau. The special purpose algorithms will not have any effect on the data collecion aspect, the data validation aspect, the solution analysis, or the implementation of the results. Their virtues are truly only a certain amount of economy in computer usage. In sporadic instances, the use of special purpose algorithms allows the solution of problems that cannot normally be handled by general purpose algorithms, but meaningful applications of this type have truly been limited to only the most sophisticated users of linear programming. When a new linear programming based system application is proposed, we suggest the caveat that when such a system development can be justified only on the basis of a special purpose algorithm, extreme caution be taken, because many have failed in similar endeavors. If nothing else, we suggest that the overall system be initially constructed and made operational with the aid of general purpose algorithms—they are capable of solving almost all meaningful problems—and after an initial implementation, a secondary review will be made to determine if the development's expense for a special purpose algorithm can be justified on the basis of reduced computing, manpower usage, or potential further profit enhancement, solely as the result of replacing the general purpose algorithm by a special purpose one.

If so, the new system development is probably well justified.

In the past, the practical use of special purpose algorithms, except for the basic transportation algorithm and to a lesser extent the bounded variable algorithm, has been somewhat limited. The future is expected to bring a relaxation in this direction. In the next few sections, we will describe special purpose algorithms that either have found more than minimal acceptance in usage, or appear to have a high degree of probability of becoming of age. Chapter 4 contained a brief discussion of the basic transportation algorithm, describing how it differed from the general purpose simplex algorithm and why it is such an efficient algorithm. We will not further discuss it here.

## BOUNDED VARIABLE ALGORITHM

This algorithm is an extension of the basic simplex algorithm, and it has been in successful use for a few years. The algorithm takes special cognizance of the fact that many variables in a linear programming solution are often restricted to a lower and/or upper bound. For example, manufacturing machine capacities are often restricted to a maximum of 720 hours in a month. This is purely an upper bound. In a conventional linear programming algorithm, this constraint must be shown as a separate equation in the model. In the bounded variable algorithm, this information can be presented to the linear programming solution code without requiring the incorporation of a special row or equation in the matrix. At the same time, if there were a policy constraint to use a machine at least 400 hours per month, this could be similarly indicated directly. We see, thus, that a bounded variable algorithm allows the use of smaller

| Component | BU | LN | HN | CN | CR | | |
|---|---|---|---|---|---|---|---|
| Objective | 5.2 | 6.4 | 8.3 | 10.2 | 11.0 | | |
| Total volume | 1 | 1 | 1 | 1 | 1 | = | 10.0 |
| Octane specification | 120 | 84.5 | 73 | 96 | 99 | ≥ | 950.0 |
| Vapor pressure | 60 | 18 | 4 | 6.4 | 2.5 | ≤ | 110.0 |
| Volatility | 105 | 30 | 12 | 15 | 3.0 | ≥ | 180.0 |
| BU volume | 1 | | | | | ≤ | 1.7 |
| LN volume | | 1 | | | | ≤ | 1.0 |
| HN volume | | | 1 | | | ≤ | 2.3 |
| CN volume | | | | 1 | | ≤ | 6.2 |
| CR volume | | | | | 1 | ≤ | 4.0 |

With a bounded variable algorithm, the volume equations are not needed as part of the matrix.

**Fig. 12-1** Blending model from Chapter 5.

model matrices, and in fact, the knowledge and specification of upper and lower bounds on selected variables are not incorporated into the matrix but are rather made available to the solution algorithm directly. The result is that with bounded variable codes, the actual solution matrix is smaller, and therefore the amount of input-output transferred during linear programming solution is smaller. The number of iterations to reach an optimal solution is seldom, if ever, affected, and improved solution efficiencies are therefore due only to the reduction of input-output time available with this algorithm as compared to a general purpose linear programming algorithm. We firmly expect that all future major linear programming codes will contain the bounded variable features. Figure 12-1 displays graphically the matrix size reduction obtainable with a bounded variable algorithm.

## GENERALIZED UPPER BOUND

In a generalized upper bound algorithm (GUB), cognizance is taken of the fact that oftentimes a number of variables together are limited to some maximum. In a multi-product manufacturing model, for example, a machine M may be used in the manufacture of products P, Q, and R. The model therefore will have separate variables for the manufacture of these products by machine M; in addition, it will have an equation describing that the total number of machine hours available to the manufacture of P, Q, and R will be limited to a number. The generalized upper bound algorithm allows this information to be incorporated directly into input data, without requiring that a special constraint row be incorporated into the linear programming model. As in the bounded variable approach, we see that in effect, a part of the matrix structure is written into the algorithm rather than into the matrix, and this is where the generalized upper bounding algorithm obtains its computational advantage.

| | OH1 | OH2 | OH3 | BO | ELEC | Relation | RHS |
|---|---|---|---|---|---|---|---|
| | 120 | 140 | 87 | 103 | 45 | = | 8100 |
| | 104 | 130 | 80 | 94 | 42 | = | 1938 |
| | 62 | 70 | 55 | 97 | 35 | = | 1020 |
| | | | | 88 | 37 | = | 2128 |
| | 1 | | | | | ≤ | 30 |
| | | 1 | | | | ≤ | 29 |
| | | | 1 | | | ≤ | 27 |
| | | | | 1 | | ≤ | 30 |
| | | | | | 1 | ≤ | 28 |

Column headings (read vertically): OH1|CAS, OH1|CA, OH2|CAS, OH2|CA, OH3|CAS, OH3|CA, OH3|C, BO|CAS, BO|CAL, BO|CA, BO|C, ELEC|CAS, ELEC|CAL, ELEC|CCA, ELEC|CCS — DE&M / CAP.

The rows with right-hand sides 30, 29, 27, 30, 28 are annotated:

> These rows represent generalized upper bounds and hence are not required with a GUB algorithm.

**Fig. 12-2** Multiproduct manufacturing model.

A number of special applications of this algorithm have been made. We expect that robust and reliable systems using this algorithm will become available. Figure 12-2 shows how the matrix format differs when a generalized upper bound algorithm is employed.

## SEPARABLE PROGRAMMING

Separable programming is a special procedure intended to deal with nonlinear conditions that often occur in industrial situations and that need to be incorporated into a linear programming model. Figure 12-3 shows an example of a nonlinear response. In separable programming, the nonlinearity is broken up in a number of small segments, each of which is linear by itself. Throughout the solution procedure, the algorithm ascertains that the linear approximation to the nonlinear response curve is followed. In this way, some nonconvex linearities can be handled quite efficiently; often more efficiently than taking the ultimate approach available through describing the problem via the mixed integer route. A number of successful applications of this algorithm have occurred, and through more extensive usage it should become a reliable and generally well tested procedure.

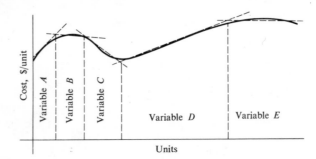

Figure 12-3

## DECOMPOSITION

Decomposition means the breaking up of a large linear programming model into a number of smaller submodels that lend themselves to independent solution and subsequent reaggregation. Since the computer solution time generally correlates as the third power of the number of rows in the matrix, halving the size of the matrix would tend to make the solution time for each of the smaller models $\frac{1}{8}$ of the larger one. This therefore is often a very attractive scheme; the difficulty, however, is that once the individual models are solved, there is little assurance that the suboptimizations so obtained represent a global optimum as available from the total model. The smaller model solutions therefore are accepted merely as suggestions or proposals, and after the smaller models are solved, an optimization of the overall model is begun based on the proposal suggested by the smaller models. This in turn produces some suggestions for changes in the operations of the smaller models. This ping-pong procedure continues until it is proven that a global optimum solution has been obtained. In the past, decomposition algorithms have often been suggested as a

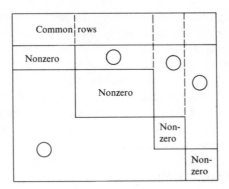

**Figure 12-4**

procedure for dealing with very large problems, so large that they exceeded the then current linear programming solution capabilities on the largest electronic computers. The successful or routine applications of this approach have been limited, but nevertheless, an adequate amount of experience has been built up so that it should be expected that future good linear programming solution codes will contain a decomposition capability. Figure 12-4 show hows the traditional decomposition methods have dealt with a large structured linear programming matrix.

The most widely used decomposition algorithms have been of the "primal" decomposition type, as shown in Fig. 12-4. In these models, an attempt is made to suboptimize sets of variables or columns that are interlinked with a common set of constraints. An example of such an operation is the use of a number of blending components in the preparation of a large number of final products. The only attempt is to obtain the true optimal solution, but hopefully with some reduction in computer usage time. On problems of less than 1000 equations, this attempt has generally been unsuccessful.

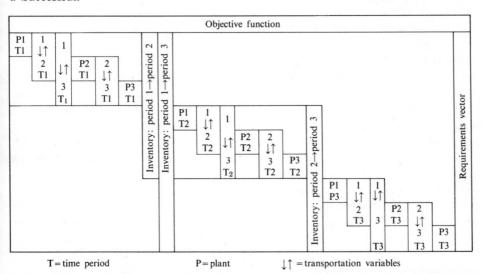

T = time period          P = plant          $\downarrow\uparrow$ = transportation variables

**Fig. 12-5** Sample multiplant-multitime period linear programming model structure.

In a way, it is unfortunate that so much emphasis has been placed on primal decomposition algorithms, because many of the most meaningful problems have a different matrix structural configuration as shown in Fig. 12-5. Here we see that the common factors in the smaller modules are not represented by a common set of constraints, but rather the interrelationships occur in the form of variables. Many of the large commercial linear programming system usages result from the simultaneous modeling of several plants in the development of an appropriate operating schedule extending over several time periods. The interactive effects between the plants are transportation variables and the interactive effects between time periods are the inventory variables. In these truly large problems that occur as the result of multitime period simulations, the common aspects between the modules or sections of the matrix are not in the rows but rather they are in the columns. This, therefore, suggests the use of a different decomposition procedure, namely, a dual decomposition. As yet, the actual algorithm development and computer codings of such a procedure have been quite limited, but this approach is promising because it lends itself so well to many typical problems occurring throughout industry.

## GENERALIZED TRANSPORTATION

In Chapter 4, the transportation algorithm was described. However, in this algorithm it was assumed that all materials are shipped from one location to another and thus the coefficients in both the supply and demand equations are 1.0 each. However, models can be constructed that exhibit an almost similar structure as a transportation model, but in which one set of the coefficients is not equal to 1.0.

Witness for example the multiproduct manufacturing model shown in Fig. 12-2. This model differs from a pure transportation model only in the fact that the coefficients in the last four rows are not 1.0's, but rather, they are a nonunity manufacturing rate. These rows cannot be scaled to result in all 1.0's, because the various products just have different manufacturing rates on the individual machines.

The generalized transportation algorithm has the capability to deal with such a matrix or model structure in a manner similar to that of the regular transportation algorithm. As such, it has great promise for solving multiproduct manufacturing type problems. To date, the number of successful computer programs using this algorithm have been scarce, but with the advent of large scale total corporate models, they are bound to increase. Also, a combination of a generalized transportation algorithm with a dual decomposition procedure appears to be a most powerful combination of algorithms, especially for dynamically planning total corporate operations involving many plants and many time periods. The decomposition can then span the region between the plants or across the time periods, and the generalized transportation model can evaluate the smaller segments.

We should note here that these special purpose algorithms all take cognizance in one way or another of special structures in matrices, and in fact, incorporate some of this structural detail into the solution procedure. As such, their use is limited to the matrices that display the selected pattern, and their justification lies in reductions in computer usage, with sporadic instances where their usage enables the solution of problems that are otherwise unmanageable.

# Using Computers for Linear Programming Problems                    13

The example in Chapters 1 and 2 lent itself well to manual solution methods, in this case even graphical, but those of the following chapters started to test the capability of ordinary human mathematical problem solving. Meaningful industrial problems often have hundreds of constraints, and many hundreds of variables. This always exceeds the capacity of manual computation. It has indeed been fortunate that simultaneously with the development of mathematical programming technology, there has been a tremendous development in computer technology. Mathematical programming technology has greatly benefited from the enormous strides made in computer technology, and conversely computer technology has been enhanced at least to some extent by the demands placed on it by mathematical programming applications. In plain words, all but trivially small linear programming problems require the use of electronic computers. Also, it is quite possible, and at times even attempted, to formulate linear programming problems that exceed the computational capabilities of the largest scale computer facilities in the world. Because of this interrelationship between mathematical programming and computer technology, we will describe how computers have been useful to solving linear programming problems in the past, and how they may be useful in the future.

## COMPUTER DEFINITION

In basic concept, a computer is a very simple device. A good clerk with a desk calculator can do all the tasks that a computer can do, but the clerk tends to be much slower. The only basic functions that computers can perform are: data input and output, addition, subtraction, storage of data for later retrieval, and most importantly, computers can determine whether one number is larger or smaller than another. The main virtues of the computer are the tremendous speed by which these actions are carried out and the virtually perfect reliability of carrying out the actions. The operational speed of a computer is such that multiplication is performed as a series of multiple additions and yet the action can be completed in just a few microseconds. For example, the multiplication of $13 \times 24$ is done by computer as multiple addition in the following form:

$$
\begin{array}{r}
13 \\
13 \\
13 \\
13 \\
130 \\
130 \\
\hline
312
\end{array}
$$

When done manually, we would have performed $(4 \times 13) + (20 \times 13)$ to arrive at the same result. We can see here that a computer, in essence, reverts to a multiple addition instead of using normal multiplication tables. Computers can afford this luxury; they are so fast that it is preferable to use multiple addition rather than looking up the multiplication table and using the appropriate entry from such a table.

**Fig. 13-1** UNIVAC 1108, a large-scale computer system. (Courtesy: UNIVAC Division, Sperry Rand Corporation.)

All the pre-1968 computers contained three main modules: an input-output module (I/O), an arithmetic and control module, and a memory module. The I/O module was the part of the computer that handled all input and output. Input can be in such physical forms as punched cards, punched paper tape, or direct typewriter signals; in magnetic forms such as magnetic tapes, disks, drums, or bulk storage; or in plain signal form from normal telephone or other communication lines. Output can be in all these same forms, and also as printed reports; newer devices include teletype units, crt displays, and audio response units. Figure 13-1 shows a modern electronic computer with a line printer located on the right. Figure 13-2 shows a communications terminal consisting of a keyboard and a crt display device. The computer I/O module simply follows orders from the arithmetic and control module in "reading" or "writing" the appropriate data on a specified I/O device. In a typical late 1960's computer, the I/O module and its assorted I/O devices generally accounted for 40 to 60% of the total computer cost.

The arithmetic and control module (AC) is the "thinking" part of the computer. This module executes the program as instructed. It initiates requests for data, does arithmetic, stores data in the memory, and makes the comparisons to "decide" on further actions. The quotation marks around "thinking" and "decide" are intentional; computers do not think or decide, they merely carry out tasks as instructed. The AC module of a computer can account for 20 to 35% of the total cost.

The memory module of a computer is a device capable of storing sizable volumes of data. The AC module can put data there for later referral. Such data can stay

**Fig. 13-2** The Uniscope 300 visual communications terminal. (Courtesy: UNIVAC Division, Sperry Rand Corporation.)

there for a long time, several hours, or it can be recovered in a microsecond or less. In a modern computer, the memory module can account for 15 to 35% of the total cost. In newer generations of computers we can expect different arrangements of the individual computer modules, more related to the actual functions to be carried out rather than to the components contained in the module. For example, input and output used to be considered as purely electromechanical devices. This is no longer so, especially in view of crt and communications equipment. Similarly AC contained all the logic elements, but functionally it is not necessary to combine arithmetic and logical control. In future generations of computers, we should look toward completely functional designs.

As computer technology has grown, major changes have come about in equipment types used, and in the physical arrangements between the modules that make up a computer. In the late 1940's and early 1950's, electronic computers existed only in research laboratories. Soon thereafter they were introduced into industry, and since then, we have witnessed a full three generations of computer technology. Now, in the last third of the 1960's, the fourth generation computers are being designed with initial operation scheduled before 1970. The overall technology has undoubtedly grown more rapidly than any other prior technological development.

## COMPUTER TECHNOLOGY

### First Generation

The first generation of industrial computers used vacuum tubes in their control modules. Input of data was by means of punched cards, and output was done by a line printer. The memory module of the first generation computers generally consisted of a revolving metal drum with a magnetic surface on which data was stored in the form of magnetized spots. The absence or presence of such magnetized spots formed the coded image of the stored data.

The first generation computers were, by current standards, relatively slow-speed devices; they were slow in executing their commands or program, and yet, input and output of data was at least another order of magnitude slower than computation.

As applications grew, emphasis was placed on improved input-output devices, because punched cards and printed reports were both bulky and slow to process. The next innovation therefore was the development of magnetic tapes, onto which information was encoded by magnetizing selected spots on the tape. Experience had been obtained with the first generation computers by storing data as magnetized images on magnetic drums. Since such drums were quite expensive, a search was made for a lower cost storage medium, and magnetic tapes were found to serve this purpose. In this manner, the surface of a rotating metal drum was actually simulated by a metallic oxide coating on a plastic tape. This allowed a much greater volume of data to be stored, but at the expense of larger data retrieval times. The first magnetic tapes actually became operational with the last of the first generation computers. However, magnetic tape units did not really come of age until the second generation of computers

**Fig. 13-3** The IBM 2420 magnetic tape unit. (Courtesy: IBM Corporation.)

was introduced in the late 1950's. Figure 13-3 shows a modern magnetic tape handling unit.

The first generation computers were capable of solving linear programming problems with up to about 40 constraints or equations, and with 40 to 80 variables.

### Second Generation

In the second generation, the computer control module was constructed with transistors rather than vacuum tubes. Also, the data storage module consisted of banks of magnetic cores instead of magnetic drums. While magnetic drums served their purpose well, a considerable amount of latent time was involved in retrieving a data point which was randomly stored on the surface of the drum. On the average, one-half of a drum revolution was lost in the search for such a randomly stored data point and this could amount to 9 to 33 milliseconds. With banks of core memories, every word of data in memory could be addressed and retrieved in the same amount of time, usually about 2 to 50 microseconds, depending on the make and model of computer. The second generation computers operated at much higher speeds than the first generation machines, due to the use of transistors in the control module and

**Fig. 13-4** CDC 3600, a large-scale computer system. (Courtesy: Control Data Corporation.)

magnetic core banks in the memory module. With the increase in speed, there developed a divergence in operating characteristics between the computer control module and the memory module on the one hand and the I/O module on the other. Frequently, the I/O unit would be 10 to 100 times slower than the control or memory modules. Hence, much potential computation time was wasted while the control module was waiting for input-output actions to be completed. Because of this, simultaneous processing was introduced, i.e., input and output actions were started, and during their execution, the computer would continue to operate in the computer mode on other jobs, returning to the I/O operation only after completion of the I/O action. Simultaneous operating is known as overlapping or buffering; the simultaneous actions can take place on various input-output channels. Several of the second generation computers, especially the larger ones, were capable of simultaneous input-output operations; all the third generation computers have this capability.

Another feature which emerged during the second generation was the use of magnetic disks for storage of data. These disks operate much like a vertically placed jukebox with a movable pickup arm that slides in and out between the stack of records and reads or writes data as magnetic spots on the faces of the disks as they are rotating. Some units operate with a single arm that travels up and down along the side of the stack and then moves inward and outward to find the proper track of a disk. Other units have one read-write head between every two disks.*

---

* Still other units have only a single disk, and a read-write head for every track on the disk. These latter units have similar operating characteristics as the original drum storage units, and in fact they are competing with drums in their traditional operating areas.

While some of the second generation computers were equipped with disk storage devices, virtually all third generation computers have this type of memory. The second generation computers could comfortably solve linear programming problems with 400 constraints and up to 3,000 variables. Larger problems with 1,000 and more constraints were tried but not always solved. Figure 13-4 shows a large scale computer developed during the later stages of the second generation.

### Third Generation

Besides larger magnetic core memories, the third generation computers manifest themselves primarily with still higher speeds of operation, and either all or at least a very large percentage of monolithic integrated circuitry, the new "chips" that perform the functions of several transistors, resistors and capacitors. Figure 13-5 shows such an integrated circuit board along with 14 hybrid circuit boards more reminiscent of the second generation of computers. Third generation computers not only carry out input-output operations simultaneously with computation, they can also carry out several programs or several sets of instructions simultaneously for separate users. This is called *multiprogramming* or *time sharing;* the total time available on the computer is shared by several programs. The initial experiments with multiprogramming were carried out with second generation equipment, but this mode of operation has truly become of age with the third generation equipment. Multi-

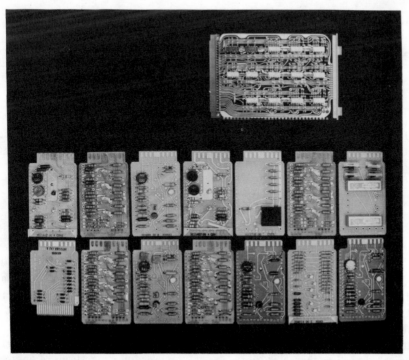

**Fig. 13-5** A monolithic integrated circuit board (top) and 14 hybrid integrated circuits. (Courtesy: UNIVAC Division, Sperry Rand Corporation.)

**Table 13-1**

**Typical Computer Characteristics**

| Characteristic | Generation | | |
| --- | --- | --- | --- |
| | First | Second | Third |
| Control module | Vacuum tubes | Transistors | Integrated circuits |
| Memory module | Drum | Cores and tapes | Cores, drums, disks, tapes |
| Input-output | Cards and printer | Cards, printer, typewriter, tapes | Cards, printer, typewriters, tapes, crt's, remote terminals |
| Typical processor speed | 100 μsec/character | 10 μsec/character | 1 μsec/character |
| Typical primary memory size | 10,000 characters | 16,000 characters | 128,000 characters |
| Reliable linear programming solution capability | 40 constraints | 400 constraints | 4000 constraints |

**Table 13-2**

**Typical Computer Memory Characteristics**

| Type | Size, million characters | Transfer rate, μsec/character | Random access time to first character |
| --- | --- | --- | --- |
| Magnetic cores | 0.032 to 0.512 | 0.2 to 2.0 | 0 |
| Magnetic drums | 1 to 4 | 1.2 to 5.0 | 4 to 20 msec |
| Magnetic disk, single | 2 to 8 | 2.0 to 8.0 | 20 to 150 msec |
| Magnetic disk, stack | 16 to 40 | 2.0 to 8.0 | 20 to 150 msec |
| Magnetic tape | 10 to 1000 | 8.0 to 24.0 | 3 min |

programming is defined here as the simultaneous operation of several programs, i.e., at any one time several operational programs can be in a semifinished state. Time sharing is defined as conversational operation of programs, with the conversation being held between the computer and a human at an I/O device such as teletypewriters or crt displays (see Fig. 13-2).

Table 13-1 shows some typical operating characteristics of the various generation computers. Table 13-2 shows a comparison between various data storage devices and their typical operation characteristics. The first and second generations of computers

Fig. 13-6 The large-scale IBM System/360 Model 85 computer. (Courtesy: IBM Corporation.)

each have had a life span of about 5 years. With each new generation, the typical performance has improved about 10-fold. At the same time, purchase cost or monthly rental for similar size equipment has remained about level, thus giving a 100 to 1 improvement in price to performance ratio in only 10 years' time. This growth rate has been unprecedented; from initial infancy, around 1950, the technology has matured to where there are now close to 40,000 general purpose digital computers in operation throughout the world. The growth in performance is bound to slacken off in the future because physical and operational constraints are being approached even though the growth of applications is still accelerating. In future years, the price to performance factor may well be increased by another factor of 10, but future growth in performance will slow from the dizzying pace of the past. A physical limitation which is being approached is the speed of light or of electricity, 186,000 miles per second. This is equivalent to approximately 1000 feet per microsecond. The control units of some of the largest third generation computers operate at a speed of 0.1 microseconds and of necessity, the circuitry involved in such an operation must be less than 100 ft in total. The fourth generation computers that are being designed should be expected to operate at still higher speeds, employ more efficient memories (such as plated wire, laser memories, or cryogenic memories), make more use of time sharing, remote processing, and proceed further along the path of operational control. However, a computer's speed cannot exceed the speed of electricity, and this may well become a limitation to the size of linear programming problems that can be solved by current techniques. Figures 13-6 and 13-7 show some truly large electronic computer complexes which are capable of solving very large linear programming problems.

**Fig. 13-7** The UNIVAC 1108 computer system. (Courtesy: NASA Manned Spacecraft Center, Houston, Texas.)

## LINEAR PROGRAMMING SOLUTION PROCEDURES

Standardized linear programming solution procedures are available for almost all modern computer systems. Many of the major computer manufacturers are supplying standard linear programming solution procedures to their customers. In addition, good solution procedures have been developed by various independent software development companies and by individual service bureaus. These latter programs are generally available on a fee basis, either as an outright purchase, or as a surcharge fee on top of normal computer rental. Chapter 7 contains suggestions on how to use such "canned" linear programming solution procedures most economically.

We must note here that there are three basic modes for computer solution of linear programming problems. In the first mode, the problem originator uses the computational facilities of his own company. Only in sporadic cases, such as in the petroleum refining business, can a computer installation be entirely justified for linear programming alone. In the remaining cases, therefore, the individual with a linear programming problem must use a computer that also has other uses. Such a computer is most frequently a part of a firm's accounting or controller's department.

In the second mode of operation, the problem originator's company does not employ its own electronic computer facility and, hence, the problem must be solved on the computing facilities of a commercial service bureau. This mode of linear programming solution is considerably less popular than the first one because it puts a great burden on the problem originator in the form of communication with the data center management and the data center programs. Also, under such circumstances, the problem originator frequently has greater difficulty in convincing his management of the economic attractiveness of such program and model development, and such a company's personnel tends to be less familiar with modern data processing procedures.

A third mode of operation consists of problem solution using a remote input-output device to a computer. In this case, the problem originator generally has a small, remote computer input-output device at his disposition. Such a device can consist of a simple card reader, a printer, and at times a remote card punch unit. With this remote device, the originator can phone in and send his problem to a major computer center. His problem is solved at the remote site, and the answers are returned via telephone line to his remote terminal. This is the newest mode of operation and it may well supplant the second mode of operation within a few years. When the linear programming solution requests are infrequent, i.e., less than once a week, or if the problems are small, it may be difficult to justify the rental of a remote job entry terminal at $800 to $1,200 per month plus telephone call costs. In such a case, using a local qualified service bureau is the preferred mode. On the other hand, when the problems are large, such as total corporate models, and if leased lines or Wide Area Telephone Service (WATS) are available, remote job entry can often be justified, especially if the remote terminal can have other uses when linear programming models are not being solved. This can be accomplished if there is a small inhouse computer that can be equipped with a data transmission unit; because such a computer can be used as a remote terminal device with linkage to a larger machine when not used for inhouse purposes.

It is our experience that mode 1, use your own company's computer, is far more desirable than modes 2 and 3. But even if this mode of operation does exist, there are some advantages to modes 2 and 3. Linear programming problems can often be solved on larger computers than those employed in mode 1, and the economies of scale are such that actual solution costs—the time to calculate a solution multiplied by the hourly rental cost of the equipment—decrease rapidly when larger computers are used. Also, modern "computer utilities" tend to give very fast turnaround times, invariably less than 2 hours. Such service is seldom available on inhouse computers. The examples of linear programming solutions cited in Chapters 7 and 8 have been solved using all three modes of operation, and using at least seven different types and models of central computers. Extensive use was made of remote job entry devices to prove that this was a feasible approach to solving large linear programming problems. In this regard, terminals and central computers were matched as well as mixed among the various computer brands.

## DISCUSSION TOPICS AND PROBLEMS

1. What kind of computers are available to you? What type and model computer does your company operate? What is its charged cost to users?

2. Which commercial service bureau's are offering what type of equipment *and* service for the solution of mathematical programming problems?

3. Is remote computer usage a possibility for your problems? Who offers such service? What is the cost for computation and for data transmission?

# Pearce Container
# Corporation
# A Case Study*

**14**

The Pearce Container Corporation is engaged in the manufacture of a wide variety of containers, primarily for the food industry but also for the packaging of other perishable materials. The main line of products consists of glass containers such as bottles for soft drinks, beer, milk, catsup, and peanut butter. To nonfood industries, Pearce supplies such items as jars for ointments, hand-cleaning compounds, bottles for medicinal alcohol, and liquid soaps. The company operates five glass container plants located in Boston, Indianapolis, Saint Louis, Waco (Texas), and San Francisco. In addition, the company also operates four plants for the manufacture of wax coated paper and plastic containers. Annual sales are approximately $200 million for glass products and $80 million for the other types of containers.

In the particular market in which Pearce operates, it is customary to quote to customers a price on a delivered basis, and hence the manufacturer absorbs the delivery costs of the materials.

As can well be imagined, there is a great seasonality in the demand for Pearce's products, since in the summer months there is a larger demand for beer and soft drink bottles especially. Also, there are frequent variations in manufacturing capacity,

---

\* This case study is largely based on an actual project carried out by the Owens Corning Fiberglas Corporation.

because glass furnaces need to be overhauled and rebuilt periodically. Whenever this occurs, such a furnace is generally out of service for 45 to 60 days. There is, therefore, a variation in supply capacity during the course of a year.

Ever since its inception, Pearce Container Corporation has carried out its production planning operation on a manual basis. However, operations planning became a very complex and time-consuming task, because Pearce now manufactures 189 lines of products with a total of over 36,000 individual manufacturing items. The great variety of items is due to the large mix that occurs for different bottle sizes, different colors, different shapes, and different capping procedures.

Pearce was interested in determining whether it would be possible to carry out the production planning operation with the aid of electronic computers. In order to investigate this, the corporation assigned a study team.

## TOTAL CORPORATE MODEL

The study team quickly determined that adequately planning the operations of all manufacturing units would be a herculean task. To this end, it was decided to initially concentrate efforts on the glass container area, since it formed the bulk of the company's operation. In total, the company operated 40 basic glass furnaces located in the five plants. In addition, there had been consideration to build an additional sixth plant near Pensocola, Florida.

After extensive reviews with the production planning manager, it was determined that:

1. Total operations planning for all glass plants would be attractive, especially if an optimum production plan could be established.
2. To adequately deal with the seasonality inherent in the operation, it would be necessary to use a time horizon of *more* than 1 year.
3. For the initial study, restricting the planning operation to the manufacture of glass containers only was quite acceptable.
4. The costs to be minimized were to be the variable costs of manufacture plus the finished goods delivery costs. The variable manufacturing costs were to include raw materials, direct labor, packaging, purchased materials, inventory, etc.

## CONSTRAINTS

The team began by investigating what the constraints on the total operational model would be. They found the following:

1. Manufacturing capacity was limited. The actual output of a given glass furnace and its associated bottle lines was limited. At some times, the limitation was on the rate at which the glass could be drawn, and at other times, the limitation was on the speed of the bottle lines. But whatever the limitation, an appropriate production rate by machine and type of product could be established. The point worth noting is

that such production planning is essentially equipment time allocation with a given machine assigned to a product for a given number of hours which results in a quantity produced.

2. Inventory space available for the storage of seasonal stocks, i.e., those stocks that are preproduced prior to a peak selling season, was limited. Additional warehouse space could be leased, or commercial warehousing space could be used, but only at relatively high costs.

3. Actual product demands would have to be met. Pearce had over the years established a policy of first-class service, and this included quick and reliable delivery of all goods ordered.

4. During the slack season, Pearce had a management policy to not lay off idle workers at selected plants, because these plants were remote from other industrial areas, and such layoffs could cause key personnel to leave the area and find other jobs elsewhere.

If the team was to develop a linear programming model for the corporate production planning, it would have to contain manufacturing capacity restraints for each of the 40 basic manufacturing machines, inventory capacity constraints for each of the five plants, production demand balances for each of the lines of products manufactured at each plant—which ran well over 500—plus the minimum manpower constraints, one for each plant. In addition, the team felt that a linear programming model should be a multitime period model to cover at least 18 months of operation. A model of this type covering only the manufacturing end, and ignoring the plant to customer distribution problem, would undoubtedly entail well over 10,000 constraints. This was beyond the then reliable solution capabilities of available computers. We will see later how this problem was dealt with.

## VARIABLES

The actual variables to be contained in the model should be the combined activity of manufacturing a given product on a given machine in a given time period. In addition, there would have to be inventory variables, describing the amount of goods manufactured in one time period and used in a later time period. Also, at times the company did ship manufactured goods from one plant to another, even though this was deemed to be quite uneconomic.

The number of manufacturing variables would be equal to the actual machine-product line combinations. Frequently, certain manufacturing machines were not used for certain product lines, even though they were entirely capable of doing so. This occurred because in the past, production planning personnel had established that these products could be manufactured at lower costs on other machines. The team, however, decided that if a linear programming model were to be employed, this model should be representative of all the production flexibility that existed, even though production planning personnel in the past had deemed certain machine-product line combinations as undesirable.

Of course, each machine-product line combination activity would have to be duplicated in each time period, because in effect, a different activity exists in month 3 than in month 2. So, for an 18-month time period model, and with each of the 40 machines capable of producing an average of 15 distinct products, there appeared to be immediately $18 \times 40 \times 15 = 10,800$ manufacturing variables. A similar number of inventory variables was anticipated, especially if consideration was to be given to storing inventory in self-owned warehouses, leased warehouse space, and/or commercial warehouse space. Again, the model appeared to be too large for solution by the then reliable computational capabilities, even before the finished goods distribution problem was appended.

## SYSTEM SIMPLIFICATION

The team quickly established that if a linear programming approach could be useful, some drastic simplifying actions would be required. The first step therefore was to put primary emphasis on the manufacturing operation alone and for the time being, to shelve consideration of the finished goods distribution system. This could be done by grouping the forecasted demands by "traditional" plant service areas, and thus coming up with only a single demand for each product category-plant combination.*

It was also felt that even though actual operations scheduling for a full 18-month time period was requested, production planning management would be much more interested in the near term time periods, and be less interested in the time periods occurring a year or so later. Because of this, the team revised the operational schedule to consider the first 3 months on a month-by-month basis and then to consider the other 15 months on a quarterly basis, thus giving an 8-time-period model, consisting of 3 months and 5 quarters of operation. This immediately brought the number of time periods down from 18 to 8. Consequently, the size of a potential model was similarly reduced.

Next, the team decided to investigate whether it would not be possible to combine many of the individual product lines into so-called product categories, or groups of lines that had similar manufacturing rates and costs. A considerable amount of time was spent in trying to establish this simplification, because as has been noted earlier, the actual number of product lines and the demand for products in each of these lines make up the majority of the model constraints. At various times, the team suggested as few as 20 and as many as 65 individual product categories. No real agreement could be reached between the study team and production planning management. Nevertheless, the team still felt that a linear programming approach to production planning would be very useful. They therefore suggested that before embarking on the development of a full scale production planning system, they would initially demonstrate the principles of the process with a much smaller pilot model. The production planning

---

* There is a fallacy in this, because it assumes that the traditional mode of operation was optimal or nearly so! This was later on realized and modified!

management agreed to this scheme, and suggested that this pilot model contain the two highest dollar volume product lines. With these ground rules, the team began to develop the demonstration model.

## DEMONSTRATION MODEL

The project team decided to construct a demonstration model of the overall allocation problem. It was felt that such a demonstration model would be useful to acquaint production planning management with the methods, data requirements, and overall system analysis required for a full scale production allocation system. Also, through the use of a demonstration model, it was felt that some experience could be gained in data gathering, model development, and results analysis, and that estimates of system operating costs both in terms of man-hours and computer costs could be established on the basis of the pilot model operations.

The team collected, with management's approval, appropriate data for the two product categories that represented the largest dollar volume of production, about 34%. Also, the two product categories selected were manufactured in at least four of the five existing plants, and they would most likely also be manufactured in any new facilities to be added to the overall manufacturing capabilities.

## DATA REQUIREMENTS

In order to build the demonstration model, appropriate data had to be developed for the manufacturing operations, for inventories, and for plant-to-plant transfers and plant-to-customer delivery of finished goods. By grouping the individual forecasted customer demands for products to the lowest aggregate cost of manufacturing plus delivery, i.e., to the plant that had the lowest combination of variable manufacturing *plus* delivery cost, an ideal manufacturing and distribution schedule could be established. Such a schedule would be at least as good and quite possibly better than the traditional plant service area assignment. However, with such an ideal system, it was not certain that all the demands allocated to each plant could be manufactured there. The project team therefore decided to allow, at least in the demonstration phase, that finished goods be transported from one plant to another to make up the shortages in manufacturing capability as necessary, thus assuming that adequate production capacity existed in the nation! It was felt that if manufacturing deficiencies occurred in one or more plants, a subsequent realignment of allocation of demand could be done with a straightforward transportation algorithm. Figure 14-1 shows this graphically.

Within the manufacturing section of the model, data would be required on the number of containers that each glass furnace and production line could manufacture in a single day. This, of course, was the most important set of data, because effectively, daily production or machine hours were to be allocated to the overall demand, so as to minimize the total manufacturing costs. The next set of data therefore covered the variable manufacturing cost of each machine-product category combination. As

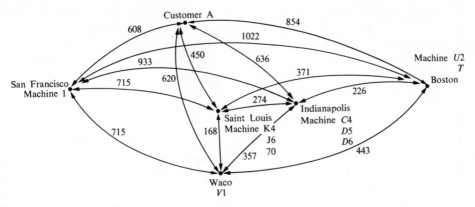

**Fig. 14-1** Pearce Container interplant transportation costs and manufacturing capacities for one product.

noted earlier, not only those machines-product combinations that had been used in the past were important, but also all other manufacturing capabilities that appeared to have a reasonable chance of being used by the mathematical model. In fact, providing additional manufacturing capabilities increases the flexibility of the model, and it *may* produce a lower total manufacturing cost.

Since in allocating production to plants, it was necessary to guarantee a minimum number of jobs, it was also necessary to provide data on the number of men that are employed at each machine-product category combination. Finally, another necessary data point was the coefficient to employ between manufacturing machine days, and manufacturing machine capacities. Since both dimensions were expressed in the daily volume capacities, these coefficients were all equal to 1.0. For the manufacturing capacities when manufacturing time is being allocated, it can best be expressed in operating days, and it should also be expected that the manufacturing facility availability would then be expressed in days. Operating hours would of course be equally acceptable; the criterion is that available machine time is being allocated to various production operations.

## INVENTORY VARIABLES

With the great seasonality and demand, inventory played a major role in the total allocation process. The actual cost of inventory was made up of two major components, i.e., the handling cost or the cost involved in moving the materials into seasonal storage and out again, and the actual storage cost, which must include the cost of capital tied up during the storage period. The actual matrix coefficients to be used for the inventory variables were simply devised. In the time periods that the materials were placed in inventory, there would be a normal subtraction from the demand balance equation, and at the time period in which they were withdrawn from inventory, there would be a normal credit to the then current demand balance equation.

Various experiments were conducted regarding optimum closing inventory strategy. It was found, during the construction and initial operational phase of the model, that it would be quite difficult to develop an optimum closing inventory strategy, and because of this, it was decided for the time being, to ignore such closing inventories.

## TRANSPORTATION VARIABLES

The transportation variables from one plant to another took on much of the same configuration as the inventory variables. The variable cost of transportation was to be used, the plant supplying the materials was to be debited in its demand balance equations, and the plant receiving the goods was to be credited with the materials. Since all five plants could ship to the four others, there would be a total $5 \times 4 = 20$ transportation variables for each product category in each time period.

It should be realized, of course, that the demonstration model was essentially a single-stage manufacturing multitime period, multiplant model as described in Chapters 4 and 5. Also, because of the particular structure of the model, the objective function became a present value function, i.e., one that carried out appropriate discounting of future cash flows to develop an optimum operating strategy based on today's dollar value.

An actual 8-time-period model was constructed consisting of 14 machine capacity constraints, 9 plant-demand constraints,* 5 inventory constraints, and 5 manpower constraints for each time period. This thus resulted in 33 equations per time period or a total of 264 equations in the model. The number of variables amounted to 18 machine-product combinations for each time period, 32 intraplant transportation variables, and a variable number of inventory activities, depending on the starting and finishing dates of each possible inventory cycle.

## SYSTEM DEVELOPMENT

Since the model was to be used primarily as a demonstration model, it was felt that variable or direct costs, based on the current standard cost system, would be adequate. The actual standard cost system included also such fixed expenses as depreciation and overhead. Adequate data, however, were extracted from the standard cost system to portray only the variable cost fraction. The other data to be put into the model, especially on manufacturing rates, the unit capacities, and direct labor employed in manufacturing were developed on a joint effort by the team and the production planning organization. From this process, much was learned regarding the necessary data collection. This proved invaluable when it was decided later to develop a full scale, all-product model encompassing the overall production allocation system.

The initial pilot model was developed by manual means, i.e., the entire linear programming matrix was developed in punch card form for submission to an electronic computer. Since this was a matrix of 264 equations and over 400 variables, it was a

---

* Product type 35 is manufactured only in four plants.

PEARCE CONTAINER DEMONSTRATION MODEL- BASIC INPUT DATA

```
1                                   MANUFACTURING
   35 1D5   760  .097 18
   35 1D6   879  .103 18
   35 1C4   733  .080 23
   35 2U2   790  .109 12
   35 3K4  0758  .119 12
   35 3J6  0799  .119 12
   35 370  0888  .140 13
   35 41   0933  .113 08
   42 1C4  0454  .037 09
   42 1D5  0476  .061 13
   42 1D6  0529  .068 11
   42 2T   0520  .043 23
   42 2U2  0668  .056 23
   42 3K4  0509  .061 19
   42 3J6  0521  .056 19
   42 370  0625  .093 19
   42 41   0538  .061 12
   42 5V1  0503  .061 20
2                                   DEMANDS
   35 1    01393014230139901404
   42 1    02893027870305803228
   35 2    00233002570025600257
   42 2    02614025510272002893
   35 3    00661006660067100675
   42 3    01673016080175301887
   35 4    00031000320003400036
   42 4    01168011650126001305
   42 5    01110011380120401206
3                                   TRANSPORT
   35 1    00000002240027400933000000000000
   35 2    00224000000037101022000000000000
   35 3    00274003710000000071500000000000
   35 4    00941010320071500000000000000000
   42 1    00000002260027400933003570000250
   42 2    00226000000037101022004430028600
   42 3    00274003710000000071500016800309
   42 4    00941010320071500000071500979
   42 5    00357004430016800715000000000304
   42 6    00250002860030900089800304000000
4                                   CAPACITY
      1 C4   88    89    89    88
      1 D5   88    89    89    88
      1 D6   72    63    58    65
      2 U2   81    88    87    55
      2 T    88    75    89    88
      3 K4   88    89    89    88
      3 J6   37    89    39    86
      3 70   54    84    85    73
      4 1    42    71    70    68
      5 V1   88    89    89    88
5                                   INVENTORY CAP.
      1    376   325   348   410
      2    055   048   062   058
      3    875   642   573   813
      4    010   015   030   024
      5    103   103   103   103
6                                   MANPOWER



      1
      2
      3
      4
      5
7                                   INVENTORY COST
   35       85    98    75    90    00    00
   42       70    98    75    80    67    67
8                                   OPENING INV.
   35      005    01    00    00    00    00
   42      050    00   332    00    04    00
9                                   ENDFILE
```

**Fig. 14-2** The basic input data for the Pearce Container demonstration model.

large task. However, by doing it manually the first time, much was learned on how a full scale system matrix generator might have to be developed. Finally, the pilot or demonstration model was solved, and the results were very encouraging. In the majority of the cases, the actual production and the uses of seasonal inventory were anticipated. Also, some plant-to-plant transfers of finished goods would occur, primarily to cover the product requirements at the Saint Louis plant where a major equipment shutdown was anticipated. The model results did contain some surprises, however, in that the project operating strategy did not fully conform to the anticipation of the production planning department. These surprises, however, could easily be rationalized, and they appeared to make quite adequate sense. It was because of these surprises that the production planning department personnel readily accepted linear programming as a possible mode for operations scheduling. It was felt that with linear programming, an optimum production planning strategy could be found, while with manual methods, only good operational plans could be developed, since the production planning personnel could not investigate all possible alternatives available to it. The surprises in fact are the difference between evaluating a manually developed strategy and finding an optimum strategy by a computer based routine.

The combined manufacturing, inventory, and transportation model did carry out appropriate tradeoffs in manufacturing costs to deliver a lowest total variable operating cost schedule. It should be noted here, that in the past, the production planning group had not generally planned the operations on the basis of a variable operating cost but rather on the basis of standard operating cost. The project team expended a reasonable amount of effort to convince the production planning personnel that more appropriate operating decisions could be made on the basis of the variable costs. This advice was accepted in due time. Figure 14-2 shows the actual data used for the demonstration model in compact format. It can easily be seen that the total volume of data was not overly large, but still it was a tremendous task to collect and verify it all.

The demonstration system developed up to this point did not yet concern itself with actual demand forecasts, which are a definite prerequisite for a full scale production allocation system, and neither did it cover the problems associated with the development of an optimum finished goods delivery schedule. Corporate staff was adequately impressed with the demonstration model, however, to authorize the development of a full scale forecasting system that would attempt to forecast the demands in each product category within a specific trade area (T/A). In total more than 120 T/A were designated, each representing a cluster of market activity. Demand forecasts for all products in each T/A were established by a combination of statistical and market forecasting procedures. At this point, the forecasted demands were assigned to plants on the basis of minimum variable manufacturing plus delivery costs. All demands assigned to each plant were then aggregated and the minimum costs summed to give the "ideal solution." Next the manufacturing linear programming model was started, and a feasible best solution calculated. Whenever this solution suggested some plant-to-plant transfers it was deemed advisable to review and reoptimize the transportation system. An example of this is shown in Fig. 14-3. It is not

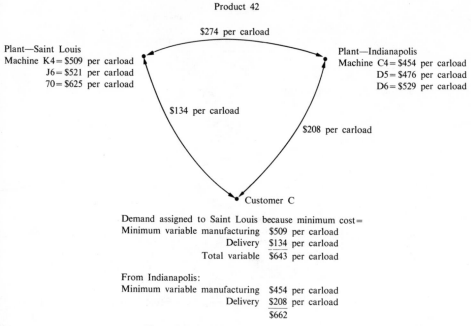

Product 42

$274 per carload

Plant—Saint Louis
Machine K4= $509 per carload
       J6= $521 per carload
       70= $625 per carload

Plant—Indianapolis
Machine C4= $454 per carload
       D5= $476 per carload
       D6= $529 per carload

$134 per carload

$208 per carload

Customer C

Demand assigned to Saint Louis because minimum cost=
Minimum variable manufacturing  $509 per carload
Delivery  $134 per carload
Total variable  $643 per carload

From Indianapolis:
Minimum variable manufacturing  $454 per carload
Delivery  $208 per carload
$662

**Fig. 14-3** Sample allocation scheme.

advisable to transport from Indianapolis to Saint Louis and then to a customer C for a cost of $274.00 + $134.00 = $408 if direct shipment from Saint Louis to the customer will incur only $208. But customer C was "assigned" to Saint Louis on the basis of the *ideal* system.

The next step therefore is, whenever a plant-to-plant transshipment occurs in the linear programming solution, to reoptimize the original demand assignments. This can be done by the efficient transportation algorithm. This, of course, has to be carried out for each product category in each time period in which a plant-to-plant shipment is suggested. The result of this step then is a very good operating plan. It will be at higher cost than the ideal plan, because operational constraints are now taken into account. If the difference between "ideal" and "very good" is small, one might consider the plan to be finished. Actually, a still better solution may exist between the ideal and reoptimized solutions. Consider the example from Fig. 14-3. Customer C was assigned to Saint Louis because it represents the potentially lowest total cost. But if the demand on Saint Louis is so large that the last increment of production is assigned to unit 70, and the demand on Indianapolis is so light that the incremental production takes place on machine C4, then we see that customer C is supplied at an actual cost of:

| Manufacture | $625/carload |
|---|---|
| Delivery | $134/carload |
| Total | $759/carload |

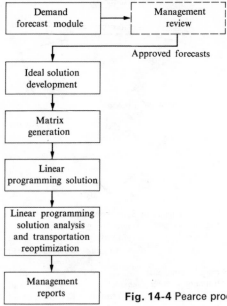

**Fig. 14-4** Pearce production planning system.

but he could have been supplied from Indianapolis at a cost of:

|  |  |
|---|---|
| Manufacture | $454/carload |
| Delivery | $208/carload |
| Total | $662/carload |

From this example we see thus that the reoptimized solution is not guaranteed to be the "global optimum solution." A major block diagram of the Pearce system is shown in Fig. 14-4. This system can easily be extended to search for such further optimizations as described here. We should note that the full system does not reach the global optimum solution in one pass because of the *ad hoc* decomposition inherent in the system—the transportation and manufacturing operations are optimized semi-independently.

Extensive actual usage of the complete system has shown that only small differences exist between the ideal and reoptimized solutions and the latter were found to be adequately appropriate for Pearce Container Corporation's needs. It was actually found that further optimization with additional tradeoffs between manufacturing and transportation would not yield a high enough return to warrant the additional system development and operations cost.

## OBSERVATIONS

A number of interesting things were learned by first developing the demonstration model. Firstly, the full scale model would undoubtedly involve between 1200 and 1700 equations and approximately 6000 to 8000 variables. Arranging a linear programming matrix of this size by manual means is unthinkable. Hence, it became necessary to employ a matrix generator program. Some consideration was given to the use of a general purpose linear programming matrix generator and the available programs were reviewed. None were found that could adequately satisfy the needs of the system to be developed.

Therefore, a special purpose matrix generator program development was started. This program would accept data on manufacturing, inventory, transportation, manufacturing unit capacities, inventory capacities, and demand forecasts as prepared by the forecasting system. The actual data input format was not unlike the sample shown in Fig. 14-2. From this data the program constructs an appropriate linear programming matrix. At the same time, the matrix generator carries out extensive consistency checks on the data. An example of such a consistency check is to verify that appropriate capacity data is available for a manufacturing unit when there is an indication that this manufacturing unit can be used to manufacture one or more products. As it turned out, the main bulk of the matrix generator program was in the area of consistency checking, since the actual routine development of matrix elements with appropriate row and column labels is quite straightforward.

In the initial operational effort with the full scale production allocation model, little attention was paid to the sizeable volume of output. The results were initially interpreted by manual means. It was quickly developed, however, that such analysis was an extremely cumbersome task. The actual linear programming solution procedure was therefore instructed to store all the calculated results on a specially designated memory device at the computing center, where the data could be interrogated by the transportation reoptimization system, as well as by a variety of special purpose report generating programs. These programs were subsequently developed. They contain the planned operations schedule by machine and by product category in each time period, the anticipated buildup of seasonal stock in owned as well as leased warehouses, and a large variety of other combinations in which the final outcome of the actual results can be indicated.

## SENSITIVITY ANALYSIS

During the development of the demonstration model, and the total corporate system, emphasis was also placed on the ease of sensitivity analysis, because, although the model was initially developed as an operations planning tool to develop optimum operating strategy, it was quickly found that excellent uses of the total system could also lie in extensive sensitivity analyses and in future operations simulations. For example, Pearce Container was considering the construction of a new plant near Pensacola, Florida. Economic review studies had been carried out, but only certain aspects of the total operation could be included in these conventional economic studies. Now, with the aid of a model as encompassing as the one developed for the operations planning system, it was a relatively easy task to include a hypothetical new facility, and to accurately predict the economic benefits to be obtained from such a facility, taking full cognizance of all manufacturing interactions existing in the overall operation. In this way, it could be established whether there was an economic payout for an investment to be made in Pensacola.

A final comment in this particular case is in order. The production planning personnel had cooperated extensively and they readily accepted the development of a total corporate production planning model. Such ready acceptance is not always forthcoming immediately. Furthermore, even after the initial quick acceptance, the full scale model had to be demonstrated to be fully operational for 6 months before product planning management fully adopted it as *the* operational production planning tool. In general, operational management is frequently reluctant to accept such elaborate and advanced production planning tools without having seen them demonstrated to be accurate, correct, and useful over a considerable amount of time. Also, in order to keep the total corporate system operational, the company did have to add several new well qualified staff members to its organization. The gross benefit therefore to be obtained from such a system development effort are often offset by some increase in well trained manpower, and in computer operational costs. However, the net benefit to the firm can be extensive, especially if the total variable manufacturing and distribution costs exceed $50 million annually. Also, one should consider that the system development effort for such a total corporate system can exceed $100,000. This should be viewed as an investment that can be repaid only by improved subsequent operations. We indicate this here because we feel that although the development of total corporate planning models along linear programming lines can be very attractive, the developing organization should realize the cost involved in the development and in the operation of such a system.

# European
# Petroleum Market
# Simulation
# A Case Study                                          15

Petrochemical companies purchase large quantities of light petroleum fractions, which they convert into chemical products. The petroleum fractions of prime interest to the petrochemical companies are propane, butane, and now also naphtha. These petroleum products are cracked to produce ethylene, a basic building block for a wide variety of petrochemical products, including polyethylene (plastic), ethylene glycol (antifreeze), and many others. European ethylene demand has sky-rocketed in the last few years, from 113,000 metric tons in 1956 to 270,000 tons in 1960 and 520,000 tons in 1964. The forecasted 1970 demand* for ethylene in Europe was 1,700,000 tons.

In the U.S., the primary feed stock for ethylene manufacture is propane and butane, which are relatively abundant in the southwest. These petroleum gases are coproduced along with crude oil. In Western Europe, ethylene has traditionally been manufactured from coal, because propane and butane are not readily available. The demand growth for ethylene has been so considerable that propane and butane supplies are starting to become somewhat limited in the U.S.; at the same time coal is becoming more and more expensive to produce in Europe. Also, the coal based processes are less economical than the petroleum based ones. Luckily, a technological breakthrough occurred with the development of high severity naphtha crackers, chemical process

---

* Forecast made in 1965.

Table 15-1

Daily Average Crude Oil Production Rates Per Country
During First 6 Months of 1967*

| Country | Volume, thousands of barrels per day |
|---|---|
| U.S. | 8511 |
| U.S.S.R. | 5605 |
| Venezuela | 3456 |
| Saudi Arabia | 2625 |
| Iran | 2490 |
| Kuwait | 2309 |
| Libya | 1474 |
| Iraq | 1001 |
| Canada | 912 |
| Algeria | 695 |
| Nigeria | 578 |
| Indonesia | 507 |
| Western Europe in total | 402 |
| Abu Dhabi | 365 |
| Mexico | 356 |
| Qatar | 288 |

* Source: *Oil and Gas Journal*, **65**, No. 52 (Dec. 25, 1967).

units that can crack naphtha into ethylene and coproduce benzene, toluene, and xylene. Naphtha is the petroleum fraction that is primarily used for gasoline manufacture. Naphtha has a higher boiling point than propane and butane, but a lower boiling point than jet fuel, diesel fuel, or fuel oil. The demand for benzene, toluene, and xylene is also growing rapidly. These so-called *aromatics* are used in the manufacture of nylon and many other products. Because of these coexisting factors of shortage of traditional raw materials, new manufacturing technology, and ready outlets for the aromatic by-products, most of the new European ethylene manufacturing capacity is of the naphtha cracker type.

Several large petrochemical companies have rapidly expanded their operations in Western Europe. However, before fully commiting themselves to new naphtha cracking plants and prior to entering into negotiations for naphtha supply contracts with their potential suppliers, these petro-chemical companies funded a research study to determine the future availability and the possible price range of naphtha in Western Europe for the years 1970 and 1975. This chapter contains a description of the study that was carried out in 1965. A few initial comments may be helpful in describing international petroleum operations.

Crude oil is found in many places on the globe, but the availability varies considerably from one location to another. At present, more than ⅔ of all proven oil reserves exist in the Middle Eastern Countries, primarily those around the Persian Gulf. Crude oil demand in that region is quite small, and hence much of the oil is exported to consuming nations in Europe, the Orient, Australia, Japan, South America, and the U.S. Table 15-1 contains a listing of crude oil production rates for the major oil producing nations.

Until about 1945 the Western Hemisphere was the prime oil producer, with major fields in the U.S., Venezuela, Colombia, Peru, and Argentina. Even after World War II, much oil was shipped from the U.S. and Venezuela to Western Europe. Europe's energy needs, however, were primarily supplied by coal, and petroleum product usage was limited mostly to transportation energy, i.e., gasoline, diesel fuel, and ships bunker oil.

Although Iran and Iraq had been oil-exporting countries before and during World War II, major new fields and production in Kuwait, Saudi Arabia, and other Persian Gulf countries began only in the late 1940's and early 1950's. The first oil well of any importance in Africa did not come in until the early 1950's, in Algeria. Extensive oil discoveries have since been made in Libya, Egypt, Nigeria, and Angola as well.

Oil production in the U.S. averages about 13 barrels per day (bbl/day) per well, production in Venezuela is about 300 bbl/day, and in the Middle East it is about 4,600 bbl/day. Zelten 1, the first commercial well in Libya, began initial flow at 17,000 bbl/day. Not all African oil wells are as prolific as Zelten 1, and neither are the African reserves as large as those of the Middle Eastern Countries. Currently, average production is about 1600 bbl/day.

Crude oil transportation costs from the Middle East to Southern Europe can amount to $0.50/bbl. At the same time, transportation costs from the North African oil producing countries to Southern Europe generally amount to only $0.10 to $0.15/bbl. The 1967 closing of the Suez Canal forced Middle East to Europe oil shipments to proceed around the Cape of Good Hope. This takes longer and consumes additional shipping capacity. This especially increased the transportation costs for the Middle Eastern crude oils.

Although most crude oils are generally available on a spot basis, the large majority of oil moves under long term contract. Many of the major international oil companies are vertically integrated; they operate crude producing, transporting, refining, and sales organizations. As far as possible, they attempt to use their own supplies and facilities. In addition, long term (5 years or more) crude oil supply contracts cover the major portion of the crude that moves outside of the large international oil companies. Such long term supply contracts are desirable because the arrangement allows a refiner to build and operate a plant specifically designed for the crude oil which will be used as feed stock. The actual fob price of foreign crude oils is difficult to establish because there are few open-market transactions. Besides, the few that are published are difficult to analyze, since they often involve other terms such as cash loan repayments, deferred payments, downstream participation, side deals, etc.

## PROJECT DESCRIPTION

The project sponsors were interested primarily in obtaining estimates of the future market availability and projected prices of petrochemical naphtha. Petrochemical naphtha generally is manufactured as a by-product from energy material manufacturing operations. Due to this relationship, the volume and price of petrochemical naphtha can be affected by a large variety of factors, including the availability of coal and nuclear power, market protection for indigenous energy sources, as well as the economic considerations for crude oil developments in the Middle East, Africa, and Europe itself.

The research study consisted of three major phases:

1. Demand forecast for petroleum products by product category and type.

2. Energy source material forecast by product category and type.

3. Simulation of future petroleum refining operations under a wide variety of supply patterns, demand patterns, and product specifications.

The study was concerned primarily with the future petroleum market conditions in OECD Europe. The specific countries included in the study were:

1. The EEC countries: France, Germany, Italy, Belgium, The Netherlands, and Luxembourg.

2. The EFTA countries: United Kingdom, Norway, Denmark, Sweden, Austria, Switzerland, and Portugal.

3. The nonaligned nations: Spain, Greece, Turkey, Ireland, and Iceland.

Basic inputs into the study project consisted of OECD statistical data, EEC statistical data, field interviews, and other sizable volumes of energy data.

### Refinery Model

The analysis was based on a linear programming model which was developed to simulate European refinery operations. The model contained all of the important refinery processes currently used by European refiners and all processes which might be installed to meet the future needs of the European petroleum market. This refinery model is shown schematically in Fig. 15-1. Each process in the model was specified in terms of operating costs, fuel requirements, yield pattern, and output stream quality for a range of operating conditions and a range of input streams. A number of simplifications were made to reduce the number of data points to manageable proportions, but those simplifications did not detract from the general validity of the results obtained.

The model was operated by specifying the demand and the limiting specifications for each of the important petroleum products. In addition, estimated volumes of various crude oils which the refinery had available to meet this demand were specified. The linear programming model then selected that combination of processing which minimized operating costs. In this case, raw material supplies and finished product

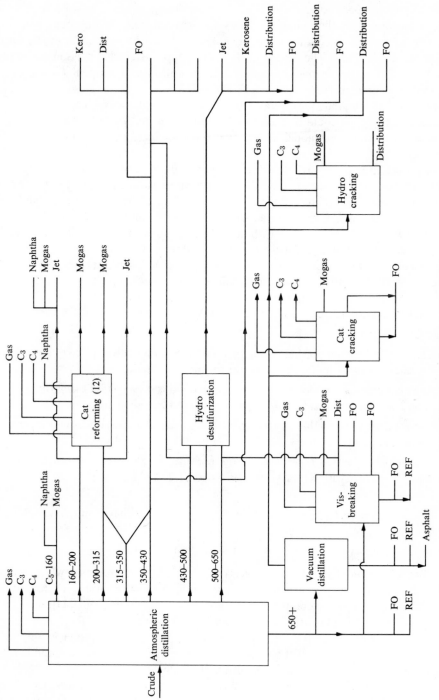

**Fig. 15-1** A model refining flowchart.

demands were specified and the linear programming model was used to simulate future operations by the refining industry. It was felt that the European petroleum refining companies could adequately be represented by a single refinery model for the purposes of this study. The obvious pitfall in this approach is that it assumes complete flexibility among the many European refineries—allowing intermediate products to be shifted around where desirable and allowing the real optimal use of all refinery components throughout the overall region. For example, a residual stream from a poorer quality crude could be used as refinery fuel for the whole refining industry, as represented by the single model, even though not all refineries would run this particular crude oil.

In order to make the whole exercise meaningful, a number of special constraints were included in the model, to describe or constrain the single model operation so that it would adequately represent the existing and future expected overall petroleum refining industry in Western Europe. Such constraints can only be defined by individuals that are thoroughly familiar with the industry, and even then, it takes considerable man-model interaction to construct the right constraints, so that a single refinery model can adequately represent a whole regional refining industry. The models so constructed must carefully be measured against current or historical operations before they can be used to assess the future.

Nevertheless, a representative model was built, and the bases used for the economic evaluation were:

1. The total petroleum market in a major geographic region was to be quite inelastic; the sales volume was to be insensitive to price fluctuations.

2. The mathematical model of the total refining industry was used primarily to determine marginal product manufacturing costs and marginal crude oil values.

3. The model used variable operating costs. In selected cases, an investment component was added to the variable operating costs.

4. Marginal product manufacturing costs and crude values were based on replacement economics with Kuwait crude priced at $1.20/bbl fob, or $1.69 cif in Southern Europe.

5. In a totally free and stable market, prices could approach marginal costs plus nominal return on investment.

6. Typical refinery – 100,000 barrels per stream day (B/SD).

The refinery model was tested under a wide variety of conditions in which product demand pattern, product specifications, and crude slates were varied. Historical data for individual European countries (having widely differing demand patterns), crude slates, and processing facilities were analyzed to verify the model's ability to duplicate actual conditions. The basic information presented in the naphtha supply curve (Fig. 15-2) relates to the 1970 position in OECD Europe. In this case, the effect of continually increasing naphtha demand was studied while all other variables were held constant. In fact, a parametric linear programming procedure was used to evaluate the relative effects for wide variations in naphtha demand, as could materialize if the petrochemical companies were to install sizable capacities of naphtha cracking units.

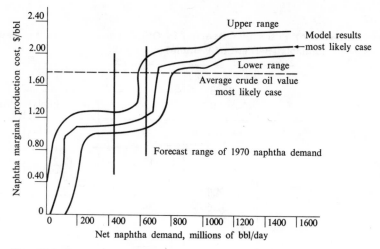

**Fig. 15-2** Marginal naphtha production costs for OECD Europe in 1970.

### Model Inputs—Petroleum Product Demand

To develop the range of 1970 demands for petroleum products (other than nonenergy uses), trends in energy requirements were examined in the different end-use sectors such as electric power generation, motor gasoline, etc. Against the sector energy demands developed in this manner were set forth the various indigenous energy sources available to meet them. Any excess of demand over indigenous supplies thus calculated was attributed to petroleum. The overall energy forecasts were largely based on available EEC forecasts updated to reflect recent trends and extended to non-EEC countries.

The future role of coal is a matter of considerable debate in Europe; therefore, there is a considerable element of uncertainty in projecting oil's share of the energy market. The uncertainty that also surrounds other indigenous energy sources such as

**Table 15-2**

**Estimated Patterns of Total Energy Demand in OECD Europe (Percent of Volume)**

| Energy source | 1963 Actual | 1970 | | |
|---|---|---|---|---|
| | | Minimum | Most likely | Maximum |
| Coal | 53.2 | 38.7 | 34.4 | 29.4 |
| Natural gas | 2.1 | 3.7 | 4.7 | 3.4 |
| Nuclear and hydropower | 9.5 | 10.8 | 10.3 | 9.9 |
| Oil | 35.2 | 46.8 | 50.6 | 57.3 |
| Total | 100.0 | 100.0 | 100.0 | 100.0 |
| Total: million tons coal equivalent | 994 | 1250 | 1310 | 1360 |

Table 15-3

**Estimated Patterns of Petroleum Demand in OECD Europe Excluding Naphtha for Town Gas and Chemicals (Percent of Volume)**

| Petroleum product | 1963 Actual | 1970 | | |
|---|---|---|---|---|
| | | Minimum | Most likely | Maximum |
| Refinery gas | 0.7 | 0.4 | 0.4 | 0.4 |
| LPG | 3.0 | 3.5 | 3.1 | 2.8 |
| Motor gasoline | 17.9 | 17.8 | 17.2 | 16.6 |
| JP-4 | 1.0 | 0.7 | 0.7 | 0.7 |
| Kerosene | 4.3 | 2.8 | 2.8 | 2.7 |
| Gas/diesel | 32.6 | 34.0 | 33.0 | 32.5 |
| Fuel oil | 37.9 | 36.7 | 39.2 | 41.0 |
| Asphalt | 2.6 | 4.1 | 3.6 | 3.3 |
| Total | 100.0 | 100.0 | 100.0 | 100.0 |
| Total: millions of barrels per day | 5600 | 8700 | 10,200 | 11,200 |

hydropower, nuclear power, and natural gas will not be critical prior to 1970 because of the much smaller absolute contribution of these sources. After 1970, however, nuclear power and natural gas will also be subject to uncertainty. However, there is a degree of compensation, since rapid development of natural gas or nuclear power reduces the security-of-energy-supply argument (but not the more fundamental political problem of labor in the mining areas) so that more rapid development of gas and nuclear power would probably be accompanied by a more rapid reduction in coal production. The forecast of a reasonable range of total energy requirements is set forth in Table 15-2.

Differences in the demand patterns for petroleum products are associated with the different energy demand patterns shown in Table 15-2. Black products, principally light and heavy heating oils, are most affected by corporate and government policies governing gas, nuclear power, and coal production. Table 15-3 shows the different petroleum demand patterns associated with the total energy forecasts shown in Table 15-2. Figure 15-3 depicts the most likely supply pattern for primary energy source material to OECD Europe between 1963 and 1975. The interesting aspect of this supply pattern is that virtually all growth in energy demand was expected to be met by petroleum.

### Model Inputs—Product Specifications

Finished petroleum products are subject to a large number of specifications. For example, motor gasoline must generally have a minimum octane rating. At the same time, its vapor pressure cannot be too high because vapor lock would result. A petroleum refiner must deliver materials that meet these specifications.

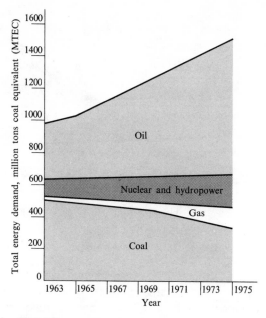

**Fig. 15-3** Primary energy supply pattern for OECD Europe.

### Model Inputs—Crude Slates

The composition of the European crude slate offers the European refiners potential flexibility in adapting to changing product demand patterns. In practice, however, this flexibility is subject to a number of constraints which, particularly in the short terms, limit European crude availabilities.

*Physical Availability.* In the short term, the availability of physical facilities, i.e., development wells, pipelines, etc., can limit crude availability. This has tended to be the case in the newer producing areas such as Libya, Algeria, and Nigeria and is a factor for individual fields in the Middle East. Companies in the more established Middle Eastern fields generally retain a cushion of producibility. In the longer term, availability, particularly of North African oil, is limited by reserves and by discovery rates.

*Corporate Position.* The corporate positions as well as degrees of self-sufficiency of individual crude producing companies differ in each of the major producing regions. Corporate availabilities can be affected by internal lifting agreements in the major concession areas of the Middle East or by long term purchase contracts. A company short on crude can develop a field in which it has sole interest rapidly, while a company long on crude may have somewhat more difficulty if it is to maintain its off-take share in multicompany concessions. Some of the newcomers to the oil producing operations in North Africa (Libya) have little crude diversification and must sell the only crudes they have available regardless of how suitable these are to market needs.

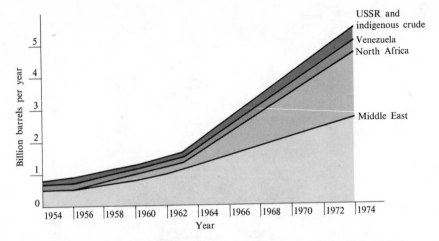

**Fig. 15-4** Crude oil supply to OECD Europe by region of origin—1954 to 1975.

*Political Considerations.* The necessity of preserving good relationships with host countries makes it difficult to effect large changes in the off-lift pattern and severely limits production in one country relative to another. Certain actions taken by consuming countries also dictate crude movements. These actions include bilateral trading arrangements with countries such as the Soviet Union, preferential treatment such as that awarded to Algeria by France, or possible direct investments by governments in exploration activities outside their own countries.

*Non-European Requirements.* Crude requirements outside of Europe also affect European crude availabilities. Market considerations outside Europe particularly affect the Caribbean and the Middle East, both of which have large refinery capacities destined for exports, as well as non-European crude markets.

**Table 15-4**

**Estimated 1970 Crude Slate Variations (Percent of Value)**

| Crude type* | Minimum North African type | Most likely | Maximum North African type |
|---|---|---|---|
| Algerian | 9.7 | 9.2 | 8.5 |
| Libyan | 24.6 | 30.8 | 37.0 |
| Iraqi | 17.4 | 15.7 | 13.9 |
| Iranian light | 16.0 | 14.7 | 13.5 |
| Kuwait | 20.1 | 18.1 | 16.1 |
| Safaniya | 7.0 | 6.4 | 5.9 |
| Venezuela | 5.1 | 5.1 | 5.1 |
| Total | 100.0 | 100.0 | 100.0 |

* Does not represent specific crudes or origins but groupings of crudes of similar qualities.

*Economics.* Those crudes which produce the greatest profit in an individual market will tend to move preferentially to that market. Profitability is a complex function of exploration, development, and production cost, government taxation, transportation differentials, and crude quality. With regard to crude quality, the model indicates that relative crude value is a function of crude slate. As the share of an individual crude increases, its value tends to drop relative to other crudes, since it is no longer possible to take advantage of its desirable qualities. For example, Libyan crude is worth very little more in a high fuel oil market than any other crude, since its more valuable middle distillate content must be partly downgraded to fuel oil.

In considering possible European crude slates, it is believed that North African-type crudes would continue to make rapid inroads in European markets. They will be limited only by availability, by retention of their premium properties, and by the condition that Middle East crude markets in Europe continue to grow in absolute terms. The range of variations in crude slate tested in the model is shown in Table 15-4. It can be seen that by 1970, North African crude types will represent 34 to 45% of the European crude slate. Figure 15-4 shows the estimate of future crude oil supplies to OECD Europe by region of origin. The patterns shown in Table 15-4 are general crude types. For example, Libyan and Nigerian crudes were considered

**Table 15-5**

**Crude Oil Classification**

| Classification | Grade |
|---|---|
| 1. Kuwait | Kuwait |
| 2. Algerian | Algerian |
| | $\frac{1}{2}$ Qatar |
| | $\frac{1}{2}$ Murban |
| 3. Libyan | Libyan |
| | Nigerian |
| 4. Agha Jari | Agha Jari |
| | Saudi Arabian Light |
| | $\frac{1}{2}$ Gach Saran |
| | Umm Shaif |
| 5. Iraq (East Med.) | Basrah |
| | Kirkuk |
| | $\frac{1}{2}$ Qatar |
| | $\frac{1}{2}$ Murban |
| 6. Safaniya | Safaniya |
| | Neutral Zone |
| | Egypt |
| | $\frac{1}{2}$ Gach Saran |
| 7. Venezuelan | Tia Juana |

**Table 15-6**

**Crude Oil Qualities**

| Characteristic | Hassi Messaoud | Libyan | Basrah | Agha Jari | Kuwait | Safaniya | Ju |
|---|---|---|---|---|---|---|---|
| Gravity—°API | 44.0 | 39.2 | 36.5 | 33.9 | 31.2 | 27.0 | 2( |
| Sulfur—Wt% | 0.14 | 0.22 | 1.98 | 1.34 | 2.5 | 2.95 | 1 |
| Distillation—Vol% | | | | | | | |
| $C_4-$ | 3.6 | 2.1 | 2.9 | 2.0 | 2.8 | 2.1 | 1 |
| $C_5-315$ | 31.6 | 23.0 | 22.9 | 20.4 | 18.1 | 15.2 | 1: |
| 315–350 | 5.3 | 4.0 | 5.4 | 4.0 | 3.1 | 2.3 | : |
| 350–650 | 38.5 | 32.4 | 31.9 | 36.3 | 25.9 | 25.3 | 3( |
| 650+ | 21.0 | 38.5 | 37.0 | 37.2 | 50.0 | 55.0 | 5: |
| Sulfur in 650$^+$—Wt% | 0.4 | 0.4 | 4.3 | 2.5 | 4.1 | 4.3 | : |
| Pour point 650$^+$—°F | 60 | 105 | 70 | 75 | 62 | 80 | 6( |
| Naphthinic | No | Yes | No | $\frac{1}{2}$ | No | No | Y |
| Market share— | | | | | | | |
| 1963 actual | 10.9 | 10.2 | 20.8 | 17.7 | 24.3 | 6.7 | • |
| 1970 base case | 9.2 | 30.8 | 15.7 | 14.7 | 18.1 | 6.4 | : |
| 1975 base case | 9.2 | 39.4 | 14.6 | 11.2 | 14.9 | 5.2 | ‹ |

together, Murban was considered to have half Algerian and half Iraqi characteristics, etc. This simplification was necessary to reduce the number of data points and analytical effort. Table 15-5 presents the crude oil classification used while Table 15-6 lists typical crude oil qualities for the crudes used in the study.

## DISCUSSION

The first step of this operations research study was a sizable effort in data collection as can be seen from the foregoing dissertation. The second step, the development of mathematical models of the operation, included statistical forecasting methods of future supplies and demands. Then the mathematical models of the forecast and the linear programming model of the refining operation were used extensively in a simulation mode to test for relative sensitivity of the parameters. The simulation mode was employed to find those items in which a small variance caused major disturbances in other factors; i.e., the simulation mode was used to isolate those parameters which cause sensitivity in the petrochemical naphtha market. When such sensitivities were observed, additional data collections were generally instituted to narrow down the range of uncertainty.

## SPECIFIC RESULTS

One of the more interesting results of the study was the development of an under-standing of the marginal value of petrochemical naphtha to a petroleum refiner. The specific relationship is shown in Fig. 15-2. As noted earlier, petrochemical naphtha is an unusual product since it is generally manufactured as a by-product from energy material manufacturing operations. A petroleum refiner must, of necessity, develop a minimum outlet for so called "white products" which include motor gasoline, aviation spirits, and jet fuel, along with the outlet for petrochemical naphtha.

Because of the nature of crude oil refining operations, unless the refiner finds a minimum white product outlet of 20 to 25% of crude, he will be faced with a surplus of white products. Polymerization of such white products into heavier fuel products is economically unattractive. A refiner with an inadequate outlet for white products may be forced to dump the excess white product material in a competitive market, or he may use this product for his own refinery fuel needs. This condition actually existed in the late 1950's and early 1960's in Western Europe and in the Caribbean area.

While a polymerization of light distillate products into heavier products is essentially unfeasible, the cracking of heavier products into lighter products is a standard operating practice. Thus, while there is a minimum amount of white product outlet requirement for petroleum refinement, there are far fewer constraints placed on high white product outlets since additional volumes can be made available through cracking processes. If a petroleum refiner has an inadequate naphtha outlet, the marginal value of this product can assume fuel oil equivalence, which is approximately 70% of fuel oil prices due to the differences in Btu content between naphtha and fuel oil. On the other hand, if the refiner obtains an adequate amount of the white product outlet, he can make more of his product available by purchasing more crude and changing his distillation tower operations and/or cracking operations in such a manner as to essentially convert one barrel of crude oil into a barrel of white product. A refiner can do so as long as he is operating within his basic refining flexibility. Therefore, the marginal value for white products in this range of operations will correlate with marginal crude costs and marginal refining operating costs. The result of this is shown in Fig. 15-2 where two basic price support levels for naphtha are given: one at fuel oil equivalence and the other at crude costs plus operating costs. The breakpoint is relatively sudden, i.e., the marginal production cost of naphtha shifts within a very narrow range between the two basic support levels.

Another interesting observation regarding the marketing procedure for petroleum products pertains to the relative values for various types of crude oil. In a hypothetical extreme case where there are no limiting specifications on petroleum products, all crude oils will be valued equally; and this evaluation is based strictly on their Btu content. As product specifications become limiting, crude oil values tend to diverge; those crude oils with "good" qualities will tend to assume higher values, while those that have poor qualities will tend to decrease in value. Our simulations noted considerable sensitivity to such product specifications as sulfur levels and pour points in the black products. When the product specifications are not binding, the relative fob values of the various crude oils differ only by Btu content and transportation differentials. As soon as these product specifications become binding, the crude oil values diverge sharply.

Also, there are sizable differences in crude oil values as related to their market penetration. Small volumes of a specific crude oil tend to have high marginal values.

As the volume of this crude increases in a given market, its good qualities tend to exceed the need for such "goodness." This then causes the marginal value of the crude to decrease.

The actual linear programming model consisted of somewhat under 200 equations and about 400 variables. It was completely developed manually, without aid of a matrix generator program or report writing programs. In this case, we should note that the model was not used to develop optimum operating strategy but rather, it assumed that future operations would be very nearly optimal, and it tried to assess future marginal operating costs (shadow prices and marginal values) under these conditions. Again, it is interesting to note the interaction between data collection, model development, model testing, and more data collection. This is a frequently occurring pattern, and part of the benefits of linear programming model development is frequently the result of taking a new look at old situations!

# Natural Gas
# Distribution
# Boston Gas Study*                                          16

A gas distribution company is a public utility that supplies gas to consumers. In former years, much consumer gas was manufactured from coal or oil, but now virtually all of it is in the form of natural gas, produced by gas wells in Texas, Louisiana, California, and elsewhere. Gas distribution companies purchase their gas supplies from the major gas transmission companies, and they then distribute the gas in their local or regional market areas.

Some typical gas distribution companies are Brooklyn Union, Boston Gas, East Ohio Gas, Laclede Gas, and Southern Counties Gas. As can be imagined, the demand for gas fluctuates extensively during the course of the year. The transmission facilities and the gas manufacturing units have a maximum delivery capability that greatly exceeds the demand during the summer months and that often becomes severely taxed in the winter months. In the past, liquified petroleum gas (LPG, propane and butane) could be stored, but until recently, there did not exist an option to store or inventory natural gas in the demand area, due to the enormous pressures and low temperatures required to liquify natural gas. Through new developments in cryogenics and metalurgy, it is now possible to store natural gas in liquid form, but investment costs are high and some additional operation costs are involved.

* This chapter was authored by J. W. Traenkle. It is presented here by permission of the author and the Boston Gas Company.

**Table 16-1**

**Gas Transmission Company Rates**

| Basis | Charge |
|---|---|
| Firm gas | Demand charge = $67.80 per thousand cubic feet (MCF) contracted. The demand charge applies to the largest volume that can be withdrawn on any day under this contract *and* the total annual volume cannot exceed 270 MCF for each MCF of demand. If fully used, this amounts to $0.25 per MCF. Usage charge = $0.32 per MCF. |
| Winter service | Additional volumes can be taken during the winter season subject to various restrictions on maximum versus average offtake. Cost is $0.92 per MCF on a take or pay basis (contract payment guaranteed whether gas is used or not). |
| Interruptible service | Additional quantities of gas that can be taken from the line when adequate gas is available. The allowable offtake times are controlled by the transmission company—offtake can be limited abruptly. This service is only somewhat reliable in the summer. |

The problem facing the Boston Gas Company was that the gas demand was growing steadily and it was starting to exceed the peak delivery capacity of purchased gas from the pipeline plus the special extra gas manufacturing capability of the old oil-gas sets and LPG. In addition, the old sets were becoming very expensive to maintain, and trained operators were becoming scarce. The Boston Gas Company now had the following options available to it:

1. Replace the oil-gas sets in kind.
2. Increase the LPG facilities with the LPG stored either under pressure or refrigerated.
3. Install liquid natural gas (LNG) facilities or import LNG with special cryogenic tankers.
4. Agree to purchase a larger volume of gas from the pipeline on a firm basis, even if this would mean paying more for gas in the summer months.

As can be seen, the main problems are to meet the peak demand and to operate at lowest total cost to the Boston Gas Company. A gas transmission company supplies several distribution companies along its right of way, and all these distribution companies face similar problems in that they prefer to offtake large quantities in the winter and small quantities in the summer. The gas transmission company, however, prefers to sell all the gas it can transmit during the entire year. In order to promote this, the transmission company has various rates as shown in Table 16-1.

Use of LPG for peak shaving requires only small investments, but high operating costs because LPG is often priced at $1.25 per MCF or higher. The caloric value of

LPG is higher than that for natural gas but only limited quantities can be sent into the network because too much LPG upsets the flame properties on burners that are normally adjusted for natural gas. Some flame property adjustment can be made by adding air to the system but this is not fully satisfactory either. Due to the overall complexity of the problem, the Boston Gas Company authorized a preliminary study of the peak shaving problem. This study was to:

1. Identify and define the alternative methods of peak shaving.
2. Define the factors which might affect the choice of a peak shaving method.
3. Assemble estimates of the various factors, noting the confidence levels with which each was forecast.
4. Develop, as a function of annual sendout, present value cash costs of each alternative, using normal and design year temperature assumptions.
5. Investigate the sensitivity of cost to changes in values of significant factors.
6. Prepare the analysis in such a form that it could be updated rapidly and at minimum cost as better or new data becomes available.


## STUDY REPORT

The first step of the analysis was to compile a list of twelve possible alternative methods of providing gas to customers. Some were eliminated right away as uneconomical (meeting all demand from pipeline gas, building additional oil gas facilities) or impractical (cavern storage of LPG, tanker delivery of LNG). All of the remaining alternatives were combinations of present facilities, pressure-stored or refrigerated LPG, or on-line LNG.

We next proceeded to gather the cost data necessary to make the economic study. This process, which involved more drudgery than ingenuity, will not be described here; suffice it to say that at the completion of this phase we had a mass of undigested data, of widely varying quality, with which to experiment. For instance, we knew how cold it would be each day in a normal, mild, or severe winter. We had a sales forecast for a normal winter, pipeline tariffs, equipment cost estimates and ratings, manning schedules, estimated fixed costs, limits on daily LPG use and interruptible sales, delays in receiving LPG after an order is placed, and, finally, an acceptable capital recovery factor.

We knew that once we had the cash flows which would result from each alternative, it would be relatively easy to pick a discount rate and find the most economical, if not the best, way to proceed. Our problem was to get the desired information from the data. We could see at the outset that the most difficult part of the analysis would be to determine the optimum mix of gases to purchase or manufacture. Boston Gas could buy under the terms of any combination of three pipeline rate schedules, could utilize any amount of oil gas or LPG up to the existing plant capacity limitation, or could use the output from LPG or LNG facilities yet to be purchased.

Our original plan was to develop a computer program which would essentially automate the manual optimization process then in use. These calculations were undoubtedly the critical part of the analysis; accuracy was essential, but the manual method was tedious in the extreme and one could never be certain that the best solution had been found.

The manual process, which could take up to four weeks to complete, proceeded through the following steps:

1. Expansion of a forecast of firm sales to sendout, considering company use and gas unaccounted for.

2. Development of load-duration data using sendout and temperature information.

3. Optimization of purchases. The analyst would choose any sensible combination of gas types and price out the annual cost. He would then vary one quantity (for example, maximum day LPG), take up the demand with, say, winter-service maximum daily quantity (MDQ), and price that combination. If the original choice of mix was judicious, he would after four or five tries have a minimum cost combination, which would then be plotted as a point on a graph of cost versus firm gas MDQ. The process would then begin all over with a different firm MDQ and continue until the curve traced by the points passed a minimum; the "optimum" could then be obtained by interpolation.

It is easy to see that the process was fraught with possibilities for error; moreover, it was slow when mixtures of three gases were considered, and nearly impossible to use for mixtures of four or five. As we observed and became familiar with the optimization method, we noted that the analyst was proceeding much as a computer does in solving an optimization problem using techniques of linear programming. This rather simple observation was the key; whether or not we could benefit by it depended on our ability to describe the economic process of optimization in formal, mathematical relationships.

Linear programming has been used extensively by the oil and chemical industries for economic process scheduling, but to our knowledge had never been successfully applied to our particular problem.

After considerable system analysis, we were able to design and formulate expressions to find the lowest cost mix of gases for Boston Gas. The final system contains four computer programs which gather data, set up the linear programming matrix, solve the linear programming problem, and interpret the output in a form readily readable by management. Without going into tedious detail, we shall outline the structure and use of each of the four programs: PEAK, PLOT, LP/11, and POST.

*PEAK.* The purpose of PEAK is to provide the linear program with information describing the total demand for all types of gas on each day. The program reads in forecast heating and nonheating firm sales for each year in the study period. These data can be presented as a series of annual estimates or as a base-year amount and an annual growth rate for each segment.

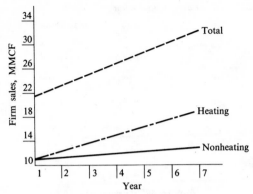

**Fig. 16-1** Seven-year forecast of firm sales.

Table 16-1

**Conversion of Actual To Block Days***

| Actual days | Block days | Number of blocks | Actual days per block day |
|---|---|---|---|
| 1 | 1 | 1 | 1 |
| 2 to 10 | 2 to 4 | 3 | 3 |
| 11 to 60 | 5 to 14 | 10 | 5 |
| 61 to 150 | 15 to 23 | 9 | 10 |
| 151 to 270 | 24 to 29 | 6 | 20 |
| 271 to 365 | 30 | 1 | 95 |

* Days arranged from coldest to warmest.

Known amounts of company-use gas and unaccounted-for gas are factored in, and the resulting forecast of sendout (Fig. 16-1) is combined with daily temperature data to develop a load-duration table. (Our temperature data tape contains daily average temperatures for normal, mild, and severe winters.) Unfortunately, our computer (IBM 1410) and linear program could not handle the problem if we attempted to consider each of the 365 days of the year for optimization, so we programmed PEAK to group the sendout into 30 "block" days. The results are 30 artificial "days" whose sendouts represent the average sendout of from 1 to 95 actual days. (The first or coldest day of the year is represented by 1 block day, the next 9 days by 3 block days, and so on, as shown in Table 16-1.) Sample pages of PEAK are shown in Figs. 16-2 and 16-3.

The resulting demands for "block" days are punched into cards for use later in LP/11 and are totaled to make sure the program did, in fact, account for all the sendout.

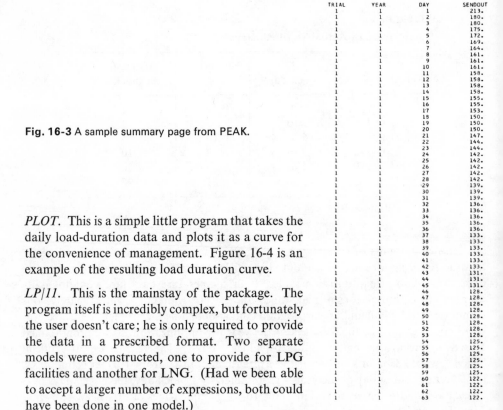

PEAK SHAVING CALCULATION - FIRM SENDOUT

COMPANY USE # 75. MMCF                    UNACCOUNTED FOR GAS PERCENT    .0375

| YEAR | NON-HEATING | ANNUAL SENDOUT HEATING | TOTAL | NON-HEATING | ANNUAL FORECAST HEATING | TOTAL |
|------|-------------|---------|-------|-------------|---------|-------|
| 1 | 12948. | 15360. | 28308. | 12388. | 14784. | 27172. |
| 2 | 13579. | 17311. | 30890. | 12995. | 16662. | 29657. |
| 3 | 14180. | 19204. | 33384. | 13574. | 18484. | 32058. |
| 4 | 14701. | 21033. | 35735. | 14075. | 20245. | 34320. |
| 5 | 15243. | 23053. | 38297. | 14597. | 22189. | 36786. |

**Fig. 16-2** First page of PEAK.

**Fig. 16-3** A sample summary page from PEAK.

| TRIAL | YEAR | DAY | SENDOUT |
|-------|------|-----|---------|
| 1 | 1 | 1 | 213. |
| 1 | 1 | 2 | 180. |
| 1 | 1 | 3 | 180. |
| 1 | 1 | 4 | 175. |
| 1 | 1 | 5 | 172. |
| 1 | 1 | 6 | 169. |
| 1 | 1 | 7 | 164. |
| 1 | 1 | 8 | 161. |
| 1 | 1 | 9 | 161. |
| 1 | 1 | 10 | 161. |
| 1 | 1 | 11 | 158. |
| 1 | 1 | 12 | 158. |
| 1 | 1 | 13 | 158. |
| 1 | 1 | 14 | 158. |
| 1 | 1 | 15 | 155. |
| 1 | 1 | 16 | 155. |
| 1 | 1 | 17 | 153. |
| 1 | 1 | 18 | 150. |
| 1 | 1 | 19 | 150. |
| 1 | 1 | 20 | 150. |
| 1 | 1 | 21 | 147. |
| 1 | 1 | 22 | 144. |
| 1 | 1 | 23 | 144. |
| 1 | 1 | 24 | 142. |
| 1 | 1 | 25 | 142. |
| 1 | 1 | 26 | 142. |
| 1 | 1 | 27 | 142. |
| 1 | 1 | 28 | 142. |
| 1 | 1 | 29 | 139. |
| 1 | 1 | 30 | 139. |
| 1 | 1 | 31 | 139. |
| 1 | 1 | 32 | 136. |
| 1 | 1 | 33 | 136. |
| 1 | 1 | 34 | 136. |
| 1 | 1 | 35 | 136. |
| 1 | 1 | 36 | 136. |
| 1 | 1 | 37 | 133. |
| 1 | 1 | 38 | 133. |
| 1 | 1 | 39 | 133. |
| 1 | 1 | 40 | 133. |
| 1 | 1 | 41 | 133. |
| 1 | 1 | 42 | 133. |
| 1 | 1 | 43 | 131. |
| 1 | 1 | 44 | 131. |
| 1 | 1 | 45 | 131. |
| 1 | 1 | 46 | 128. |
| 1 | 1 | 47 | 128. |
| 1 | 1 | 48 | 128. |
| 1 | 1 | 49 | 128. |
| 1 | 1 | 50 | 128. |
| 1 | 1 | 51 | 128. |
| 1 | 1 | 52 | 128. |
| 1 | 1 | 53 | 128. |
| 1 | 1 | 54 | 125. |
| 1 | 1 | 55 | 125. |
| 1 | 1 | 56 | 125. |
| 1 | 1 | 57 | 125. |
| 1 | 1 | 58 | 125. |
| 1 | 1 | 59 | 125. |
| 1 | 1 | 60 | 122. |
| 1 | 1 | 61 | 122. |
| 1 | 1 | 62 | 122. |
| 1 | 1 | 63 | 122. |

*PLOT.* This is a simple little program that takes the daily load-duration data and plots it as a curve for the convenience of management. Figure 16-4 is an example of the resulting load duration curve.

*LP/11.* This is the mainstay of the package. The program itself is incredibly complex, but fortunately the user doesn't care; he is only required to provide the data in a prescribed format. Two separate models were constructed, one to provide for LPG facilities and another for LNG. (Had we been able to accept a larger number of expressions, both could have been done in one model.)

The actual mathematical expressions used for Boston Gas Company's particular problem are both too complex and specialized to reproduce in detail here; the LPG model had 151 equations of 19 types, and the LNG model used 184 equations of 25 types to express the various constraints.

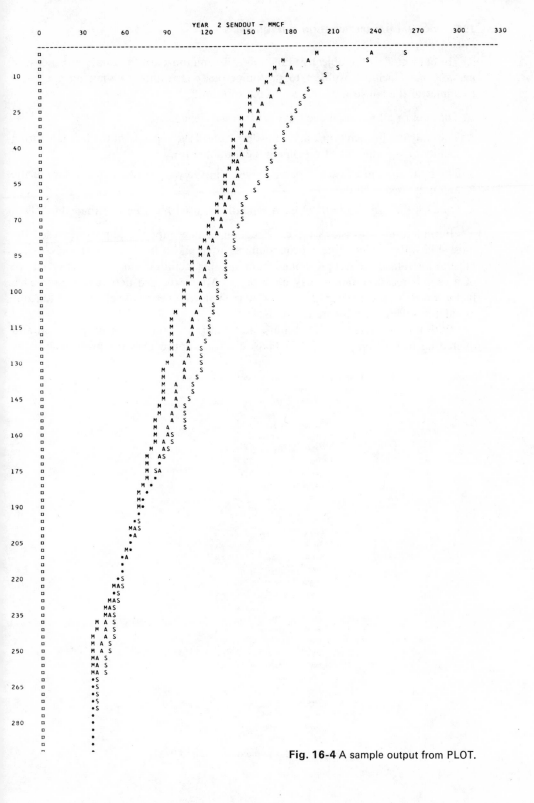

**Fig. 16-4** A sample output from PLOT.

In both models the objective function to be minimized is the total annual cost of gas and new facilities, subject to the numerous constraints. Following are a few examples of the constraints placed on the solution:

1. The sum of all gas used each day must equal demand.

2. The daily use of each type of gas must not exceed the capacity of the manufacturing facility or the amount of pipeline gas contracted for.

3. The total amount of each type of gas used in the year must equal the sum of the amounts used each day.

4. On each day, the amount of each type of gas used must be less than the MDQ.

Formulating expressions for construction of new capital equipment caused the most difficulties. Since linear programming attempts to minimize variable costs, it must be restrained but not prohibited from building facilities, which means that choice of a capital recovery factor may be critical. After extended debate, we adopted a factor which would return 12% on all new facilities over a 30-year period (all our calculations were on a before-tax basis).

With all the variables, constraints, and constants punched in proper form and offered up to the computer, LP/11 takes over and approaches the problem just the

```
1                        BOSTON GAS FOR LNG,LPG ANALYSIS DEC 1 1965
SOLUTION PRINT - FUNCTION ROW    COST -18984.952  RHS    5

        VARIABLE      LEVEL        C/J

         1FRMS       108.436       0.0

         10GS          0.0         0.0

         1VLG          0.0         0.0

         1WS          33.555       0.0

         2FRMS       108.436       0.0

         20GS          0.0         0.0

         2VLG          0.0         0.0

         3FRMS       108.436       0.0

         30GS          0.0         0.0

         3VLG          0.0         0.0

         3WS          33.555       0.0

         4FRMS       108.436       0.0

         40GS          0.0         0.0

         4VLG          0.0         0.0

         4WS          33.555       0.0

         5FRMS       108.436       0.0

         50GS          0.0         0.0

         5VLG          0.0         0.0

         5WS          33.555       0.0

         6FRMS       108.436       0.0

         60GS          0.0         0.0

         6VLG          0.0         0.0

         6WS          33.555       0.0

         7FRMS       108.436       0.0

         70GS          0.0         0.0

         7VLG          0.0         0.0

         7WS          33.555       0.0

         8FRMS       108.436       0.0

         80GS          0.0         0.0
```

**Fig. 16-5** A sample output from LP/11.

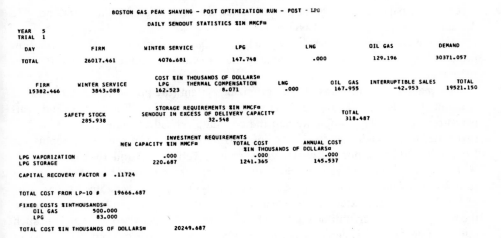

BOSTON GAS PEAK SHAVING - POST OPTIMIZATION RUN - POST - LPG

DAILY SENDOUT STATISTICS ☼IN MMCF☼

YEAR 5
TRIAL 1

| DAY | FIRM | WINTER SERVICE | LPG | LNG | OIL GAS | DEMAND |
|---|---|---|---|---|---|---|
| 1 | 104.314 | 67.951 | 40.848 | .000 | 30.000 | 243.113 |
| 2 | 104.314 | 67.951 | 8.300 | .000 | 23.903 | 204.468 |
| 3 | 104.314 | 67.951 | 8.300 | .000 | 23.903 | 204.468 |
| 4 | 104.314 | 67.951 | 8.300 | .000 | 17.462 | 198.027 |
| 5 | 104.314 | 67.951 | 8.300 | .000 | 14.242 | 194.807 |
| 6 | 104.314 | 67.951 | 8.300 | .000 | 11.021 | 191.586 |
| 7 | 104.314 | 67.951 | 8.300 | .000 | 4.580 | 185.145 |
| 8 | 104.314 | 67.951 | 8.300 | .000 | 1.360 | 181.925 |
| 9 | 104.314 | 67.951 | 8.300 | .000 | 1.360 | 181.925 |
| 10 | 104.314 | 67.951 | 8.300 | .000 | 1.360 | 181.925 |
| 11 | 104.314 | 67.951 | 6.440 | .000 | .000 | 178.705 |
| 12 | 104.314 | 67.951 | 6.440 | .000 | .000 | 178.705 |
| 13 | 104.314 | 67.951 | 6.440 | .000 | .000 | 178.705 |
| 14 | 104.314 | 67.951 | 6.440 | .000 | .000 | 178.705 |
| 15 | 104.314 | 67.951 | 3.219 | .000 | .000 | 175.484 |
| 16 | 104.314 | 67.951 | 3.219 | .000 | .000 | 175.484 |
| 17 | 104.314 | 67.950 | .000 | .000 | .000 | 172.264 |
| 18 | 104.314 | 64.729 | .000 | .000 | .000 | 169.043 |
| 19 | 104.314 | 64.729 | .000 | .000 | .000 | 169.043 |
| 20 | 104.314 | 64.729 | .000 | .000 | .000 | 169.043 |
| 21 | 104.314 | 61.509 | .000 | .000 | .000 | 165.823 |
| 22 | 104.314 | 58.289 | .000 | .000 | .000 | 162.603 |
| 23 | 104.314 | 58.289 | .000 | .000 | .000 | 162.603 |
| 24 | 104.314 | 55.068 | .000 | .000 | .000 | 159.382 |
| 25 | 104.314 | 55.068 | .000 | .000 | .000 | 159.382 |
| 26 | 104.314 | 55.068 | .000 | .000 | .000 | 159.382 |
| 27 | 104.314 | 55.068 | .000 | .000 | .000 | 159.382 |
| 28 | 104.314 | 55.068 | .000 | .000 | .000 | 159.382 |
| 29 | 104.314 | 51.848 | .000 | .000 | .000 | 156.162 |
| 30 | 104.314 | 51.848 | .000 | .000 | .000 | 156.162 |
| 31 | 104.314 | 51.848 | .000 | .000 | .000 | 156.162 |
| 32 | 104.314 | 48.627 | .000 | .000 | .000 | 152.941 |
| 33 | 104.314 | 48.627 | .000 | .000 | .000 | 152.941 |
| 34 | 104.314 | 48.627 | .000 | .000 | .000 | 152.941 |
| 35 | 104.314 | 48.627 | .000 | .000 | .000 | 152.941 |
| 36 | 104.314 | 48.627 | .000 | .000 | .000 | 152.941 |
| 37 | 104.314 | 45.407 | .000 | .000 | .000 | 149.721 |
| 38 | 104.314 | 45.407 | .000 | .000 | .000 | 149.721 |
| 39 | 104.314 | 45.407 | .000 | .000 | .000 | 149.721 |
| 40 | 104.314 | 45.407 | .000 | .000 | .000 | 149.721 |
| 41 | 104.314 | 45.407 | .000 | .000 | .000 | 149.721 |
| 42 | 104.314 | 45.407 | .000 | .000 | .000 | 149.721 |
| 43 | 104.314 | 42.187 | .000 | .000 | .000 | 146.501 |
| 44 | 104.314 | 42.187 | .000 | .000 | .000 | 146.501 |
| 45 | 104.314 | 42.187 | .000 | .000 | .000 | 146.501 |
| 46 | 104.314 | 38.966 | .000 | .000 | .000 | 143.280 |
| 47 | 104.314 | 38.966 | .000 | .000 | .000 | 143.280 |
| 48 | 104.314 | 38.966 | .000 | .000 | .000 | 143.280 |
| 49 | 104.314 | 38.966 | .000 | .000 | .000 | 143.280 |
| 50 | 104.314 | 38.966 | .000 | .000 | .000 | 143.280 |
| 51 | 104.314 | 38.966 | .000 | .000 | .000 | 143.280 |
| 52 | 104.314 | 38.966 | .000 | .000 | .000 | 143.280 |
| 53 | 104.314 | 38.966 | .000 | .000 | .000 | 143.280 |
| 54 | 104.314 | 35.746 | .000 | .000 | .000 | 140.060 |
| 55 | 104.314 | 35.746 | .000 | .000 | .000 | 140.060 |
| 56 | 104.314 | 35.746 | .000 | .000 | .000 | 140.060 |

**Fig. 16-6** A sample first page from POST for LPG analysis.

BOSTON GAS PEAK SHAVING - POST OPTIMIZATION RUN - POST - LPG

DAILY SENDOUT STATISTICS ☼IN MMCF☼

YEAR 5
TRIAL 1

| DAY | FIRM | WINTER SERVICE | LPG | LNG | OIL GAS | DEMAND |
|---|---|---|---|---|---|---|
| TOTAL | 26017.461 | 4076.681 | 147.748 | .000 | 129.196 | 30371.057 |

| FIRM | WINTER SERVICE | COST ☼IN THOUSANDS OF DOLLARS☼ LPG | THERMAL COMPENSATION | LNG | OIL GAS | INTERRUPTIBLE SALES | TOTAL |
|---|---|---|---|---|---|---|---|
| 15382.466 | 3843.088 | 162.523 | 8.071 | .000 | 167.955 | -42.953 | 19521.150 |

| SAFETY STOCK | STORAGE REQUIREMENTS ☼IN MMCF☼ SENDOUT IN EXCESS OF DELIVERY CAPACITY | TOTAL |
|---|---|---|
| 285.938 | 32.548 | 318.487 |

INVESTMENT REQUIREMENTS

| | NEW CAPACITY ☼IN MMCF☼ | TOTAL COST ☼IN THOUSANDS OF DOLLARS☼ | ANNUAL COST ☼IN THOUSANDS OF DOLLARS☼ |
|---|---|---|---|
| LPG VAPORIZATION | .000 | .000 | .000 |
| LPG STORAGE | 220.687 | 1241.365 | 145.537 |

CAPITAL RECOVERY FACTOR # .11724

TOTAL COST FROM LP-10 # 19666.687

FIXED COSTS ☼INTHOUSANDS☼
OIL GAS    500.000
LPG         83.000

TOTAL COST ☼IN THOUSANDS OF DOLLARS☼    20249.687

**Fig. 16-7** A sample last page from POST for LPG analysis.

way we did in the sample by first finding out whether there is a feasible solution. If there is no solution that will satisfy all constraints, it types out the message NO FEASIBLE SOLUTION; if there are errors in the model formulation it may inform you UNBOUNDED SOLUTION.  Assuming all goes well, the message SOLUTION FEASIBLE appears, and the computer proceeds to find the optimum solution by some recondite means.  At some point, ranging from 30 minutes to $2\frac{1}{2}$ hours after the start button is pushed, the console typewriter proudly announces PRIMAL SOLUTION, and the values of all the variables and the objective function are disgorged by the printer.  If $2\frac{1}{2}$ hours seems a long time, consider that the machine has in that time solved, say 180 simultaneous equations, each containing 200 variables about 200 times (about 100 to determine that a solution is feasible and another 100 to find the optimum).  These times may be reduced substantially (a factor of 10 to 50) by using a more powerful but more expensive machine.  Whatever machine is used, it still beats the 4 to 6 weeks required for manual calculation—and we have yet to catch it making a mistake or using an assumption which was not clearly spelled out.

Also, if you do more than one variation of a problem—for example, running the same problem for a series of years—solutions after the first are completed in a matter of 1 or 2 minutes, since the machine starts running around the solution space testing new solutions, beginning at the point of the last solution rather than from the origin, where it usually starts a new problem.

The output report from LP/11 gives the values of each variable, and if the analysis were done only for the edification of researchers, we could stop there. Unfortunately, the report is too disorganized to put before management, so we transfer some of the data to punched cards as input for the remaining routine.  Figure 16-5 shows a typical page of output.

*POST.*  This routine takes the information from LP/11 and prints it out in a format which is readable and familiar to management.  Figures 16-6 and 16-7 show sample first and last pages of reports for an LPG analysis, while Figs. 16-8 and 16-9 provide the same information for an LNG run.

Having explained what we did, we shall now discuss how we used the information presented in our analysis and how Boston Gas uses the system today for operational planning.

We made numerous runs of the optimizing system (the pile of computer printout is about three feet thick) trying different combinations of facilities, costs, and temperatures.  Eventually we felt we had the cost data refined to the extent practical at that time, so we made our final series of runs.  A summary of the POST report for LPG and LNG in a normal winter are shown in Tables 16-2 and 16-3, respectively. Note that LNG purchases must be optimized for a severe winter so that adequate supplies are available should one occur.  The analysis slightly overstates the gas costs of LNG, since to the extent a severe winter does not occur, gas can be carried over to the next year and interruptible sales can be increased.  The increased margin from such interruptible sales is insignificant, though, since interruptible customers are few in Boston and they will pay very little more than the cost of gas.

BOSTON GAS PEAK SHAVING - POST OPTIMIZATION RUN -   LNG

DAILY SENDOUT STATISTICS (IN MMCF)

YEAR 5
TRIAL 1

| DAY | FIRM | WINTER SERVICE | LPG | LNG | OIL GAS | DEMAND |
|---|---|---|---|---|---|---|
| 1 | 120.732 | 41.870 | .000 | 80.511 | .000 | 243.113 |
| 2 | 120.732 | 41.870 | .000 | 41.866 | .000 | 204.468 |
| 3 | 120.732 | 41.870 | .000 | 41.866 | .000 | 204.468 |
| 4 | 120.732 | 41.870 | .000 | 35.425 | .000 | 198.027 |
| 5 | 120.732 | 41.870 | .000 | 32.205 | .000 | 194.807 |
| 6 | 120.732 | 41.870 | .000 | 28.984 | .000 | 191.586 |
| 7 | 120.732 | 41.870 | .000 | 22.543 | .000 | 185.145 |
| 8 | 120.732 | 41.870 | .000 | 19.323 | .000 | 181.925 |
| 9 | 120.732 | 41.870 | .000 | 19.323 | .000 | 181.925 |
| 10 | 120.732 | 41.870 | .000 | 16.103 | .000 | 178.705 |
| 11 | 120.732 | 41.870 | .000 | 16.103 | .000 | 178.705 |
| 12 | 120.732 | 41.870 | .000 | 16.103 | .000 | 178.705 |
| 13 | 120.732 | 41.870 | .000 | 16.103 | .000 | 178.705 |
| 14 | 120.732 | 41.870 | .000 | 12.882 | .000 | 175.484 |
| 15 | 120.732 | 41.870 | .000 | 12.882 | .000 | 175.484 |
| 16 | 120.732 | 41.870 | .000 | 9.662 | .000 | 172.264 |
| 17 | 120.732 | 41.870 | .000 | 6.441 | .000 | 169.043 |
| 18 | 120.732 | 41.870 | .000 | 6.441 | .000 | 169.043 |
| 19 | 120.732 | 41.870 | .000 | 6.441 | .000 | 169.043 |
| 20 | 120.732 | 41.870 | .000 | 3.221 | .000 | 165.823 |
| 21 | 120.732 | 41.870 | .000 | .001 | .000 | 162.603 |
| 22 | 120.732 | 41.870 | .000 | .000 | .000 | 162.603 |
| 23 | 120.732 | 41.870 | .000 | .000 | .000 | 159.382 |
| 24 | 120.732 | 38.650 | .000 | .000 | .000 | 159.382 |
| 25 | 120.732 | 38.650 | .000 | .000 | .000 | 159.382 |
| 26 | 120.732 | 38.650 | .000 | .000 | .000 | 159.382 |
| 27 | 120.732 | 38.650 | .000 | .000 | .000 | 159.382 |
| 28 | 120.732 | 35.430 | .000 | .000 | .000 | 156.162 |
| 29 | 120.732 | 35.430 | .000 | .000 | .000 | 156.162 |
| 30 | 120.732 | 35.430 | .000 | .000 | .000 | 156.162 |
| 31 | 120.732 | 32.209 | .000 | .000 | .000 | 152.941 |
| 32 | 120.732 | 32.209 | .000 | .000 | .000 | 152.941 |
| 33 | 120.732 | 32.209 | .000 | .000 | .000 | 152.941 |
| 34 | 120.732 | 32.209 | .000 | .000 | .000 | 152.941 |
| 35 | 120.732 | 32.209 | .000 | .000 | .000 | 152.941 |
| 36 | 120.732 | 28.989 | .000 | .000 | .000 | 149.721 |
| 37 | 120.732 | 28.989 | .000 | .000 | .000 | 149.721 |
| 38 | 120.732 | 28.989 | .000 | .000 | .000 | 149.721 |
| 39 | 120.732 | 28.989 | .000 | .000 | .000 | 149.721 |
| 40 | 120.732 | 28.989 | .000 | .000 | .000 | 149.721 |
| 41 | 120.732 | 28.989 | .000 | .000 | .000 | 149.721 |
| 42 | 120.732 | 28.989 | .000 | .000 | .000 | 146.501 |
| 43 | 120.732 | 25.769 | .000 | .000 | .000 | 146.501 |
| 44 | 120.732 | 25.769 | .000 | .000 | .000 | 146.501 |
| 45 | 120.732 | 25.769 | .000 | .000 | .000 | 143.280 |
| 46 | 120.732 | 22.548 | .000 | .000 | .000 | 143.280 |
| 47 | 120.732 | 22.548 | .000 | .000 | .000 | 143.280 |
| 48 | 120.732 | 22.548 | .000 | .000 | .000 | 143.280 |
| 49 | 120.732 | 22.548 | .000 | .000 | .000 | 143.280 |
| 50 | 120.732 | 22.548 | .000 | .000 | .000 | 143.280 |
| 51 | 120.732 | 22.548 | .000 | .000 | .000 | 143.280 |
| 52 | 120.732 | 22.548 | .000 | .000 | .000 | 143.280 |
| 53 | 120.732 | 19.328 | .000 | .000 | .000 | 140.060 |
| 54 | 120.732 | 19.328 | .000 | .000 | .000 | 140.060 |
| 55 | 120.732 | 19.328 | .000 | .000 | .000 | 140.060 |
| 56 | 120.732 | 19.328 | .000 | .000 | .000 | 140.060 |

**Fig. 16-8** A sample first page from POST for LNG analysis.

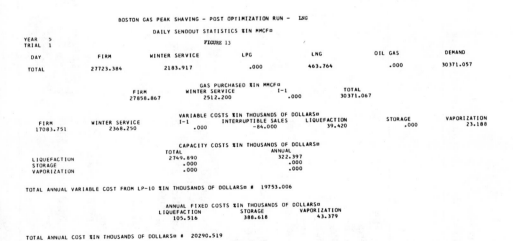

BOSTON GAS PEAK SHAVING - POST OPTIMIZATION RUN -   LNG

DAILY SENDOUT STATISTICS (IN MMCF)

FIGURE 13

YEAR 5
TRIAL 1

| DAY | FIRM | WINTER SERVICE | LPG | LNG | OIL GAS | DEMAND |
|---|---|---|---|---|---|---|
| TOTAL | 27723.384 | 2183.917 | .000 | 463.764 | .000 | 30371.057 |

GAS PURCHASED (IN MMCF)

| FIRM | WINTER SERVICE | I-1 | TOTAL |
|---|---|---|---|
| 27858.867 | 2512.200 | .000 | 30371.067 |

VARIABLE COSTS (IN THOUSANDS OF DOLLARS)

| FIRM | WINTER SERVICE | I-1 | INTERRUPTIBLE SALES | LIQUEFACTION | STORAGE | VAPORIZATION |
|---|---|---|---|---|---|---|
| 17083.751 | 2368.250 | .000 | -84.000 | 39.420 | .000 | 23.188 |

CAPACITY COSTS (IN THOUSANDS OF DOLLARS)

| | TOTAL | ANNUAL |
|---|---|---|
| LIQUEFACTION | 2749.890 | 322.397 |
| STORAGE | .000 | .000 |
| VAPORIZATION | .000 | .000 |

TOTAL ANNUAL VARIABLE COST FROM LP-10 (IN THOUSANDS OF DOLLARS) #  19753.006

ANNUAL FIXED COSTS (IN THOUSANDS OF DOLLARS)

| LIQUEFACTION | STORAGE | VAPORIZATION |
|---|---|---|
| 105.516 | 388.618 | 43.379 |

TOTAL ANNUAL COST (IN THOUSANDS OF DOLLARS) #  20290.519

**Fig. 16-9** A sample last page from POST for LNG analysis.

**Table 16-2**
**LPG with Oil Gas Normal Winter Results**

| | Year | | | | | | |
|---|---|---|---|---|---|---|---|
| | 1 | 2 | 3 | 4 | 5 | 6 | 7 |
| **Maximum day sendout, MMCF** | | | | | | | |
| Firm | 75.4 | 82.9 | 90.0 | 96.8 | 104.3 | 111.9 | 119.8 |
| Winter service | 45.0 | 51.0 | 56.6 | 61.9 | 68.0 | 74.0 | 80.3 |
| LPG | 16.9 | 23.2 | 29.0 | 34.6 | 40.8 | 47.1 | 53.7 |
| Oil gas | 30.0 | 30.0 | 30.0 | 30.0 | 30.0 | 30.0 | 30.0 |
| Total | 167.4 | 187.1 | 205.5 | 223.3 | 243.1 | 263.0 | 283.8 |
| **Annual sendout, MMCF** | | | | | | | |
| Firm | 19,496.2 | 21,179.8 | 22,799.8 | 24,325.9 | 26,017.5 | 27,708.9 | 29,486.8 |
| Winter service | 2701.7 | 3061.3 | 3392.8 | 3714.9 | 4076.7 | 4438.6 | 4816.7 |
| LPG | 103.2 | 118.9 | 129.7 | 138.6 | 147.7 | 156.9 | 166.5 |
| Oil gas | 80.3 | 89.0 | 100.8 | 113.8 | 129.2 | 144.6 | 160.8 |
| Total | 22,381.5 | 24,449.0 | 26,423.1 | 28,293.1 | 30,371.1 | 32,449.0 | 34,630.7 |
| **Capacity required** | | | | | | | |
| Storage, MMCF | 300.5 | 389.3 | 474.9 | 564.4 | 690.5 | 834.7 | 1015.2 |
| Vaporization, MMCF/day | 34.0 | 42.5 | 50.4 | 58.0 | 66.6 | 75.2 | 84.2 |
| **Gas cost, $000** | | | | | | | |
| Firm | 11,339.4 | 12,385.6 | 13,384.5 | 14,330.9 | 15,382.5 | 16,433.9 | 17,538.0 |
| Winter service | 2546.9 | 2885.9 | 3198.3 | 3502.0 | 3843.1 | 4184.3 | 4540.7 |
| LPG* | 116.1 | 134.8 | 148.0 | 159.1 | 170.6 | 182.1 | 194.2 |
| Oil gas | 104.4 | 115.7 | 131.0 | 147.9 | 168.0 | 188.0 | 209.0 |
| Interruptible margin | (17.3) | (24.1) | (30.0) | (36.1) | (43.0) | (49.8) | (57.0) |
| Total | 14,089.5 | 15,497.9 | 16,831.9 | 18,103.8 | 19,521.2 | 20,938.5 | 22,424.9 |
| **Annual fixed costs, in $000** | | | | | | | |
| Oil gas | 500.0 | 500.0 | 500.0 | 500.0 | 500.0 | 500.0 | 500.0 |
| LPG | 83.0 | 83.0 | 83.0 | 83.0 | 83.0 | 83.0 | 83.0 |

* Includes thermal compensation.

Table 16-3

LNG Optimized on Severe Winter–Normal Winter Results

| | | | | Year | | | |
|---|---|---|---|---|---|---|---|
| | 1 | 2 | 3 | 4 | 5 | 6 | 7 |
| Maximum day sendout, MMCF | | | | | | | |
| Firm | 86.3 | 95.2 | 103.7 | 111.7 | 120.7 | 129.7 | 138.8 |
| Winter service | 27.7 | 31.4 | 34.8 | 38.2 | 41.9 | 45.6 | 49.8 |
| LNG | 53.4 | 60.5 | 67.0 | 73.4 | 80.5 | 87.7 | 95.1 |
| Total | 167.4 | 187.1 | 205.5 | 223.3 | 243.1 | 263.0 | 283.8 |
| Annual sendout, MMCF | | | | | | | |
| Firm | 20,626.9 | 22,460.8 | 24,219.6 | 25,880.5 | 27,723.4 | 29,565.3 | 31,469.6 |
| Winter service | 1447.3 | 1639.8 | 1817.5 | 1990.1 | 2183.9 | 2378.8 | 2613.3 |
| LNG | 307.3 | 348.3 | 386.0 | 422.6 | 463.8 | 504.9 | 547.9 |
| Total | 22,381.5 | 24,448.9 | 26,423.1 | 28,293.1 | 30,371.1 | 32,449.0 | 34,630.7 |
| Gas purchases, MMCF | | | | | | | |
| Firm | 20,716.7 | 22,562.5 | 24,332.4 | 26,003.9 | 27,858.8 | 29,713.1 | 31,640.1 |
| Winter service | 1664.9 | 1886.4 | 2090.7 | 2289.2 | 2512.2 | 2735.9 | 2990.7 |
| Interruptible (I-1) | — | — | — | — | — | — | — |
| Total | 22,381.5 | 24,448.9 | 26,423.1 | 28,293.1 | 30,371.1 | 32,449.0 | 34,630.8 |

**Table 16-3 (Cont.)**

| | | | | Year | | | |
|---|---|---|---|---|---|---|---|
| | 1 | 2 | 3 | 4 | 5 | 6 | 7 |
| Capacity required | | | | | | | |
|   Storage, MMCF | 1493.8 | 1692.7 | 1875.9 | 2054.1 | 2254.1 | 2454.9 | 2684.9 |
|   Vaporization, MMCF/day | 70.4 | 79.8 | 88.4 | 96.8 | 106.3 | 115.7 | 125.6 |
|   Liquefaction, MMCF/day | 6.8 | 7.5 | 8.2 | 8.9 | 9.8 | 10.8 | 11.8 |
| Gas cost, $000 | | | | | | | |
|   Firm | 12,467.0 | 13,663.2 | 14,800.4 | 15,881.2 | 17,083.8 | 18,285.2 | 19,515.7 |
|   Winter service | 1569.5 | 1778.3 | 1970.9 | 2158.1 | 2368.3 | 2579.2 | 2819.3 |
|   Interruptible (I-1) | — | — | — | — | — | — | — |
|   Interruptible margin | (53.1) | (64.7) | (75.0) | (84.0) | (84.0) | (84.0) | (84.0) |
|   Total | 13,983.4 | 15,376.8 | 16,696.3 | 17,955.3 | 19,368.1 | 20,780.4 | 22,251.0 |
| Variable operating costs, $000 | | | | | | | |
|   Vaporization | 15.4 | 17.4 | 19.3 | 21.1 | 23.2 | 25.2 | 46.6 |
|   Liquefaction | 26.1 | 29.6 | 32.8 | 35.9 | 39.4 | 43.0 | 27.4 |
|   Reliquefaction | 101.6 | 115.1 | 127.6 | 139.7 | 153.3 | 166.9 | 182.6 |
|   Total | 143.1 | 162.1 | 179.7 | 196.7 | 215.9 | 235.1 | 256.6 |
| Annual fixed costs, $000 | 160.0 | 160.0 | 160.0 | 160.0 | 160.0 | 160.0 | 160.0 |

Table 16-4

LPG with Oil Gas Cost Summary for Normal Winter ($000)

| | Year | | | | | | |
|---|---|---|---|---|---|---|---|
| | 1 | 2 | 3 | 4 | 5 | 6 | 7 |
| Tax basis cost | | | | | | | |
| Gas cost | 14,090 | 15,498 | 16,832 | 18,104 | 19,521 | 20,938 | 22,425 |
| Depreciation, old plant | 227 | 227 | 227 | 227 | 227 | 227 | 227 |
| Depreciation, new plant | 20 | 41 | 54 | 68 | 81 | 105 | 132 |
| Fixed cost | 583 | 583 | 583 | 583 | 583 | 583 | 583 |
| Normal cost | 14,920 | 16,349 | 17,696 | 18,982 | 20,412 | 21,853 | 23,367 |
| Tax credit | 7896 | 8652 | 9365 | 10,045 | 10,802 | 11,565 | 12,366 |
| Investment credit | 25 | 25 | 17 | 17 | 17 | 30 | 34 |
| Total tax reduction | 7921 | 8677 | 9382 | 10,062 | 10,819 | 11,595 | 12,400 |
| Cash basis | | | | | | | |
| Gas cost | 14,090 | 15,498 | 16,832 | 18,104 | 19,521 | 20,938 | 22,425 |
| Capital expenditures | 844 | 844 | 563 | 563 | 563 | 985 | 1135 |
| Fixed cost | 583 | 583 | 583 | 583 | 583 | 583 | 583 |
| Tax credit | (7921) | (8677) | (9382) | (10,062) | (10,819) | (11,595) | (12,400) |
| Net cash cost | 7596 | 8248 | 8596 | 9188 | 9848 | 10,911 | 11,743 |

**Table 16-5**
**LNG Optimized on Severe Winter Cost Summary for Normal Winter ($000)**

| | Year | | | | | | |
|---|---|---|---|---|---|---|---|
| | 1† | 2† | 3 | 4 | 5 | 6 | 7 |
| **Tax basis cost** | | | | | | | |
| Gas cost* | 14,090 | 15,498 | 16,748 | 18,012 | 19,431 | 20,849 | 22,325 |
| Variable reliquefaction cost | — | — | 209 | 294 | 294 | 294 | 294 |
| Depreciation, old plant | 219 | 215 | 143 | 68 | 67 | — | — |
| Depreciation, new plant | — | — | 198 | 229 | 229 | 229 | 250 |
| Fixed costs | 583 | 583 | 160 | 160 | 160 | 160 | 160 |
| Normal costs | 14,892 | 16,296 | 17,458 | 18,763 | 20,181 | 21,532 | 23,029 |
| Extraordinary property loss | 95 | 44 | 2941 | — | — | — | — |
| Dismantling cost | — | — | 250 | — | — | — | — |
| Total pretax cost | 14,987 | 16,340 | 20,649 | 18,763 | 20,181 | 21,532 | 23,029 |
| Tax credit | 7931 | 8647 | 10,927 | 9929 | 10,680 | 11,395 | 12,187 |
| Investment credit | — | — | 232 | 39 | — | — | 29 |
| Total tax reduction | 7931 | 8647 | 11,159 | 9968 | 10,680 | 11,395 | 12,216 |
| **Cash basis** | | | | | | | |
| Gas cost* | 14,090 | 15,498 | 16,748 | 18,012 | 19,431 | 20,849 | 22,325 |
| Variable reliquefaction cost | — | — | 209 | 294 | 294 | 294 | 294 |
| Fixed cost | 583 | 583 | 160 | 160 | 160 | 160 | 160 |
| Capital expenditures | 525 | 3646 | 4734 | 657 | — | 433 | 433 |
| Dismantling cost | — | — | 250 | — | — | — | — |
| Tax reduction | (7931) | (8647) | (11,159) | (9968) | (10,680) | (11,395) | (12,216) |
| Net cash cost | 7267 | 11,080 | 10,942 | 9155 | 9205 | 10,341 | 10,996 |

* Includes variable costs except reliquefaction.
† LPG used in years 1 and 2, see Table 16-4.

Tables 16-4 and 16-5 illustrate the process by which the cash costs obtained from POST are adjusted to introduce the relative tax advantages of the heavy capital expenditures if LNG is adopted.  Finally, the net cash costs which appear at the bottom of Tables 16-4 and 16-5 were discounted to present value by 6% and 10% rates for both the 7-year study period and for a 20-year period, assuming that the cash flows in years 8 to 20 were identical to year 7.  The resulting present-value costs are shown in Table 16-6.

**Table 16-6**

**Present Value Costs of Alternatives**

| | Study period | | | |
|---|---|---|---|---|
| | 7 years | | 20 years | |
| | Discount rate | | | |
| Product | 6% | 10% | 6% | 10% |
| LNG | 54,058,000 | 47,418,000 | 121,211,000 | 89,001,000 |
| LPG | 51,280,000 | 44,742,000 | 121,371,000 | 88,144,000 |

**Table 16-7**

**Advantages and Disadvantages of LNG Over LPG**

Advantages

1. Favorable return on investment
2. Compatibility
3. Reduced customer complaints
4. Improved reserve to maintain service in emergencies
5. Better utilization of short-term contract quantities
6. Possibility of better economics through hedging
7. Improved pipeline load factor
8. Improved economics in severe winters or at higher than present growth rates
9. No foreseeable material shortages

Disadvantages

1. More risk
2. Building permit needed
3. Strain on borrowing capacity

Table 16-6 shows that at the conclusion of 7 years, LPG is the optimum strategy at either 6% or 10% discount rate. This is not surprising, considering the extensive capital expenditures required to get LNG on the line. (However, if the oil gas plant cannot be used the whole time, LNG becomes clearly preferable for both study periods at both discount rates.) Liberalizing the extrapolation assumptions for years 8 to 20 to reflect the expected growth in sendout also shows a significant increase in the return on investment to be achieved by an LNG plant, a return which significantly exceeds Boston Gas' cost of capital.

Although our analysis concentrated on economics, management must also recognize other considerations. A section of our report covered the noneconomic advantages and disadvantages of LNG. These are summarized without discussion in Table 16-7.

One of the most interesting aspects of this analytical method is its other uses; the following four have been found to date:

*Determination of Contract Quantities.* Periodically Boston Gas must contract with the pipeline for future gas deliveries. Prior to development of the optimization process, deciding on quantities 3 to 5 years in advance was an empirical process, to say the least. Now the latest sales forecast, expected pipeline rates, and existing or planned peak shaving capacities can be plugged in to yield a basic figure which management can then adjust as their experience dictates.

*Need for New Peak Shaving Facilities.* The model can be run with constraints on peaking capacity removed to find out whether the existing plant is in fact of optimum size. New facilities are penalized by addition of an appropriate capital cost and capital recovery factor.

*Marginal Costs.* The optimization process is presently being used to explore the marginal cost of adding new customers of various types. We are actively using this information to help obtain an economically rational and feasible rate structure. We hope that our work will also assist in orienting marketing activities to the most profitable goals.

*Financial Planning.* The Boston Gas Company has started to develop a mathematical model of the financial structure of the company. This model is beginning to be used to measure the effects on profitability and return on investment of alternative marketing strategies, rates, variations in growth, and other factors. Since gas cost is about 40% of total operating expense, the optimization process plays an important part in the model system by calculating the gas costs under an assumed set of future conditions.

## COMMENTS

Several important points are to be drawn from this case description:

1. The overall problem was so complex that a linear programming model formulation appeared necessary.

2. While the linear programming solution mechanism is well understood and canned solution programs are available, there is a need for considerable auxiliary systems development work to arrive at a useful management tool. Especially important were the matrix generator and report writer programs.

3. The overall system, which in fact became a model of the companies' distribution operations, had many beneficial side uses. This is generally what happens.

4. The outputs from the linear programming analyses were used for further financial planning by the Boston Gas Company, taking into account the normal uncertainties that surround forecasts of all types, weather as well as normal load growth and market penetration. In this subsequent analysis a number of good gas contract and equipment patterns were tested against historical weather patterns. This simulation thus sought to establish a "best" operating strategy, given the randomness and uncertainty of historical weather patterns.

Two interesting side comments may be in order:

1. After using its own IBM 1410 computer for most of the production runs reported in this case study, the project team switched later to using more powerful and larger computers. When using these large machines, solution times of 5 minutes or less were incurred for the major linear programming problem.

2. When the larger computers became available, it was felt desirable to plan the corporate operations on a 365 actual rather than 30 "block" day basis. Thus, a model of about 2400 rows was constructed and solved. However, the solution presented by the actual day model was only 0.05% better than the "block" day solution, and these benefits were less than adequate to support the several additional hours of computer running time involved in solving the larger model. In this case, it was shown that a model with some gross simplifications provided a completely satisfactory answer.

# Spot Charter
# Tanker Rates
# A Case Study*

Petroleum tankers move crude oil and products from the producing areas to the consuming areas. At present, oil transportation by tanker accounts for more than 50% of all tonnage moved by ocean vessels, and this rate is increasing.

The major oil companies all own a fleet of tankers which they use for their own purposes. In addition there are a large number of tankers owned by independent shippers which are chartered for long or short (spot) durations to the world's oil companies. The majority of these independent shippers are located in Scandinavia and in Greece.

Spot charter rates are indicative of the supply and demand balance between tanker and transportation requirements. In recent years spot tanker charter rates have varied extensively and this has prompted the following research activity.

## THE SPOT CHARTER MARKET

The spot market for tanker charters is frequently marked by wide swings in rate levels, yet the demand for tankers is exceptionally price inelastic. This results from several factors. First, transportation is only one input to a factor (oil consumption)

---

* This chapter was authored by H. L. Dick, J. L. Russel, and J. L. Lewis. It is presented here by permission of the authors.

with a relatively inelastic demand. Second, the specialized nature of ocean transportation allows no ready substitution—the alternative of pipelines is only a longterm prospect. Third, transportation costs are only a small fraction of total petroleum expenses. Finally, various geographical and institutional constraints of the oil business lead to the setting of production plans quite independently of the current cost of inputs. The timing and extent of spot rate fluctuations becomes a matter of concern to oil companies, as they seek to maintain a certain degree of flexibility by supplementing their own tanker fleets with charters in the open market. A clearer picture of the likely future trends in the spot tanker market would enable such companies to plan their own mix of ship construction, long term charters and short term or spot (less than 6 months) charters so as to minimize transportation costs.

Given the competitive nature of the industry and the important role of individual expectations, only an industry-wide study could hope to provide such a forecast of spot rates. It is the purpose of this report to examine briefly the nature of the economic forces acting upon the spot market, then to move from this base to a detailed analysis of the supply and demand factors for the next 5 years. From this, a forecast of the general trends for spot charters will be developed.

### Tanker Economics

Petroleum presently accounts for some 35% of the total demand for energy. Rising populations and improved living standards indicate a steady growth in the use of energy products, with a 7.5% annual increase seen in the consumption of oil over the next 30 years.* In recent years, oil transported by tankers has accounted for over 50% of total oil consumption. The total demand for tankers will vary, in addition to this market expansion, with the changing patterns of international oil traffic and changes in the speed and effective capacity of tankers.

The tankers available for transporting this quantity of petroleum may be divided into three segments: (1) company owned and operated, (2) long term charters, and (3) spot charters. Each of the first two groups represents some 40 to 50% of the tanker fleet, which currently totals approximately 100 million dwt. The spot market, then, consists of 5 to 15% of the active fleet (see Table 17-1). Long term charter rates, over periods of up to 15 years, generally follow the costs of building and operating the incremental tanker of the size required, plus a return on invested capital. The recent pattern has been for declining operating costs, largely the result of large scale economies associated with the trend toward larger tankers. It is in the relatively small spot market, however, that any disequilibrium of supply and demand makes itself felt. Such differences result not only from an overall tanker shortage or surplus, but from temporary effects of seasonal demand and supply, an inadequate number in the required loading areas, weather conditions, etc. Some short term adjustment is possible through conversion of vessels employed in the grain trade or reactivation of idle ships (for example, 3.5 MM dwt. were added to the fleet under the conditions of

---

* E. D. Naess, *Tanker Industry: Problems and Prospects*, Institute for Shipping Research, Bergen, 1965, p. 5.

Table 17-1

Spot Market Versus Total Tanker Charters*

| Year | Per Cent |
|------|----------|
| 1954 | 15% |
| 1955 | 19 |
| 1956 | 15 |
| 1957 | 11 |

* Source: Z. S. Zannetos, *The Theory of Oil Tankship Rates*, MIT Monographs in Economics No. 4, MIT Press, Cambridge, 1966, Chapter 6.

extreme shortage following the closing of the Suez Canal in June, 1967). Historically, however, there has been little reserve of tanker tonnage, and short term demand changes lead to major changes in the level of spot rates. Indeed, the prices of few commodities fluctuate as much as spot tanker rates.

### The Spot Market

Expectations of future conditions play a key role in the process of price determination in the spot market, and exhibit a high degree of relative price elasticity. Current rates become the result of the present impact of actions initiated in the past by expectations of future supply-demand relationships. Expectations can quickly bring about sequential shifts in the demand for spot charters, but since supply schedules cannot change without the passage of time, the rates may move from bottom to peak, or vice versa, in a matter of months. Orders for new vessels are placed primarily during periods of high rates. This can be seen in the reaction to the closure of the Suez Canal in 1956, and again in 1967. Tankers were ordered at unprecedented rates (see Fig. 17-1), out of all proportion to the anticipated requirements of the oil industry. The result was an extended period of oversupply, and a drop from temporarily high spot rates to a depressed level (Fig. 17-2). The relevant factors for shipbuilders are, simply, price and credit terms and availability, with no direct interface between shipyards and the demand for ships.

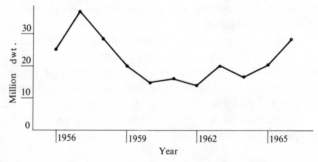

Fig. 17-1 Total dwt. under construction or on order. (Source: Sun Oil Co., *Analysis of World Tank Ship Fleets.*)

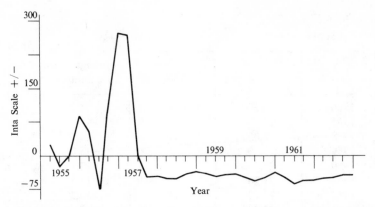

**Fig. 17-2** Quarterly average of weekly spot rates from 1956 through 1962. (Source: J. Bes, *Tanker Shipping*, Barker and Howard, London, 1963, p. 158.)

The position of supply and demand schedules is also affected, as mentioned above, by circularities of shorter duration, such as seasonal trade, repairs, and the individual needs of large users. The average size of vessels chartered tends to decrease as spot rates increase, reflecting the entry of smaller and less economical vessels into the market. This relationship weakens, however, at high spot rate levels. The supply of tankers is thus somewhat elastic below capacity levels, but becomes inelastic once the capacity level is reached. Rate stability and equilibria, then, may be possible in the short run only at the low, elastic, portion of the rate schedule.*

The supply of new tankers, in terms of numbers and total dwt., will depend upon: (1) spot rates and the expectations they generate, (2) shipbuilding costs, (3) the rate of technological obsolescence (age distribution), and (4) the pattern of ownership. The actual short term fleet capacity varies, though, with several additional factors— retirements versus deliveries, average speed, conversions, the amount of ballasted traffic, the idle time lost for repairs, loading, and unloading, and tieups. Repairs can in general be postponed if spot rates are high. The trend here is for less time spent for repairs, as ship construction and maintenance technologies increase. Conversions are relatively expensive, and a significant factor only under extreme conditions. While scrappage will vary with the fleet's age distribution and the rate of technological advances, the primary factor is the level of anticipated spot rates. Table 17-2 summarizes some of these recent patterns.

Total transportation costs for the ship owner-operator will be a result of construction costs, crew and other direct operating expenses, fuel costs, and port facilities charges, to which should be added a charge for return on capital invested. Yet it would appear that the actual short term, out-of-pocket costs will set a floor on market rates. Rates would only go lower as long as some depreciation expense allows a positive cash flow. The age distribution of the tanker fleet thus becomes a considera-

---

* A further discussion is contained in Z. S. Zannetos, *The Theory of Oil Tankship Rates*, MIT Monographs in Economics, No. 4, MIT Press, Cambridge, 1966, Chapter 6.

**Table 17-2**

**Oil Tanker Fleet***

| Year | Average dwt | Average age | Average speed knots |
|------|-------------|-------------|---------------------|
| 1956 | 16,200 | 8 yrs 4 mos | 14.2 |
| 1957 | 17,100 | 8    1 | 14.4 |
| 1958 | 18,000 | 7   10 | 14.6 |
| 1959 | 19,100 | 7    6 | 14.8 |
| 1960 | 20,200 | 7    4 | 15.1 |
| 1961 | 21,200 | 7    6 | 15.2 |
| 1962 | 22,100 | 7    8 | 15.3 |
| 1963 | 23,200 | 7    9 | 15.4 |
| 1964 | 25,300 | 7    7 | 15.6 |
| 1965 | 27,100 | 7    7 | 15.7 |
| 1966 | 29,200 | 7    7 | 15.7 |

* Source: Sun Oil Co., *Analysis of World Tank Ship Fleets.*

tion when looking at spot tanker rates. Reluctance to tie up vessels may be further increased by the costs of laying up a vessel. The conclusion, then, is that the minimum spot rate at any point in time will be that which provides some small inducement to keep the marginal vessel in operation, i.e., at least some small net cash inflow.

Several further observations deserve comment. The second closing of the Suez Canal will undoubtedly accentuate the trend toward large (200,000 dwt. and up) tankers. Although involving an added distance of 4800 miles by having to travel around the Cape of Good Hope, the large scale economies appear to offset the difference. This trend is already in progress, as total oil from the Persian Gulf via the Cape rose from 5.0 million tons in 1965 to 18.7 million tons in 1966.

## SPOT RATE FORECASTING MODEL

### Tanker Demand

A forecast of the spot charter market for the 1968 to 1972 period requires an analysis of demand for tankers on the one hand and anticipated supply of tankers for crude oil transport on the other. The demand function was defined in terms of the number of T-2 equivalents employed in international crude oil trade.* The basis for the demand projection was the determination of major sources (6) and destinations (14) of crude,

---

* For the purposes of our study, we used the following definition of T-2: 16,600 dwt., 14.6 knots, 3.5 days turnaround. While the definition of a T-2 varies between oil companies, that given above is widely accepted and consistent with the data collected.

with estimates of the amounts to be shipped between locations:

| Sources | Destinations | |
|---|---|---|
| North Africa | Mediterranean Europe | Japan-Korea-Taiwan |
| West Africa | Atlantic Europe | U.S. East Coast |
| Near East | South Africa | U.S. West Coast |
| Persian Gulf | East Africa | Canada East Coast |
| S. E. Asia | Israel | Canada West Coast |
| Caribbean | Indian Ocean | Caribbean |
| | Australasia | South America |

These forecasts indicated that the quantity of crude oil to be transported annually by tankers will undergo a sizable increase to over 23 million b/cd in 1972 (see Table 17-3). It was necessary also to take account of the pattern of crude shipments. This step involved the construction of a linear programming model using as objective function values the number of T-2's required to transport 1000 barrels per day between various locations.* The possible routes served were the activities. The constraints were the quantities to be supplied by each source or demanded at each destination. This model was programmed to solve for the minimum number of T-2's required to transport the amounts established by the constraints.

**Table 17-3**

**Petroleum Via Sea Transport**

| Year | Quantity, b/cd |
|---|---|
| 1967 | 15,208 |
| 1968 | 16,725 |
| 1969 | 18,377 |
| 1970 | 20,082 |
| 1971 | 21,514 |
| 1972 | 23,067 |

This process was repeated for each year in the 1967 to 1972 period. For the year 1967, the indicated "optimal" demand for tankers was compared with the known demand so that an "inefficiency factor" could be determined:

$$(\text{model's T-2 demand}) \times (\text{inefficiency}) = (\text{actual T-2's}).$$

This inefficiency factor, 1.08, may be explained as resulting from (1) nonoptimal route selections caused by the distribution of individual companies' oil fields and refineries, and (2) imperfect geographic matching of tankers with shipping needs. The somewhat

---

* These conversion factors were obtained from Emergency Petroleum Supply Committee data.

**Table 17-4**

**Demand for Oil Tankers**

| Year | Demand, T-2's |
|------|---------------|
| 1968 | 6080 |
| 1969 | 6760 |
| 1970 | 7550 |
| 1971 | 8125 |
| 1972 | 8660 |

**Table 17-5**

**Schedule of New Tankers (T-2's)**

| Year | 10,000–24,999 | 25,000–44,999 | 45,000–99,999 | 100,000+ | Total |
|------|---------------|---------------|---------------|----------|-------|
| 1968 | 29 | 3 | 326 | 601 | 959 |
| 1969 | 25 | 9 | 92 | 821 | 947 |
| 1970 | 9 | — | 15 | 789 | 813 |

critical assumption was made that this inefficiency factor would remain constant throughout the 5 years under consideration. This followed from the observations that oil field-refinery relationships should not vary significantly, and that the increased efficiency of new supertankers will be partly offset by their ability to use only certain harbors with adequate docking and unloading facilities.

The resulting projections of the demand for oil tankers in international crude trade are presented in Table 17-4, showing an average growth rate of 9.2%.

**Tanker Availability**

A number of sources were examined for data pertaining to the anticipated supply (in T-2's) of tankers over the next 5 years. The figures selected as most appropriate came from the Mobil Oil Company. The study conducted by the Emergency Petroleum Supply Committee shortly after the closing of the Suez Canal in 1967 meant that the data was up to date with respect to both current availabilities and ships on order. Table 17-5 summarizes this schedule of new deliveries.

Tanker availabilities for 1971 and 1972 were calculated by projecting the average trend in new vessels for 1967 to 1970. This was taken as a viable first approximation, subject to later revision if deemed necessary. It was further assumed that the coastal, nonpetroleum, and clean products trade requirements would remain constant over the period. This led to the supply-demand relationships presented in Table 17-6.

As may be seen from this table, the T-2's available in 1970 will cover the projected demand for 1971. Indeed, there will be an oversupply of tankers throughout the 5-

**Table 17-6**

**Tanker Demand and Availability, 1968 to 1972**

| Year | T-2 demand international crude | Clean products | U.S. coastal | Non-Petroleum demand | Total demand | Total supply |
|------|------|------|------|------|------|------|
| 1968 | 6080 | 770 | 350 | 245 | 7445 | 7993 |
| 1969 | 6760 | 770 | 350 | 245 | 8125 | 8940 |
| 1970 | 7550 | 770 | 350 | 245 | 8915 | 9753 |
| 1971 | 8125 | 770 | 350 | 245 | 9490 | 10617 |
| 1972 | 8660 | 770 | 350 | 245 | 10025 | 11481 |

**Table 17-7**

**Tanker Age and Size Categories**

| Size \ Age | Pre-1947 | 1947–1950 | 1951–1954 | 1955–1958 | 1959–1962 | 1963–1967 | 1968–1972 |
|------|------|------|------|------|------|------|------|
| 10,000–25,000 | × | × | × | × | × | × | × |
| 25,000–45,000 | | × | × | × | × | × | × |
| 45,000–100,000 | | | × | × | × | × | × |
| 100,000 + | | | | | × | × | × |

year period. Given this outlook, we hypothesized that spot charter rates will approach the variable operating costs of the marginal vessel employed in the transportation of crude oil. In other words, a ship owner should be willing to take any rate that covers his variable operating costs. Vessels may, of course, be laid up, at some cost to the operator, when charter rates are low and expected to remain at depressed levels. This layup versus scrap decision remains the prerogative of the owner, and appears closely related to the length of time low rates are seen as likely to prevail.

**Operating Costs**

This hypothesis required that an analysis be made of the operating costs of various tanker size and age categories. Economies of scale mean a lesser cost per dwt. for large tankers; newer vessels possess greater speed and efficiency. The approach, therefore, was to break down the existing fleet into 21 groups according to four size and seven age categories (see Table 17-7). The four groups in age class VII (1968–1972) will vary as new tankers come on stream each year. It was assumed, however, that availabilities in the other 17 classifications will remain constant throughout this period. This followed from the observations that (1) there is no necessary lifetime beyond which a tanker must be scrapped, and (2) tankers tend to enter and leave the crude oil market in response to rate changes.

It was then necessary to develop cost structures for these various tanker groupings. To do this, average 1964 operating costs per T-2 per day were estimated for:*

a) A 1956-built 16,600-dwt. tanker

b) A 1961-built 38,500-dwt. tanker

c) A 1964-built 75,000-dwt. tanker

d) A 1964-built 130,000-dwt. tanker.

These figures were taken as average costs per T-2 day for all tankers of the given age category in each of the size groups. For example, operating costs for (a) were assumed to represent the average for 10,000 to 25,000-dwt. tankers constructed from 1955 to 1958. To extrapolate for the other age categories, general efficiency factors were determined, primarily from historical trends in average ship speeds. This was felt to be the major contributor to increased operating efficiency of crude tankers. Therefore, given a 1961-constructed tanker with a normal speed of 16.6 knots, the operating costs of a 1956-built vessel with a speed of 14.6 knots could be approximated by use of a factor of 16.6/14.6, or 1.14. Once 1964 cost estimates were available for each of the 21 tanker categories, the necessary data for the 1968 to 1972 period was generated by applying inflation rates to the various cost components. (See Table 17-8 for 1968 cost figures.) Table 17-9 presents estimates of average rates of inflation in tanker operating costs, which were obtained from interviews with oil company representatives. With this cost data, it was possible to return once again to our hypothesis that spot rates over the next 5 years will tend to approximate the variable operating costs of the marginal tanker category.

In order to determine the least efficient vessel that would be required in any given year, a simple linear programming model was constructed using daily operating costs per T-2 as the objective function values, the age-size of tankers as activities, and the availability of each age-size class as right-hand side values in the constraint equations, along with our estimates of total T-2 demand. Some minor adjustments were first made in the tanker supply data, as vessels for clean products and coastal trades were subtracted out of the availability of the 10,000–25,000-dwt. group, proportionately from all age categories. It was felt, however, that tankers in the nonpetroleum trades (245 T-2's) were of secondary importance, i.e., a marginal area into which tankers entered as an alternative to being laid-up, and from which they could be brought if spot rates rose (as occurred after the 1967 Suez crisis). The total requirements for these last two trades, when compared with the amounts "leftover" in each year after all crude demand had been met, were in no case in excess of total tanker availability. The model was then solved to minimize total operating costs.

---

* These estimates rest largely upon information provided by Arthur D. Little, Inc. and a paper by Michael Hubbard, *The Comparative Costs of Oil Transport*, Institute of Petroleum, London, 1966.

**Table 17-8**

**1968 Tanker Operating Cost Figures, $/T-2/Day**

| Tanker category | | Crew expenses | Insurance, victualling, and stores | Repairs and misc. | Fuel-in-port and bunker | Total |
|---|---|---|---|---|---|---|
| Age | Size (dwt.) | | | | | |
| Pre-1947 | 10,000–24,999 | 394.0 | 369.0 | 230.0 | 507 | 1500.0 |
| 1947–1950 | 10,000–24,999 | 385.0 | 360.0 | 225.0 | 495 | 1465.0 |
| 1947–1950 | 25,000–49,999 | 201.0 | 172.5 | 106.0 | 360 | 839.5 |
| 1951–1954 | 10,000–24,999 | 369.0 | 344.0 | 215.5 | 474 | 1402.5 |
| 1951–1954 | 25,000–49,999 | 192.0 | 164.5 | 102.5 | 345 | 809.0 |
| 1951–1954 | 45,000–99,999 | 113.5 | 96.3 | 60.6 | 254 | 524.4 |
| 1955–1958 | 10,000–24,999 | 348.0 | 325.0 | 204.0 | 446.5 | 1323.5 |
| 1955–1958 | 25,000–49,999 | 184.0 | 157.5 | 98.0 | 329 | 768.5 |
| 1955–1958 | 45,000–99,999 | 109.5 | 92.3 | 58.0 | 244 | 503.8 |
| 1959–1962 | 10,000–24,999 | 307.5 | 287.0 | 180.0 | 295 | 1169.5 |
| 1959–1962 | 25,000–44,999 | 164.5 | 140.2 | 87.6 | 294.3 | 686.6 |
| 1959–1962 | 45,000–99,999 | 99.5 | 84.1 | 53.0 | 223 | 459.6 |
| 1959–1962 | 100,000+ | 64.8 | 54.8 | 34.0 | 138 | 291.6 |
| 1963–1967 | 10,000–24,999 | 266.0 | 249.5 | 156.0 | 342 | 1013.5 |
| 1963–1967 | 25,000–49,999 | 147.5 | 126.5 | 78.5 | 264 | 616.5 |
| 1963–1967 | 45,000–99,999 | 91.3 | 77.3 | 48.5 | 204.6 | 421.7 |
| 1963–1967 | 100,000+ | 59.2 | 50.2 | 31.2 | 151.1 | 291.7 |
| 1968–1972 | 10,000–24,999 | 238.0 | 22.0 | 139.5 | 306 | 905.5 |
| 1968–1972 | 25,000–49,999 | 139.0 | 118.5 | 74.0 | 249 | 580.5 |
| 1968–1972 | 45,000–99,999 | 86.0 | 72.7 | 45.5 | 192 | 396.2 |
| 1968–1972 | 100,000+ | 55.8 | 47.2 | 29.4 | 142 | 274.4 |

**Table 17-9**

**Inflation Rates: Tanker Operations**

| Cost item | % per year |
|---|---|
| Crew expenses | 6 |
| Insurance | 3 |
| Victualling | 3 |
| Stores | 3 |
| Repairs | 5 |
| Miscellaneous | 5 |
| Fuel-in-port | 0 |
| Bunker fuel | 0 |

**Table 17-10**

**Forecast of Operating Costs and Spot Rates**

| Year | Marginal tanker group | | Operating cost per T-2 day | Intascale rate |
|---|---|---|---|---|
| | Size | Age | | |
| 1968 | 25,000–44,999 | 1955–1958 | $768.5 | −66% |
| 1969 | 25,000–44,999 | 1955–1958 | 787.8 | −65 |
| 1970 | 25,000–44,999 | 1955–1958 | 809.0 | −64 |
| 1971 | 25,000–44,999 | 1959–1962 | 745.8 | −67 |
| 1972 | 25,000–44,999 | 1959–1962 | 767.3 | −66 |

## RESULTS

### Spot Tanker Rates

The linear programming model provided estimates of daily operating costs per T-2 for the marginal tanker category determined to be in service, as shown in Table 17-10. Inflation causes a slight increase in costs through 1970. After that, a growing condition of oversupply means that some less efficient vessels will no longer be used. These costs set the tradeoff point between operation and lay-up, and so are equal to the revenue per T-2 day required to keep these tankers in service. The Intascale rates roughly corresponding to these revenues* are also presented in Table 17-10, and represent our forecast of the general level of spot charter rates for 1968 to 1972. These projections suggest a depressed market condition, close to the rates prevailing before the 1967 Suez crisis. It may be observed that the shift to a more efficient marginal category after 1970 (25,000 to 44,999 dwt., built from 1959 to 1962) will lead to a decline in spot rates of nearly 8%.

In order to put these figures into specific terms for actual tanker runs, a small program was devised to print out the rates in dollars per long ton associated with the Intascale rates given above. This was done for all possible route combinations on our source-destination matrix and repeated for each of the 5 years (Fig. 17-3 contains a sample).

### Seasonal Fluctuations

The observation that spot rates may vary because of seasonal effects on the supply-demand relationship led to an examination of the impact of introducing into the model certain assumptions regarding seasonal changes. The assumptions used in this analysis were:

1. Peak seasonal tanker needs will occur in December and January.

2. Rates will rise smoothly from the base level beginning in October, peak in December-January, and fall back to regular levels by March.

---

* This computation was made by converting into rates per long ton, which involved division by the appropriate coefficient from the EPC supply-destination table. When done for several routes, a common Intascale level was determined.

| ORIGIN. | DESTINATION | 1968 RATE | 1969 RATE | 1970 RATE | 1971 RATE | 1972 RATE |
|---|---|---|---|---|---|---|
| MED. EUROPE | ATL. EUROPE | .916764 | .939787 | .965077 | .889684 | .915332 |
| MED. EUROPE | NORTH AFRICA | .498015 | .510522 | .52426 | .483304 | .497237 |
| MED. EUROPE | W. AFRICA | .968127 | .992441 | 1.01915 | .939531 | .966616 |
| MED. EUROPE | NEAR EAST | .558499 | .572525 | .587931 | .542002 | .557626 |
| MED. EUROPE | U.S. EAST COAST | 1.57958 | 1.61925 | 1.66282 | 1.53292 | 1.57711 |
| ATL. EUROPE | MED. EUROPE | .916764 | .939787 | .965077 | .889684 | .915332 |
| ATL. EUROPE | ATL. EUROPE | .287993 | .295226 | .303171 | .279487 | .287544 |
| ATL. EUROPE | NORTH AFRICA | .837338 | .858367 | .881465 | .812604 | .83603 |
| ATL. EUROPE | W. AFRICA | 1.58396 | 1.62374 | 1.66744 | 1.53718 | 1.58149 |
| ATL. EUROPE | S. AFRICA | 2.21018 | 2.26569 | 2.32666 | 2.1449 | 2.20673 |
| ATL. EUROPE | INDIAN OCEAN | 3.6553 | 3.7471 | 3.84794 | 3.54733 | 3.64959 |
| ATL. EUROPE | S.E. ASIA | 4.13208 | 4.23585 | 4.34984 | 4.01003 | 4.12563 |
| ATL. EUROPE | U.S. EAST | 1.19544 | 1.22547 | 1.25844 | 1.16013 | 1.19358 |
| ATL. EUROPE | CANADA EAST | 1.16373 | 1.19295 | 1.22506 | 1.12935 | 1.16191 |
| ATL. EUROPE | CARIBBEAN | 1.55375 | 1.59277 | 1.63563 | 1.50786 | 1.55133 |
| ATL. EUROPE | SOUTH AMERICA | 1.90711 | 1.95501 | 2.00762 | 1.85078 | 1.90414 |
| NORTH AFRICA | MED. EUROPE | .361132 | .370201 | .380163 | .350465 | .360568 |
| NORTH AFRICA | ATL. EUROPE | .837338 | .858367 | .881465 | .812604 | .83603 |

**Fig. 17-3** Forecast of spot rates for period 1968 through 1972—$/LT.

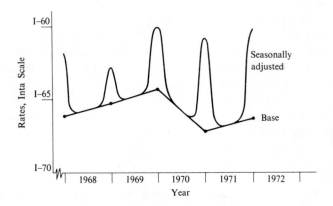

**Fig. 17-4** Rate projections, 1968 to 1972.

3. Maximum tanker demand in this period will be 1.07 times the yearly base line needs. This was derived from the fact that tankers operate at lower effective capacities during the winter months.

4. Variable operating costs per T-2 per day during the peak season will, therefore, be 1.07 times the "normal" costs.

With these modified inputs to the tanker allocation model, the seasonal pattern shown in Fig. 17-4 was obtained. The maximum seasonal fluctuation in rates is roughly six points Intascale. Certainly this is only a rough attempt at anticipating

Table 17-11

Spot Rates with Operation of Israeli Pipeline

| Year | T-2 savings | Cost per T-2 day | Revised Intascale | Original Intascale |
|------|-------------|------------------|-------------------|--------------------|
| 1969 | 399 | $705.2 | −69% | −65% |
| 1970 | 396 | 725.1 | −68 | −64 |
| 1971 | 399 | 668.2 | −71 | −67 |
| 1972 | 396 | 687.5 | −70 | −66 |

short term rate changes. Yet, as a basis of comparison, the maximum difference in the quarterly average of weekly rates during the 1958 to 1963 period was 15 percentage points on Intascale.

### Trans-Suez Pipeline

An additional attempt at demonstrating the usefulness of the tanker allocation model in assessing future spot rate levels involved an analysis of the impact of operation of the 1,200,000 b/cd Trans-Suez pipeline, planned for completion in 1970. The input values of the tanker demand model were adjusted for a 1,200,000 b/cd increase in Red Sea port imports, and for a corresponding increase in exports (Near East source location). The model was then solved for this new traffic pattern, giving a revised T-2 demand which in turn was introduced into the allocation model. The results, shown in Table 17-11, suggest a small but noticeable drop in spot rates from the initial nonpipeline forecast. The operation of the pipeline will reduce total tanker transportation of crude oil by replacing long runs around the Cape with shorter runs to and beyond the Suez Canal. Rates will drop by four points Intascale as the spot tanker fleet competes for the reduced demand, driving additional less efficient vessels out of service.

### Suez Canal

The possibility exists that the Suez Canal will reopen, with the effect of reducing the total T-2 demand figures by cutting travel time and distance from the Persian Gulf to European and other destinations. Yet the earliest this could occur appears to be late 1970, well into the period under investigation. Even if the Canal opens, we consider it unlikely to regain its former significance. The new supertankers could travel the Canal only one way, in ballast, if at all. The proposed Trans-Suez pipeline will further divert oil from this route. A quick estimate of the operating costs likely to prevail with use of the Suez Canal led to the conclusion that the impact on spot rates would be relatively minor.

### Profitability of Tanker Operations

One final question remains: Is tanker operation in the spot market an attractive business for an investor? Specifically, given a projection of spot rates of Intascale −66%, could an investor achieve a reasonable return over a 15-year period by constructing a large (200,000 dwt.) tanker for use in the spot market? While somewhat unrealistic in that a new vessel could be expected to engage in longer term charters, this was seen as one approach to an approximate answer. The following assumptions were employed:

1. Construction costs of $75 per dwt., or $15 million.
2. Down payment of 20%, with a 10-year, 8% ship loan for the remainder, amortized evenly.
3. A tax rate of 52%, with SOYD depreciation over 15 years.
4. Ship in service by 1970, to operate 350 days per year.
5. An average speed of 20 knots, equivalent to 17.4 T-2's.
6. A salvage value of $3 million in 1985.

Using the costs already developed for a 100,000+ dwt. tanker, as well as an inflation factor, a present value analysis gave these results:

• At a 10% discount rate, $PV = \$3,091,000$.
• At a 15% discount rate, $PV = \$1,519,000$.

The implied internal rate of return was found to be 24.5%. Although appearing to be an attractive investment, these results proved quite sensitive to changes in spot rates. For example, the lowest Intascale rate at which the investor could earn 15% is I-70, and the minimum rates to achieve a 10% return is I-72. In view of the spot rate forecasts, which drop below I-70 with operation of the Trans-Suez pipeline, the answer is by no means obvious. Still, our hypothetical tanker would be operating at quite efficient levels relative to the spot tanker fleet, particularly in the initial years.


## SUMMARY AND CONCLUSIONS

Several points stand out in the preceding analysis. Perhaps most significant is the demonstration that it is possible to employ linear programming techniques using commonly available data to obtain what appear to be reasonable forecasts of the general level of spot charter rates on an annual basis. These projections may readily be converted into dollar rates for any particular tanker route.

The spurt in shipbuilding that occurred after the 1967 closing of the Suez Canal, plus the trend to ever more supertankers, implies that an oversupply condition will exist in the oil tanker market, even though sea transport in terms of b/cd will rise by 52% in the next 5 years. As the major impact of changing supply-demand relationships is reflected in the spot market, rates are expected to return rapidly to pre-Suez levels. The actual rates we see as prevailing throughout the period from late 1968 to the end of 1972 are in the range of Intascale −65% to −70%.

The approach adopted in this study is limited by the aggregate nature of much of the data. The rate levels are dependent on the use of fairly broad tanker groupings. Also, we were unable to compare the results directly with the 1967 base year, since the Suez crisis caused a soaring of spot rates. The short-term condition of undersupply

Table 17-12

Sensitivity Analysis

| Year | Upward change in T-2 demand to change solution | % | Downward change in T-2 demand to change solution | % |
|---|---|---|---|---|
| 1968 | 364 | 6.0 | 216 | 3.6 |
| 1969 | 556 | 8.2 | 24 | 0.4 |
| 1970 | 570 | 7.6 | 10 | 0.1 |
| 1971 | 269 | 3.2 | 374 | 4.6 |
| 1972 | 588 | 6.8 | 55 | 0.6 |

Table 17-13

Spot Rates with New Solution Basis

| Year | Forecast of Intascale (original) | Cost with new solution from upward demand change | Inta-scale | Cost with new solution from downward demand change | Inta-scale |
|---|---|---|---|---|---|
| 1968 | −66% | $809 | −64% | $686.6 | −70% |
| 1969 | −65 | 826 | −63 | 705.2 | −69 |
| 1970 | −64 | 848 | −62 | 725.1 | −68 |
| 1971 | −67 | 831 | −63 | 668.2 | −71 |
| 1972 | −66 | 856 | −62 | 687.5 | −70 |

of T-2's seen in late 1967 is a contrary situation to that which we project for 1968 to 1972.

Yet the analysis does have the merit of relying upon industry-wide data and sources, thus moving beyond the rather restricted view of a single oil company or single tanker charterer. Also, a supply-demand comparison based on current data and expectations is felt to be a more reasonable approach than a simple projection of historical trends, as is often seen in oil industry literature. By making certain assumptions regarding seasonal changes in demand, we were able to demonstrate the model's flexibility in forecasting rough seasonal fluctuations as well as general rate levels. Similarly, the analysis could readily be modified to consider the impact on spot rate levels of a major new pipeline.

### Sensitivity Analysis

While linear programming solutions do not lend themselves to an analysis of uncertainty through use of probabilistic estimates, the results were checked to determine the extent of changes in T-2 demand which would be required to change the solution and the associated costs per T-2 day. Table 17-12 points out that the basis holds for fairly broad ranges, particularly in the upward direction. Even when a change of basis does occur, the impact on the spot rates associated with the new operating costs is limited to some three points Intascale (see Table 17-13).

Part of this apparent insensitivity is the result of the design of the model, using as it does only a limited number (21) of age-size tanker categories. Another factor, however, is the rather small variation in marginal tanker costs relative to the seasonal swings caused by changes in effective availability and capacity. The stability of the output over these ranges in T-2 demand indicates a high likelihood that actual spot rates will be near the predicted values.

## BIBLIOGRAPHY

### Books and Articles

Bes, J., *Tanker Shipping*, Barker and Howard, London, 1963.

Hubbard, Michael, *The Comparative Costs of Oil Transport*, Institute of Petroleum, London, 1966.

Naess, E. D., *Tanker Industry: Problems and Prospects*, Institute for Shipping Research, Bergen, 1965.

Newton, W. L., *Economics of Tanker Operations*, Petroleum Institute. Talk given at Northwestern, April 8, 1965.

————, *The Long-Term Development of the Tanker Freight Market*. London, 1964.

Zannetos, Zenon S., *The Theory of Oil Tankship Rates*, MIT Monographs in Economics, No. 4. MIT Press, Cambridge, 1966.

### Periodicals

*Fortune*, "Tankers Move the Oil That Moves the World," September, 1967.

*Oil and Gas International*. Petroleum Publishing Company, The Hague, monthly.

*Oil and Gas Journal*. The Petroleum Publishing Company, Tulsa, weekly.

*Petroleum Press Service*. London, monthly.

### Oil Company Publications

British Petroleum Co., Ltd. *Statistical Review of the World Oil Industry*, Britannic House, London, 1966.

John I. Jacobs & Co., Ltd. *World Tanker Fleet Review*, London.

Sun Oil Company, *Analysis of World Tank Ship Fleets*, Philadelphia.

Standard Oil Company, *Register of Tank Vessels*, New York.

# Bibliography

1. ACKOFF, R. L. (editor), *Progress in Operations Research*, Wiley, New York, 1961. (This work is a continuation of *Introduction to Operations Research*, by Churchman, C. W., Ackoff, R. L., and edited by Arnoff, E. L.  Wiley, 1957 and Dunod, 1960.)
2. ARROW, K. J., HURWICZ, L., and UZAWA, H., *Studies in Linear and Non-Linear Programming*, Stanford University Press, Stanford, 1958.
3. BALAS, E., "An Additive Algorithm for Solving Linear Programs with Zero-One Variables," *Op. Res.*, **13**, 4, 1965.
4. BAUMOL, W. J., *Economic Theory and Operations Analysis*, Prentice Hall, Englewood Cliffs, N.J., 1961.
5. BEALE, E. M. L., "An Alternative Method of Linear Programming," *Proc. Cambridge Phil. Soc.*, **50**, 4, 1954.
6. BELLMAN, R., "On the Computational Solution of Linear Programming Problems Involving Almost Block-Diagonal Matrices," *Man. Sci.*, **3**, 4, 1957.
7. CHARNES, A., "Optimality and Degeneracy in Linear Programming," *Econometrica*, **20**, 2, 1952.
8. CHARNES, A., and COOPER, W. W., "The Stepping Stone Method of Explaining Linear Programming Calculations in Transportation Problems," *Man. Sci.*, **1**, I, 1954.

9. CHARNES, A., and COOPER, W. W., "Duality, Regrouping and Warehousing," *ONR Research Memorandum No. 19*, Carnegie Institute of Technology, Pittsburgh, 1954.

10. CHARNES, A., and COOPER, W. W., "Generalizations of the Warehousing Model," *ONR Research Memorandum No. 34*, Carnegie Institute of Technology, Pittsburgh, 1955; or in *Operational Research Quarterly*, **6**, 4, 1955.

11. CHARNES, A., and COOPER, W. W., "Management Models and Industrial Applications of Linear Programming," *Man. Sci.*, **4**, 1, 1957.

12. CHARNES, A., COOPER, W. W., and HENDERSON, A., *An Introduction to Linear Programming*, Wiley, New York, 1953.

13. CHARNES, A., COOPER, W. W., and MELLON, R., "Blending Aviation Gasolines: A Study in Programming Interdependent Activities in an Integrated Oil Company," *Econometrica*, **20**, 2, 1952.

14. CHARNES, A., and LEMKE, C. E., "The Bounded Variables Problem," *ONR Research Memorandum No. 10*, Carnegie Institute of Technology, Pittsburgh, 1954.

15. COLVILLE, A. R., "Mathematical Programming Codes," *Technical Report No. 320-2925*, IBM New York Scientific Center, 1968.

16. DANO, Sven, *Linear Programming in Industry*, Springer-Verlag, New York, 1965.

17. DANTZIG, G. B., "Programming in a Linear Structure," *Econometrica*, **17**, 1, 1949 (summary).

18. DANTZIG, G. B., "Recent Advances in Linear Programming," *RM-1475*, The RAND Corp., 1955; or in *Man. Sci.*, **2**, 2, 1956.

19. DANTZIG, G. B., "On the Status of Multistage Linear Programming Problems," *P-1028*, The RAND Corp., 1957; or in *Man. Sci.*, **6**, 1, 1955.

20. DANTZIG, G. B., "On the Significance of Solving Linear Programming Problems with Some Integer Variables," *P-1468*, The RAND Corp., 1958; or in *Econometrica*, **28**, 1, 1960.

21. DANTZIG, G. B., *Linear Programming and Extensions*, Princeton University Press, Princeton, 1962.

22. DANTZIG, G. B., FULKERSON, D. R., and JOHNSON, S. M., "On a Linear Programming-Combinatorial Approach to the Traveling Salesman Problem," *RM-2321*, The RAND Corp., 1959; or in *Op. Res.*, **7**, 1, 1959.

22a. DANTZIG, G. B., and ORCHARD-HAYS, W., "Alternate Algorithm for the Revised Simplex Method Using Product Form for the Inverse," *RM-1268*, The RAND Corp., 1953.

23. DANTZIG, G. B., and ORCHARD-HAYS, W., "The Product Form for the Inverse in the Simplex Method," *Math. Tables and Aids to Computation*, **8**, 46, 1954.

24. DANTZIG, G. B., and WOLFE, P., "A Decomposition Principle for Linear Programs," *P-1544*, The RAND Corp., 1958.

25. DANTZIG, G. B., and WOLFE, P., "Decomposition Principle for Linear Programs," *Op. Res.*, **8**, 1, 1960.

26. DRIEBEEK, N. J., "An Algorithm for the Solution of Mixed Integer Programming Problems," *Man. Sci.*, **12**, 7, March 1966.

27. DENNIS, J. B., *Mathematical Programming and Electrical Networks*, Wiley, New York, 1959.

28. DORFMAN, R., SAMUELSON, P. A., and SOLOW, R. M., *Linear Programming and Economic Analysis*, McGraw-Hill, New York, 1958, and Dunod, Paris, 1962.

29. EISEMANN, K., "Linear Programming," *Quart. Appl. Math.*, **13**, 3, 1955.

30. FLOOD, M. M., "Application of Transportation Theory to Scheduling a Military Tanker Fleet," *Op. Res.*, **2**, 2, 1954.

31. FLOOD, M. M., "The Traveling-Salesman Problem," *Op. Res.*, **4**, 1, 1956.

32. FORD, L. R., and FULKERSON, D. R., "Solving the Transportation Problem," *RM-1736*, The RAND Corp., 1956; or in *Man. Sci.*, **3**, 1, 1956.

33. GASS, S. I., *Linear Programming: Methods and Applications*, McGraw-Hill, New York, 1958.

34. GLOVER, F., "A Bound Escalation Method for the Solution of Integer Linear Programs," *Cahiers du Centre d'Etudes in Recherche Operationnelle (Brussels)*, **6**, 1964.

35. GOMORY, R. E., "An Algorithm for Integer Solutions to Linear Programs," *Technical Report No. 1*, Princeton-IBM Mathematics Research Project, 1958.

36. GOMORY, R. E., "All-Integer Integer Programming Algorithm," *Research Report RC-189*, IBM Research Center, 1960.

37. GOMORY, R. E., "An Algorithm for the Mixed Integer Problem," *RM-2597*, The RAND Corp., 1960.

38. GOMORY, R. E., and BAUMOL, W. J., "Integer Programming and Pricing," *Econometrica*, **28**, 3, 1960.

39. HADLEY, G. F., *Linear Algebra*, Addison-Wesley, Reading, Mass., 1961.

40. HADLEY, G. F., *Linear Programming*, Addison-Wesley, Reading, Mass., 1962.

41. HADLEY, G. F., and SIMONNARD, M. A., "A Simplified Two-Phase Technique for the Simplex Method," *Nav. Res. Log. Qu.*, **6**, 3, 1959.

42. HELD, M. and KARP, R. M., "A Dynamic Programming Approach to Sequencing Problems," *J. Soc. Indust. Appl. Math.*, **10**, 1, March 1962.

43. KENDRICK, DAVID, *Branch and Bound Algorithms for Investment Planning Problems Project for Quantitative Research in Economic Development*, Center for International Affairs, Harvard University, Cambridge, Mass., 1967.

44. LAND, A. H., and DOIG, A., "An Automatic Method of Solving Discrete Programming Problems," *Econometrica*, **28**, 3, 1960.

45. LEMKE, C. E., "The Dual Method of Solving the Linear Programming Problem," *Technical Report No. 29*, Carnegie Institute of Technology, Pittsburgh, 1953; or in *Nav. Res. Log. Qu.*, **1**, 1, 1954.

46. LITTLE, J. D. C., MURTY, K. G., SWEENEY, D. W., KAREL, C., "An Algorithm for the Traveling Salesman Problem," *Op. Res.*, **11**, 1963.

47. MANNE, A. S., "Notes on Parametric Linear Programming," *P-468*, The RAND Corp., 1953.

48. Manne, A. S., *Scheduling of Petroleum Refinery Operations*, Harvard Economic Studies, 48, Harvard University Press, Cambridge, 1956.

49. MEISELS, KURT, *A Primer of Linear Programming*, New York University Press, New York, 1962.

50. ORCHARD-HAYS, W., "A Composite Simplex Algorithm, II," *RM-1275*, The RAND Corp., 1954.

51. ORCHARD-HAYS, W., "Background, Development and Extensions of the Revised Simplex Method," *RM-1433*, The RAND Corp., 1954.

52. ORCHARD-HAYS, W., "Evolution of Linear Programming Computing Techniques," *Man. Sci.*, **4**, 2, 1958.

53. ROY, B., NGHIEM, Ph. T., BERTIER, P., "Programmes linearies en nombres entiers et procedure S.E.P.," *Metra*, **4**, 3, 1965.

54. SIMONNARD, M. A., *Linear Programming*, Prentice Hall, Englewood Cliffs, N.J., 1966.

55. SIMONNARD, M. A., "Transportation-Type Problems," *Interim Technical Report No. 11*, Massachusetts Institute of Technology, Cambridge, 1959.

56. SIMONNARD, M. A., and HADLEY, G. F., "Maximum Number of Iterations in the Transportation Problem," *Nav. Res. Log. Qu.*, **6**, 2, 1959.

57. SYMONDS, G. H., *Linear Programming: The Solution of Refinery Problems*, Esso Standard Oil Company, New York, 1955.

58. VAJDA, S., *Mathematical Programming*, Addison-Wesley, Reading, Mass., 1961.

59. WAGNER, H. M., "A Comparison of the Original and the Revised Simplex Methods," *Op. Res.*, **5**, 3, 1957.

60. WITHINGTON, F. E., *The Use of Computers in Business Organizations*, Addison-Wesley, Reading, Mass., 1966.

61. WOLFE, P., (editor), *The RAND Symposium on Mathematical Programming: Linear Programming and Recent Extensions*, proceedings of a symposium held in March, 1959, The RAND Corp., Santa Monica, 1960.

62. WOLFE, P., "An Extended Composite Algorithm for Linear Programming," *P-2373*, The RAND Corp., 1961.

63. WOLFE, P., "A Technique for Resolving Degeneracy in Linear Programming," *RM-2995-PR*, The RAND Corp., 1962.

# Index